CONTENTS

Cover Design by Jennifer Thomson

Pastime Publications Ltd gratefully acknowledge the assistance of The Scottish Tourist Board, Area Tourist Boards and others in compiling this guide.

Published by Pastime Publications Ltd., 32-34 Heriot Hill Terrace, Edinburgh EH7 4DY. Tel: 031-556 1105.

First published by The Scottish Tourist Board 1970
U.K. Distribution by A.A. Publishing Ltd.
Typesetting by Newtext Composition Ltd.
Printed by bound by Eyre & Spottiswoode.
Worldwide Distribution by The British Tourist Authority.

ADVERTISERS' INDEX
DISPLAY ADVERTISEMENTS

(ALSO SEE COLOUR ADVERTS)

CLASSIFIED ADVERTISEMENTS

HOTELS & GUEST HOUSES

SELF CATERING

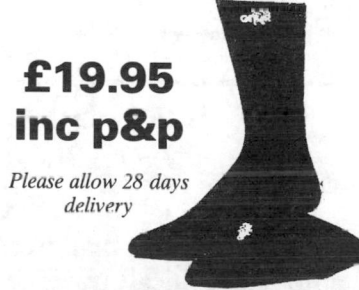

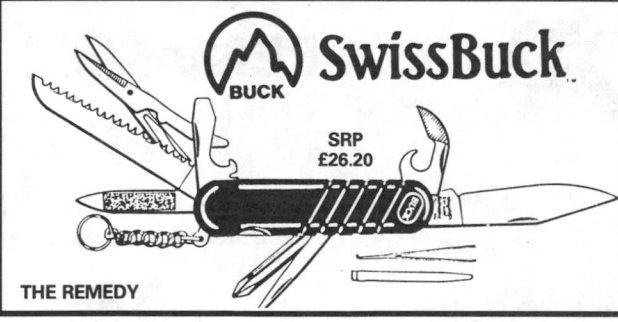

CASTLE LOCH
Lochmaben, Dumfriesshire

The Loch offers some of the best coarse fishing in Great Britain throughout the year and is well stocked with vendace, roach, perch, eel and large specimens of bream. Subject to booking, clubs may also be accommodated. Daily and weekly tickets available from the Castle Loch filling station, Lochmaben and ourselves.

An attractive and secluded Caravan and Camping Park with modern facilities is situated near the Loch.

Further details from: McJerrow & Stevenson
55 High Street, Lockerbie, Dumfriesshire. · Tel: (0576) 202123.

Norrie and Chris Young, formerly of Ardshealach Lodge, Argyll welcome you to.....

THE COLQUHONNIE HOTEL

Nine miles of mostly double bank fishing on the River Don for trout and salmon; also loch fishing. Excellent cooking, no menu fatigue. Quality wines at affordable prices.

All rooms ensuite. On the Castle and Whisky Trails. Golf nearby. For details of inclusive fishing breaks please contact:

The Colquhonnie Hotel,
Strathdon AB36 8UN.
Tel: (09756) 51210.

STOP INSECTS BITING!
use

X - GNAT

the Unique New
INSECT REPELLENT

X–Gnat is applied to articles of clothing - **not** to the skin and provides protection for up to **two weeks** from a single application.

X–Gnat is non-toxic and is safe to use with children Available from most Chemists, Sports outlets and Service stations - or direct from

HOTLINE -

041 - 777 - 6954

A superb mansion house hotel, totally re-furbished, overlooking sea front with superb en-suite accommodation and two first class restaurants.

Deep sea, trout and salmon fishing available in close proximity. So let us organise your fishing break. Facilities for storage of your catch.

For further information please contact:

General Manager,
Windmill Hotel,
Millgate Loan,
Arbroath DD11 1QG.
Tel: (0241) 72278.
Fax: (0241) 430441.

STB
♦♦♦

ABERDEENSHIRE ANGUS

TRADES DESCRIPTION ACT

The accommodation mentioned in this holiday guide has not been inspected, and the publishers rely on information provided. The publishers have every confidence in their advertisers but cannot be held responsible for the accuracy of the descriptions published.

A Y R S H I R E

DUMFRIESSHIRE

DUNBARTONSHIRE

FIFE

Please mention this Pastime Publications guide

18

INVERNESS - SHIRE

KIRKCUDBRIGHT

Please mention this Pastime Publications guide.

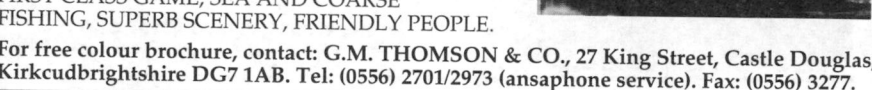

KIRKCUDBRIGHTSHIRE

LANARKSHIRE

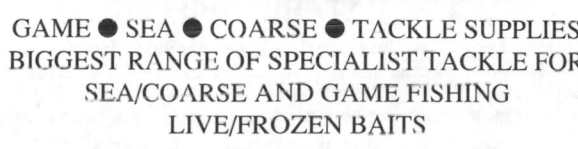

24

FOR ROAD MAPS
SEE PAGES 165-170

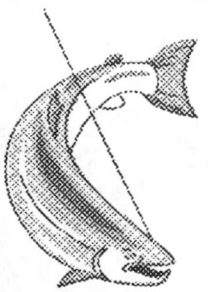

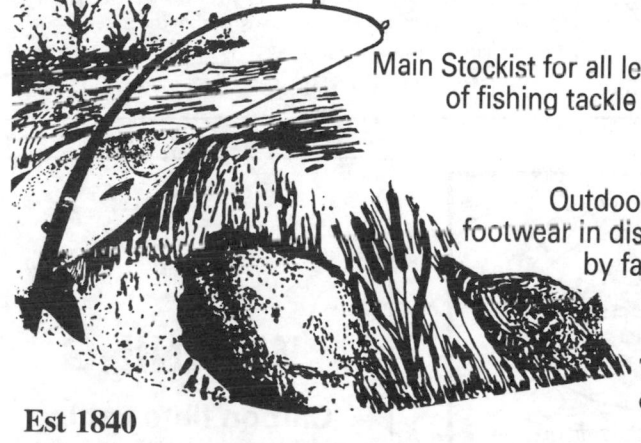

STIRLINGSHIRE

SUTHERLAND

Please mention this Pastime Publications guide

WIGTOWNSHIRE NORTH UIST

A cod takes a tope bait, off Port Logan, and pays the price.

	Type of accommodation	Type of Fishing	Permits available	Drying facilities	Freezing facilities	Price p.p. B/B or B.B.E.M.	Special features

Michael Waller & Margaret Cockburn, School of Casting, Salmon & Trout Fishing, Station House, Clovenfords, Galashiels TD1 3LU. Tel: (089695) 293.

Weekly fly fishing courses for novice and experienced fishers. The oldest established school with a fine reputation for the teaching of casting and fishing. Full equipment hire including waders. A wonderful holiday by mountain and moorland.

HOTELS & GUESTS HOUSES

ANGUS
Forfar

Name	Type of accommodation	Type of Fishing	Permits available	Drying facilities	Freezing facilities	Price p.p. B/B or B.B.E.M.	Special features
William & Edith Douglas (Mr. & Mrs.), Chapelbank House Hotel, 69 East High Street, Forfar. Tel: (0307) 463151.	Hotel 4 Crowns Highly Comm	Trout Salmon	-	Limited	Limited	B.&B. £30 B.B.E.M. £45	Situated in the heart of Strathmore Valley, Tayside.
Deanna Linsday (Mrs.), Wemyss Farm, Montrose Road, Forfar. Tel: (0307) 462887.	Farm Commended/ Listed	Trout Salmon Coarse	Yes	Yes	Yes	B. & B. from £13. B.B.E.M. from £21.50.	Only a few minutes walk from Rescobie Loch Trout Fishing.

Kirriemuir

Name	Type of accommodation	Type of Fishing	Permits available	Drying facilities	Freezing facilities	Price p.p. B/B or B.B.E.M.	Special features
Maureen Marchant, The Welton of Kingoldrum, Kirriemuir DD8 5HY. Tel: (0575) 74743.	F'house 3 Crowns Commended	Fly fishing by boat & bank for wild brown trout	At Lintrathen Loch	Yes	Yes	B.& B. £14-£17.50 B.B.E.M. £20-£24.50	Local salmon. Also Tay, Ericht, South Esk within easy reach.

Montrose

Name	Type of accommodation	Type of Fishing	Permits available	Drying facilities	Freezing facilities	Price p.p. B/B or B.B.E.M.	Special features
A. Ruxton (Mrs.), Muirshade of Gallery Farm, Montrose. Tel: (0674) 840209.	House 2 Crowns Commended	Fly Fishing	Ask	Yes	Yes	£15 B.&B. £22 B.B.E.M.	Beautiful house with superb views over Grampians. 2 double, 1 twin rooms. Superb food.

ARGYLL
Dunoon

Name	Type of accommodation	Type of Fishing	Permits available	Drying facilities	Freezing facilities	Price p.p. B/B or B.B.E.M.	Special features
M.J. Greig (Mr.), Royal Marine Hotel, Hunter's Quay, Dunoon PA23 8HJ. Tel: (0369) 5810.	Hotel 4 Crowns Commended	Ghillie service	Yes	Yes	Yes	D.B.B. from £30.00 Special rate breaks on request	Warm welcome. Good food. Friendly staff. Beautiful area. Great fishing.

AYRSHIRE
Cumnock

Name	Type of accommodation	Type of Fishing	Permits available	Drying facilities	Freezing facilities	Price p.p. B/B or B.B.E.M.	Special features
Ewing Hope (Mr.), Royal Hotel, Cumnock. Tel: (0290) 420882.	Hotel 2 Crowns Commended	Various	Ask	Yes	Yes	B. & B. from £23.	B. & B. available all year. Children and pets welcome.

Kirkoswald

Name	Type of accommodation	Type of Fishing	Permits available	Drying facilities	Freezing facilities	Price p.p. B/B or B.B.E.M.	Special features
M.N. Appleyard, Kirkton Jeans Hotel, Main Street, Kirkoswald KA19 8HY. Tel: 065-56-220.	Hotel	Brn trout salmon pike, perch, Roach, rudd	Ask	Yes	Yes	B.&B. from £15.00	9 bedrooms all ensuite. Colour TV and tea/coffee facilities. Restaurant, 2 bars - bar food.

Sorn

Name	Type of accommodation	Type of Fishing	Permits available	Drying facilities	Freezing facilities	Price p.p. B/B or B.B.E.M.	Special features
K. McFadzean (Mrs.), Sorn Inn, 35 Main Street, Sorn KA5 6HU. Tel: (0290) 551305.	Inn	Trout Salmon Grayling	Yes	Yes	Limited	£21.00 B.&B.	Situated 100 yds from River Ayr. B.&B. in twin and double rooms.

	Type of accommodation	Type of Fishing	Permits available	Drying facilities	Freezing facilities	Price p.p. B/B or B.B.E.M.	Special features
DUMFRIESSHIRE **Dumfries** Cairndale Hotel & Leisure Club, English Street, Dumfries DG1 2DF. Tel: (0387) 54111.	Hotel 4 Crowns Commended	Coarse Loch Rivers	Yes	Yes	Yes	Single - £69. Double/twin - £79. Bargain breaks rate - Min. 2 nights: from £65 p.p.p.n.	76 bedrooms, all ensuite. Leisure fac. inc. 14m swimming pool, sauna, spa bath, sunbeds, toning tables.
DUNBARTONSHIRE **Balloch** M. Harris (Mr.), Cameron Cottage, Old Luss Road, Balloch. Tel: (0389) 59779.	Cottage Pending	-	No	Yes	-	B.&B. from £14-£20 B.B.E.M. from £20-£30	
FIFE **Freuchie** Van Beusekom (Mr.), Lomond Hills Hotel, Freuchie. Tel: (0337) 57498.	Hotel 4 Crowns Commended	Fly rainbow brown trout Salmon	-	Yes	Yes	From: £37 D.B.B. min 2 days.	All rooms with facilities. Free use of leisure centre.
INVERNESS-SHIRE **Aviemore** The Red McGregor Resort Hotel, Grampian Road, Aviemore PH22 1RH. Tel: (0479) 810256.	Hotel	Salmon Trout	Yes	Yes	Yes	D.B. & B. from £29.50	Friendly hotel. All rooms ensuite. Leisure centre. Restaurant, bistro and 'Anglers Rest' Pub.
Beauly Iain Campbell (Mr.), Caledonian Hotel, Beauly. Tel: (0463) 782278.	Hotel 2 Crowns	Trout & salmon	Yes	Yes	Yes	£205.00 B.B.E.M. incl. pack lunch.	Boat engine incl. "Fish a loch a day for your stay"
Kincraig L.E. Rainbow (Mrs.), Ossian Hotel, Kincraig PH21 1NA. Tel: (0540) 651242.	Lic. Hotel 4 Crowns Commended	Trout & Salmon on Loch & River	Bank & Boat permits	Yes	Yes	B.&B. from: £15.00-£29.50	Family-run hotel, good food and wines, ensuite bedrooms.
Whitebridge Ian Milward (Mr.), Knockie Lodge, Whitebridge IV1 2UP. Tel: (045 63) 276.	Hotel 3 Crowns Deluxe	Brown Trout (Fly only)	N/A	Yes	Yes	B.B.E.M. from £62.50	Family-run hotel in magnificent setting on hills above Loch Ness.
KIRKCUDBRIGHTSHIRE **New Galloway** N. Swain (Mr.), Kenmure Arms Hotel, High Street, New Galloway, Castle Douglas. Tel: (06442) 240.	Lic. Hotel	Coarse, trout, pike etc.	Yes	Yes	Yes	B.&B. from £13.50 B.B.E.M. from £20.50	Loch Ken 2 mins. Boat & rod hire. Open all year. Fridges for baits, freezer for catches.
MORAYSHIRE **Dallas** Jim Mountford (Mr.), Dallas Hotel, Main Street, Dallas IV36 0SA. Tel: 034-389-323.	Hotel	Salmon Sea/ Brown/ Rainbow Trout	Yes	Yes	Yes	On Appl.	Friendly, comfortable, family-run hotel. Central to many fishing areas - fishing on Lossie River.

	Type of accommodation	Type of Fishing	Permits available	Drying facilities	Freezing facilities	Price p.p. B/B or B.B.E.M.	Special features
PEEBLESHIRE							
Peebles							
Norman Kerr (Dr.), Kingsmuir Hotel, Springhill Road, Peebles EH45 9EP. Tel: (0721) 720151.	Hotel 3 Crowns Commended	River Tweed trout (Spring) salmon Autumn	Ask	Yes	Yes	B.&B. £27-£37 E.M. £5-£11	Family run hotel, all rooms ensuite. Traditional Scottish cooking using fresh local produce.
Walkerburn							
C. Miller (Mr.), Tweed Valley Hotel, Walkerburn EH43 6AA. Tel: 089 687 636.	Hotel 4 Crowns	Salmon Fly	Yes	Yes	Yes	B. & B. £40. B.B.&E.M. £59.	Private beats on River Tweed, and hotel has own smokehouse.
PERTHSHIRE							
Auchterarder							
Diana Buchanan (Mrs.), Lawhill House, Trinity Gask, by Auchterarder. Tel: 031-661 1889.	F'house	Salmon Trout Grayling	Yes	Yes	Yes	B.&B. £15.00 D.B.B. £25.00	Fishing River Earn. Superb views. Spacious comfort. Scrumptous food.
Blairgowrie							
Aldchlappie Hotel, Kirk Michael, by Blairgowrie PH10 9NF. Tel: (0250) 881224.	Hotel 3 Crowns	Trout Salmon	Yes	Yes	Yes	B.&B. from £20 B.B. & E.M. from £28	Ensuite rooms with TV. Malt bar stocking real ales.
Killin							
R. Bedwell (Mr.), Fairview House, Main Street, Killin FK21 8UT. Tel: (0567) 820667.	Guest House 2 Crowns Commended	Loch & river	From local Angling Club	Yes	Yes	B.&B. £14-£16 B.B.E.M. £22-£24	Local boatman available for salmon fishing. Brown trout from rivers.
J. Mallinson (Mr.), Clachaig Hotel, Falls of Dochart, Killin. Tel: (05672) 270.	Hotel 3 Crowns	Game	Yes	Yes	Yes	B.&B. £21.00	Loch Tay and River fishing organised. Own beat available to guests. Ensuite facilities.
Kinloch Rannoch							
Jennifer Skeaping (Mrs.), Bunrannoch House, Kinloch Rannoch PH16 5QD. Tel: (0882) 632407.	Guest House S.T.B. Approved	Coarse	Day/week	Yes	Yes	B.&B. from £16. D.B.&B. from £27.	Good food, a warm welcome and relaxing atmosphere ensures that you will want to return.
Perth							
C.J. Longden (Mr.), Ballathie House Hotel, Kinclaven, by Stanley PH1 4QN. Tel: (0250) 883 268.	Hotel 4 Crowns Deluxe	Salmon, trout on Tay	Hotel's residents only.	Yes	Yes	From: £60 D.B.B.	Delightful grounds by river. Award winning cuisine.
Pitlochry							
J.C. Wilson (Mrs.), Craigower Hotel, 134 Atholl Road, Pitlochry. Tel: (0796) 472590.	Hotel	Salmon Sea Trout Perch	Yes	Yes	Yes	B. & B. £20-£25.	Ghillie/boatman available. Boat hire. Bait purchased locally. Shooting. All bedrooms ensuite.
G.M. Ogg (Mr.), Duntrune Guest House, 22 East Moulin Road, Pitlochry PH16 5HY. Tel: (0796) 472172.	Guest House 2 Crowns Commended	Salmon Trout	Yes	Yes	Ask	B. & B. from: £16.50	5 ensuite rooms with TV and tea/coffee facilities. Good parking facilities.

	Type of accommodation	Type of Fishing	Permits available	Drying facilities	Freezing facilities	Price p.p. B/B or B.B.E.M.	Special features
ROSS-SHIRE **Contin** H. Ponty (Mrs.), Achilty Hotel, Contin IV14 9EG. Tel: (0997) 421355.	Hotel	Salmon & trout	Yes	Yes	Yes	£17.50-£24.50 B.&.B. £30-£37 D.B.B.	First class accommodation and food. Excellent fishing on River Blackwater.
Strathpeffer Martyn A. Hill (Mr.), Coul House Hotel, Contin, by Strathpeffer IV14 9EY. Tel: (0997) 421487.	Hotel 4 Crowns Highly Comm	Salmon sea/ brown rainbow & trout Fly and Spin	Rivers Conon and Beauly various lochs.	Yes	Yes	B.&B. from £32. B.B.E.M. from £49.	Secluded country mansion; incomparable Highland setting. "Taste of Scotland" restaurant. All rooms ensuite.
Ullapool M. Errington (Mrs.), Four Seasons Hotel, Ullapool IV26 2SX. Tel: (0854) 612905.	Hotel 3 Crowns Commended	Sea & river salmon/ trout	Yes	Yes	Yes	£28.00 B.&B.	Quiet hotel on Loch Broom. 2 mins. village. Excellent food (a la carte menu).
SELKIRKSHIRE **Selkirk** Philipburn House Hotel, Selkirk. Tel: (0750) 20747.	Hotel 4 Crowns Commended	Salmon trout coarse	Yes	Yes	Yes & smoking fac	B.&.B. £38-£50 B.B.E.M. £55-£75	Including lodge and cottage apartments. Ideal for fishing holidays.
SUTHERLAND **Lairg** D.A. Walker (Mr.), Sutherland Arms Hotel, Lairg IV27 4AJ. Tel: (0549) 2291. Fax: (0549) 2261.	Hotel & S/C 3 Stars	Wild brown trout/ salmon. Fly only.	Yes	Yes	Yes	On Appl	Fully inclusive fly fishing holidays available. Details on request.
Lochinver N.L. Gorton (Mr.), Inver Lodge Hotel, Lochinver IV27 4LU. Tel: (0571) 4490.	Hotel 4 Crowns Highly Comm	Trout & Salmon	Daily or Weekly	Yes	Yes	From £60 per night D.B.B.	Boats available on lochs Kirkaig, Inver, Upper Oykel. Salmon rivers.
SCOTTISH ISLANDS **Mull** H.R.R. Kay (Mr.), Assapol Country House Hotel, Bunessan PA67 6DW. Tel: 068 17 258.	Hotel 3 Crowns Commended	Loch for salmon sea & brown trout	Yes	Yes	Yes	B.&B. from £24 B.B.E.M. from £37.50	Overlooking Loch Assapol. Taste of Scotland. Private facilities. Boat available.
Orkney A. MacDonald (Mr.) Merkister Hotel, Loch Harray KW17 2LF. Tel: 085 677 366. Fax: 085 677 515.	Hotel 3 Crowns	Wild brown trout & sea trout	N/A	Yes	Yes	Low: £20-£29.50 B.&B. £35-£41.50 D.B.B.	Excellent boats with Evinrude Motors, own pier 100 yds from hotel.

SELF CATERING

	Type of accommodation	Type of Fishing	Permits available	Drying facilities	Freezing facilities	Price per unit	Special features
Write to: Pam Copeland (Mrs.), Bailey Mill, Bailey, Newcastleton Roxburghshire TD9 0TR. Tel: (06978) 617.	Houses Flats	Esk & Liddle Salmon & trout Lake fishing.	Yes	Laundry room	Yes	£78-£398	House and flats on farm complex, sleep from 2-10 x 5, near Longtown, Cumbria. On site recreation available. Bar.
ABERDEENSHIRE **Aboyne** Glen Tanar Estate, Brooks House, Glen Tanar, Aboyne AB34 5EU. Tel: (03398) 86451.	Cottages 3 Crowns Comm-Highly Comm 5 Crowns	Salmon sea/ rainbow trout	Day or weekly	Yes	Yes	£130-£396 p.w	Carefully restored traditional cottages set in beautiful countryside on a private estate.
Monymusk J.M. Uren (Mr.), Write to: Priory Farm, Appledore Road, Tenterden, Kent TN30 7DD. Tel: (0322) 38 4646/ (0580) 764161.	Lodge Sleeps 6 3 Crowns	Salmon Sea trout Brown trout	2 miles single bank River Don	Yes	Yes	£188 per week.	10 named pools on the River Don at the Place of Tilliefour, near Monymusk. Fishing £188 - 2 rods per week.
ARGYLL **Dalavich** S.A. Watts (Mrs.), Write to: The Old Rectory, Alphamstone, Bures, Suffolk CO8 5HH. Tel: (0787) 269340.	2 Houses 3 Crowns Approved	Fly - salmon, trout. Coarse - pike trout etc.	Yes	Yes	Ask	From £95 p.w. inc. Elec. and linen.	2 lochs - boat hire on both and shore fishing Awe. Short walking distance - shore and boats. Avich short drive - fly only.
Loch Awe Jonathan C. Soar (Mr.), Sonachan House, Portsonachan, by Dalmally PA33 1BN. Tel: (08663) 240. Fax: (08663) 241.	Lux. flats House Chalets C'vans 4 Crowns Comm-Highly Comm	Brown Trout Rainbow Trout Sea Trout Salmon, Coarse	Yes	Yes	Yes	£115-£440 per week	Lochside mansion house. Free shore fishing ⅓ mile. Boat hire. Permits.
INVERNESS-SHIRE **Fort William** T. Legg (Mrs.), Write to: Moss Cottage, Corran Caravans, Onich, by Fort William. Tel: (08553) 208.	C'van	Sea loch	Not required	Yes	Yes	From £120 p.w.	Idyllic lochside location. Panoramic views. Quiet family site. Caravan sleeps 6.
PERTHSHIRE **Pitlochry** MacFarlane (Mr.), Logierait Pine Lodges, Logierait, by Pitlochry. Tel: (0796) 482 253.	Chalets 3 Crowns Commended	Coarse trout & salmon	Rivers Tay & Tummel	No	Yes	£120-£388 p.w.	So peaceful on the banks of River Tay.

WRASSE - THE MULTI-COLOURED SCRAPPER

by Jim McLanaghan

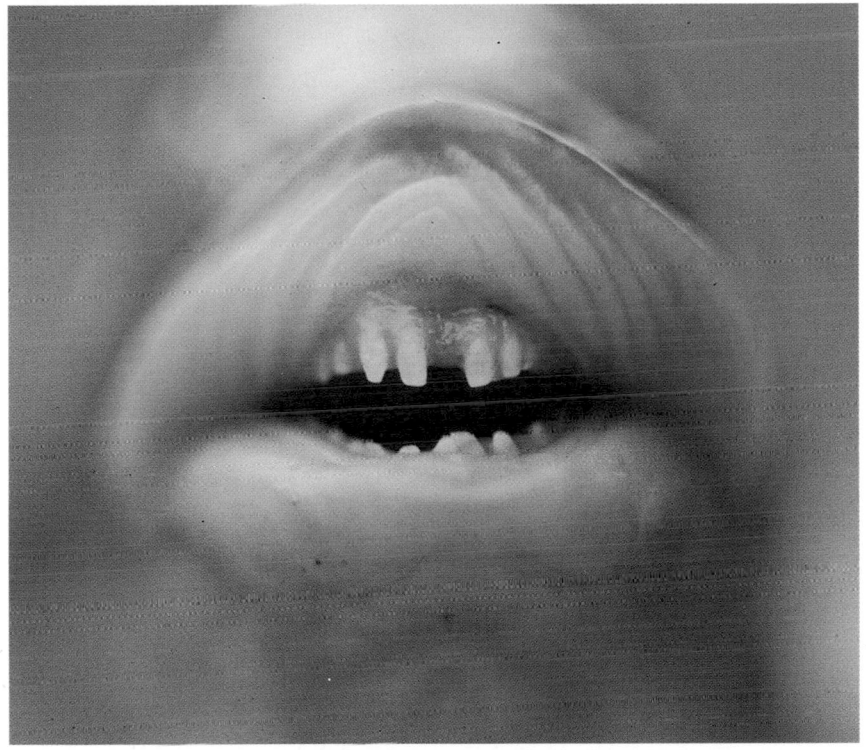

Close up of Wrasse's teeth.

The float bobbed cautiously then was still. Knowing my quarry, I did not despair but waited patiently. Back he came. This time the float had a more urgent movement to it as it moved frantically in the water sending out the ringlets which discern a fish from normal wave movement. Down - up - down - up - I fed an extra yard of line and watched. Finally, down went the float, completely out of sight even from my elevated view on the cliffs, and I struck.

This was what I had come to this rocky headland for - the wrasse, a lover of rockiest places imaginable and a stocky powerhouse of a fish. My rod bent as the hook went home and line was gently eased off against the clutch when to my surprise the fish stopped! Regaining some lost line I felt slightly cheated as I had thought this a good fish and as I tightened the clutch I prepared to lift the fish out of the water. Before I could make another move, the fish flicked over, dived and doubling the rod over proceeded to tear about 20ft of line off my reel before fish and I parted company. The line had gone at the knot as the curly end tail showed, not surprising considering the strain it was under. I sat back dejectedly and considered where I had gone wrong. My tackle? - No, I had a good carbon 8ft spinner coupled with my trusty Mitchell 300 and 12 lbs line. The answer probably lay with the fish itself as it was undoubtedly the most powerful wrasse I'd ever hooked and with a splendid array of teeth it should have been no surprise that he could chomp through line or a knot.

Like so many holiday anglers, I had brought only freshwater gear, only to find conditions were not at all suitable with barely any water in the local rivers. Intent on getting some fishing in, I had dug myself a few lug and headed south to Burrow Head on Scotland's south west, a superb rock mark which can produce wrasse, pollack, dogfish, conger, tope and possibly even shark. My quarry, however, was the wrasse, one of the most obliging of saltwater fish in all senses of the word. Firstly, no great distance needs to be attained by casting as they can be caught literally under your feet, a couple of feet or so out from the cliffs. Secondly, bait, always a problem for visitors, but the wrasse is not a fussy feeder in the least - mussels, worms, winkles, limpets, crab, squid, almost anything. The only bait which I do not have great faith in is mackerel or herring as the wrasse tends to shred it with its teeth before you can set the hook but if it's all you have, use it!

Since you don't have to cast far, virtually any spinning or freshwater rod will do but, as I found out, a good reel and at least 10-12 lbs line is a must. Hook size is mainly a matter of preference but anything from No 1 to 2/0 is OK but with smaller hooks the strike should be earlier to avoid deep hooking since all wrasse should be returned alive to the waters. One added bonus when a wrasse is caught is the breathtaking array of colours which these fish present ranging from scarlet and brown to rich green and reds. If this seems multi-coloured it fades into insignificance against the cuckoo wrasse with his fluorescent yellows and golds and neon blue spots, truly a magnficent fish which no-one with any soul could contemplate keeping. Floats should be large enough to carry the bait and split shot or whatever you are using for a weight. If no float is being used, I would suggest old scrap metal or spark plugs as weights as ·these fish frequent the most horrendously rocky areas and tackle losses can be VERY high.

A small haversack will normally carry enough tackle for a day's wrasse fishing and as it can involve a climb over rocks and sometimes over fields, I would make two pleas. Firstly, take great care on rocky stances and never go alone. Watch the sea always. Secondly, when crossing or using farmland, please do not drop litter or damage crops. Scotland has some very beautiful countryside and fantastic angling, let's enjoy and conserve both.

Almost any rocky stance - and there are literally millions along Scotland's indented shoreline - will provide good wrasse prospects. So, if like me you find yourself on holiday and at a loose end, go look for some wrasse. Your spinning gear is ideal for it and the wrasse will give you sport well worthy of the effort.

SCOTTISH BIG GAME UP-DATE

by Jim McLanaghan

It was prophesied, and now it is fact, the largest porbeagle shark ever taken on rod and line has been landed at Scrabster in Scotland! Everyone who ever fished there knew it was just a matter of time before the world record went and Robert Richardson from East Kilbride showed the way last year with his superb 414lbs fish, a world record on 50lbs line, it paved the way for the record breaking monster.

The weather in the early part of the year had been atrocious and, although I had three separate weekends booked, none were fishable. Some boats out during the week with cod anglers on board had sharks all round the boats but when the anglers with suitable gear arrived the sharks vanished - Sod's Law!

This was all to change however and in April the right angler with the right gear met the right fish. After a prolonged and tiring struggle, the new world record of 507lbs was finally boated by Chris Bennet of Invermoriston. Incidentally, he had taken another shark of 170lbs earlier that same day.

Not only are Scottish waters proving to be world beaters but anglers are now using some very up-to-date gear and techniques previously reserved for tropical waters. No longer do we rely on the humble baitfish or livebait but some very exotic lures up to 12 inches long are being trolled behind the boats with porbeagle and who knows what else in mind.

Tackle to fight these giants is also being made in Scotland and with an emphasis on shorter stand-up rods, it means an angler can apply colossal pressure to a large fish with minimum effort to himself. Essential if you have quarter of a ton of fish on your line. New butt pads which are more comfortable and far less tiring are also being produced to suit this new breed of rod.

Another angling scene which is making headlines is the large skate being caught off Lochaline near Mull. So prolific an area is this that in three days Kirkintilloch rod maker, Stan Massey, took 14 skate with the largest being a hernia inducing 192lbs. These fish demand strong rods, big reels and equally strong backs as they surge in the tideraces like 7ft wide kites. Even anglers with dinghies are getting in on the act and to date 37 fish have been taken - all being returned alive. Any angler contemplating catching one of these huge flatfish from a dinghy should take the very greatest care as fish of this weight will certainly cant a dinghy well over in the water.

The last in the mighty trio of big fish which Scotland has to offer, the halibut, has surfaced again metaphorically and literally. By far the most desirable species, the halibut has had a long absence from our catch list but they are still there as a small band of dedicated anglers proved earlier this year.

Fishing out of a small port in Scotland's north west, the skipper said one morning 'Let's go halibut fishing' and the anglers thought "Aye, and some marlin too!" and so they set forth. Nothing eventful happened till late afternoon when one of the anglers had a savage take and a "huge angry something" took off for America with his bait. A long battle of give and take then ensued, mostly take on the fish's side, but eventually it neared the boat and the anglers saw it. A huge halibut estimated at over 200lbs, it took one look at the boat, or maybe it saw the gaff, and dived. Now there are very few fish, or submarines for that matter, which can dive like a halibut and in a flash all the line recovered had gone. This happened a couple of times more and the fish was once more beside the boat. This is where the real problems start with any big fish and where most are lost. Good gaffs are essential but unfortunately were not available on this boat. The fish was part way over the gunwhale when it went berserk, flicked over, back into the sea and with a derisory splash left the skipper and anglers to ponder what might have been.

The big three - halibut, porbeagle and skate - are the magnets which draw anglers to Scotland year after year, not only for the fish they catch or the fish they put back but sometimes for the ones they lose. The spirit of Zane Grey lives on.

190lb. Porbeagle.

FOR FISHERS, THE SUN IS RISING IN THE NORTH

By Bill Currie

The Ghillie takes a fish to the hut.

One of the remarkable things about Scotland is that, small as it is, you can travel in quite a short time from what seems to be one country into another. It is not just that Scotland has two long and interesting coastlines, one on the Atlantic and one on the North Sea - each with radically different weather, waters and fishing. It is much subtler than that. From a centre like Inverness, two hours' driving can take you through the fertile Black Isle and up over the Cromarty Bridge to the north east, past long sandy beaches, then along a fine cliffy coast to the lowlands of Caithness. All the way you are aware that you are in a different kind of 'Highlands', beside a different sea. When you reach Caithness, you are into a still more unusual land - the Northern Lowlands beyond the Highlands.

If, however, on your drive north from Inverness, you were to turn north west at Muir of Ord, or at Bonar Bridge, you would spend your next couple of hours driving through the North Western Highlands - beautiful hills deeply intersected by sea lochs, glimpses of islands, vistas of sandy beaches and prospects of loch after loch after loch lying in the heather. Yet only fifty miles at the most separates this 'Interlaken' country from the cliffy east coast. Between north west and north east the weather is different, the waters are different and the fishing is different. North west and north east are both rich in fishing, but they are so different that it is sometimes hard to believe that they are part of one, quite small, section of a not very large country.

In the North West Highlands and the islands of the western sea, lie a vast resource of natural hill lochs, most of which are good wild trout fishing. The Hebrides abound in trout lochs and those over the shell sand we call 'machair' are often outstanding for size and quality of fish. This resource of trout fishing is linked in my mind with the delights of holiday fishing. It is in wild, unspoiled, remote country with lochs often set in memorable pockets of mountain scenery and lonely moor. It is, for me and for many game fishers, a landscape of quite magical qualities. When the pressures of business rise, I often find myself thinking of being in a boat somewhere in the north west drifting down a rocky, heathery shoreline with natural birches and rowans leaning over the water and trout splashing at the fly in the ripple. I know this sounds like a dream landscape - and for many it is - but it is so easy to make this kind of dream come true in Scotland. It is all just a short drive away from our main centres, but it feels like a different land.

Scotland is also a package of different 'countries' as far as it migratory game fish go - the salmon and the sea trout. To many, these fish are the spectacular quarry, alluring, longed for and much hunted. In the last two or three years a remarkable picture of new fishing prospects for salmon and sea trout has emerged in Scotland, considerably altering how a visitor or a resident should plan fishing. Partly because of the buying off of Icelandic and Faroese nets (by the visionary Icelandic businessman. Orri Vigfusson, head of the North Atlantic Salmon Fund) a whole series of rivers in the north are revitalising. In 1992 and again in 1993 the rivers of the north coast and north east coasts have had wonderful sport. In July 1993 I spoke to a friend from Tongue, in the middle of the north coast, who said that rivers from the Borgie and Forss round to the Thurso and right down the east coast to Inverness (including the Ness) were having their best summer runs for many years. He even went as far as to say that these small waters, having had a bad time for years, now were experiencing their best fishing for a generation. I know the more substantial rivers of the north east had excellent runs in the summer of 1993, reflecting a general upsurge of sport which began in 1992. Many smaller waters in the north also had good to excellent runs of summer salmon and grilse. Of the major rivers of the area, Helmsdale, Conon and Beauly had substantial runs of fish in late June and July 1993 and the runs continued into August. The Ness, a river of a different type, being backed by the largest lochs in Scotland, was also excellent last July, having enjoyed a much needed revival of fishing in 1992. I am strongly inclined to believe that a radical change has resulted from the netting changes in Iceland and the

Faroes which I have mentioned. It is a good pointer that Iceland itself has had a great upturn in its fishings too in the last two or three years. In salmon fishing terms, the sun is rising in the north.

Another important change took place in 1993 which will add to the improvement of sport. In July, after pressure from anglers, the damaging nets at Speymouth were taken off. This will radically improve the numbers of fish returning to the lovely salmon fishings of the Spey, which for some years have been in serious decline. One of the good things about this excellent river is that it has many places where the public can have reasonably priced visitor access to salmon fishings. Take the Grantown-on-Spey area as an example. Over 10 miles of the Spey are available for daily and weekly fishing there. This water not only has

A ten pounder on the fly.

Netting a sea trout.

salmon running in from early spring to late summer, but has first class sea trout fishing in June and July. In addition to the Strathspey Angling Association and the Abernethy Angling Association, both issuing visitor tickets for their extensive waters, there are hotel-based angling courses in Grantown, for example based on Seafield Lodge and further downstream at Blairfindy Lodge, Glenlivet (on the Livet, the Avon and the Spey), each with access to normally private beats.

In fishing terms, it is quite a long way from the trout lochs of the north west, through the small and medium sized salmon rivers of the north and east to the big-river fishings of the Ness and Spey, and on to the Dee and Tay. In terms of miles, however, these rivers are not very far apart. In purely geographical terms, in Scotland, it is usually just a short hop from one region to another. When salmon and sea trout migrate into our waters, however, two distinct spheres of fishing may share the same waters.

The migratory fish lay, as it were, a different map over the trout fishing terrain. Many regions good for trout loch fishing from June also offer good sea trout and salmon sport right through the summer. So, thinking about geographical regions is useful, but it does not necessarily reveal the whole truth. A careful study of the fishing maps in "Scotland for Fishing" will show you regions like the north west and the Hebrides where trout lochs abound, yet the stillwaters are interlaced with good small salmon rivers. This is typical of the north and west. In the north east of Scotland, where there are fewer lochs, it tends to be the salmon fishings which dominate. There are areas near the east coast, north of Inverness, where there is some good trout loch fishing - for example - the Badanloch area inland from Helmsdale, and the excellent trout lochs of Caithness - but the scene in the east is generally dominated by excellent medium-sized salmon rivers. Further south, the Moray-Buchan area of Scotland east of Inverness, turning the corner down to Aberdeen, has a few trout lochs, but is very much more famous for its salmon rivers like the Spey, Deveron, Don and Dee.

Reading this guide and making a few telephone calls to likely areas will help your detailed planning, but, with the recent return of salmon and sea trout in strength to the northern rivers, your choice may well be not so much between different regions of Scotland, as between different waters in the far north. In that case you will likely come close to dealing with an embarrassment of riches. I can tell you, it is many years since I felt confident enough to make a remark like that.

In discussing the fishing resources of our small country, you will not have failed to notice that this year I have used most of my space to deal with lands north of Inverness. That does not mean that the waters of the south west are without merit. Absolutely not. There is a whole world of interesting fishing from the Firth of Clyde round to the Nith, including a dozen salmon waters, many trout lochs and scenery to rival the north. Nor does it mean that there is nothing to discuss south of the Tay. Far from it! In the south east of Scotland we have the great Tweed district, the largest area of river drainage in Scotland with many miles of burns, waters and rivers in it. That is good spring and summer trouting country, but its main claim to fame is that it is autumn salmon territory par excellence. There, too, you would be right to feel that on Tweedside you were in another country. You would certainly feel the same in Galloway and south Ayrshire. All these different terrains, each with its special fishings, are described in this booklet. For a comparatively small country, Scotland has a remarkable range of fishing choice for its home fishers and its visitors. That would be true in any year, but 1994, I think, will be special. If follows what we may well look back on as the two years of revival of the migratory fishings of the north. This change up north has biased me. I know that the world of Scottish fishing does not wholly begin and end north of the Great Glen, but I feel strongly in 1994 that the regions lying north and west of Inverness 'are putting love on me', as the song says, and I too will be one of the visitors there.

(Bill Currie is Consultant Editor of Salmon, Trout and Sea-trout. His recent book, The River Within, is published by Merlin Unwin Books).

USEFUL ADDRESSES IN
SCOTTISH SPORT FISHERIES

Scottish Tourist Board
23 Ravelston Terrace,
Edinburgh EH4 3EU.
Tel: 031-332 2433.

**Department of Agriculture
& Fisheries for Scotland**
Pentland House, 47 Robb's
Loan, Edinburgh EH14 1YQ.
Tel: 031-244 6015.

**Inspector of Salmon
Fisheries**
Pentland House (Room 407),
47 Robb's Loan,
Edinburgh EH14 1YQ.
Tel: 031-244 6227.

S.O.A.F.D.
Officer in Charge,
Freshwater Fisheries
Laboratory, Faskally,
Pitlochry PH16 5LB.
Tel: (0796) 472060.

**S.O.A.F.D. Marine
Laboratory**
P.O. Box 101, Victoria Road,
Aberdeen AB9 8DB.
Tel: (0224) 876544.

**Secretary, Scottish River
Purification Boards
Association**
1 South Street,
Perth PH2 8NJ.
Tel: (0738) 27989.

Scottish Sports Council
Caledonia House, South
Gyle, Edinburgh EH12 9DQ.
Tel: 031-317 7200.

Scottish Natural Heritage
12 Hope Terrace,
Edinburgh EH9 2AS.
Tel: 031-447 4784.

Forestry Commission
Dawn McNiven, Information
Officer, 231 Corstorphine
Road, Edinburgh EH12 7AT.
Tel: 031-334 0303.

Scottish Hydro-Electric plc
16 Rothesay Terrace,
Edinburgh EH3 7SE.
Tel: 031-225 1361.

**Institute of Fisheries
Management**
Secretary (Scottish branch),
Gordon Struthers,
"Torshavn", Lettoch Road,
Pitlochry PH16 5AZ.
Tel: (home) (0796) 472846.
Tel: (work) (0796) 472060.

**Scottish Anglers' National
Association**
Administrative Office,
Caledonia House, South
Gyle, Edinburgh EH12 9DQ.
Tel: 031-339 8808.

**Central Scotland Anglers'
Association**
Secretary, Kevin Burns,
53 Fernieside Crescent,
Edinburgh.
Tel: 031-664 4685.

**Esk Valley Angling
Association**
Secretary, Kevin Burns,
53 Fernieside Crescent,
Edinburgh.
Tel: 031-664 4685.

**Federation of Highland
Angling Clubs**
Secretary, W. Brown,
Coruisk, Strathpeffer,
Ross-shire IV14 9BD.
Tel: (0997) 421446.

**Department of Forestry and
Natural Resources**
University of Edinburgh,
Kings Buildings, Mayfield
Road, Edinburgh EH9 3JU.
Tel: 031-650 1000.

Institute of Aquaculture
University of Stirling,
Stirling FK9 4LA.
Tel: (0786) 73171.

The Effects of POLLUTION may take years to disappear from a river
REPORT ALL CASES IMMEDIATELY
Keep samples of dead fish
Please telephone
Forth River Purification Board
031-441 1674 (24 hours) or 0786 51741
or Forth District Salmon Fishery Board 0836 722 647
or your local Police Office

GAME ANGLING CLUBS

CLUB	SECRETARY
Aberfeldy Angling Club	G. MacDougall, 60 Moness Crescent, Aberfeldy, Perthshire PH15. Tel: (0887) 20653
Airdrie Angling Club	Roy Burgess, 21 Elswick Drive, Caldercruix, Lanarkshire.
Annan & District Angling Club	J. Glen, 110 High Street, Annan, Dumfriesshire.
Badenoch Angling Association	J. Dallas, The Mills, Kingussie, Inverness-shire.
Berwick & District Angling Association	D. Cowan, 3 Church Street, Berwick TD15 1EE. Tel: (0289) 330145
Blairgowrie, Rattray & District Angling Association	W. Matthew, 4 Mitchell Square, Blairgowrie, Perthshire. Tel: (0250) 3679
Brechin Angling Club	D.E. Smith, 3 Friendly Park, Brechin, Angus.
Castle Douglas & District Angling Association	Ian Bandall, Tommy's Sports Shop, Castle Douglas, Kirkcudbrightshire. Tel: (0556) 2851
Chatton Angling Association	D. Boyle, 12 West End, Chatton, Alnwick, Northumberland NE66 5PP. Tel: (06685) 388.
Coldstream & District Angling Association	Brian Turnbull, Binning Cottage, Duns Road, Coldstream, Berwickshire TD12 4DR. Tel: (0890) 2941.
Cramond Angling Club	E. McCrindle, 36 John Humble Street, Mayfield, Dalkeith, Midlothian EH22 5QZ. Tel: (0875) 22506
Dalbeattie Angling Association	G.W. Garroch, 7 The Meadows, Dalbeattie DG5 4SA. Tel: (0556) 611050
Devon Angling Association	R. Breingan, 33 Redwell Place, Alloa, Clackmannanshire FK10 2BT. Tel: (0259) 215185
Dreghorn Angling Club	Mr. S. Wallace, 14 Lismore Way, Dreghorn. Tel: (0294) 218475.
Dumfries & Galloway Angling Association	D. Byers, 4 Bloomfield, Edinburgh Road, Dumfries DG1 1SG. Tel: (0387) 53850
Dunkeld & Birnam Angling Association	Mr. K.L. Scott, "Mandaya", Highfield Place, Bankfoot, Perthshire PH1 4AX. Tel: (0738) 87448.
Dunoon & District Angling Club	A.H. Young, "Ashgrove", 28 Royal Crescent, Dunoon PA23 7AH. Tel: (0369) 5732
Earlston Angling Association	P. Hessett, 2 Arnot Place, Earlston, Berwickshire TD4 6DP. Tel: (089 684) 577
Eckford Angling Association	R.B. Anderson, W.S., Royal Bank Buildings, Jedburgh, Roxburghshire. Tel: (0835) 3202
Elgin & District Angling Association	W. Mulholland, 9 Conon Crescent, Elgin, Moray.
Esk & Liddle Fisheries	G.L. Lewis, The Buccleuch Estates Ltd, Ewesbank, Langholm, Dumfriesshire DG13 OND.
Esk Valley Angling Improvement Association	K. Burns, 53 Fernieside Crescent, Edinburgh.

Eye Water Angling Club, W.S. Gillie,
2 Tod's Court,
Eyemouth,
Berwickshire
TD14 5HR.
Tel: (08907) 50038.

Ford & Etal Estates Fishing Club W.M. Bell,
Heatherslaw,
Cornhill on Tweed.
Tel: Crookham
(089 082) 221

Fyvie Angling Association J.D. Pirie,
Prenton,
South Road,
Oldmeldrum,
Aberdeenshire
AB51 0AB.

Gordon Fishing Club Mrs. M. Forsyth,
47 Main Street,
Gordon,
Berwickshire.
Tel: (057 381) 359

Greenlaw Angling Club J. Purves,
9 Wester Row,
Greenlaw,
Berwickshire
TD10 6XE.

Hawick Angling Club R. Sutherland,
20 Longhope Drive,
Hawick.
Tel: (0450) 75150

Inverness Angling Club G.M. Smith,
50 Nevis Park,
Inverness.

Irvine & District Angling Club A. Sim,
51 Rubie Crescent,
Irvine.

Jedforest Angling Club J.T. Renilson,
4 Canongate,
Jedburgh,
Roxburghshire.

Kelso Angling Association Euan Robson,
33 Tweedsyde Park,
Kelso TD5 7RF.
Tel: (0573) 225279.

Killin, Breadalbane Angling Club D. Allan,
12 Ballechroisk,
Killin.
Tel: (05672) 362

Kilmaurs Angling Club J. Watson,
7 Four Acres Drive,
Kilmaurs,
Ayrshire.

Kintyre Fish Protection & Angling Club F.W. Neate,
Kilmoray Place,
High Street,
Campbeltown,
Argyll.

Kyles of Bute Angling Club R. Newton,
Viewfield Cottage,
Tighnabruaich,
Argyll.

Ladykirk & Norham Angling Association R.G. Wharton,
8 St. Cuthbert's
Square,
Norham.
Berwick-upon-Tweed
TD15 2LE.
Tel: (0289) 382467

Lairg Angling Club J.M. Ross, St. Murie,
Church Hill Road,
Lairg,
Sutherland IV27 4BL.
Tel: (0549) 2010

Larbert & Stenhousemuir Angling Club A. Paterson,
6 Wheatlands Avenue,
Bonnybridge,
Stirlingshire.

Lauderdale Angling Association D.M. Milligan,
Gifford Cottage,
Main Street, Gifford,
East Lothian
EH41 4QH.

Lochgilphead & District Angling Club Inter Sport,
Lochnell Street,
Lochgilphead, Argyll.

Loch Keose & Associated Waters M. Morrison,
Handa, 18 Keose
Glebe,
Lochs, Isle of Lewis
Tel: (085 183) 334

Loch Lomond Angling Improvement Association R.A. Clements, C.A.,
224 Ingram Street,
Glasgow.

Loch Rannoch Conservation Association Mrs. Steffen,
Coilmore Cottage,
Kinloch Rannoch,
Perthshire.

Melrose & District Angling Association T. McLeish,
Planetree Cottage,
Newstead, Melrose.
Tel: (089 682) 2232

Morebattle Angling Club H. Fox,
Orchard Cottage,
Morebattle.

Murthly & Glendelvine Trout Angling Club	Chairman, A.M. Allan, Drummond Hall, Murthly, Perthshire.
New Galloway Angling Association	J. McCubbing, Carsons Knowe, New Galloway. Tel: (064 42) 448
North Uist Angling Club	J. Cheyne, 6 Clachan, Locheport, North Uist PA82 5EU. Tel: (08764) 322
Peeblesshire Trout Fishing Association	D.G. Fyfe, 39 High Street, Peebles. Tel: (0721) 720131
Perth & District Anglers' Association	A. Fraser, 4 Fairhill Avenue, Perth.
Pitlochry Angling Club	R. Harriman, Sunnyknowe, Nursing Home Brae, Pitlochry, Perthshire. Tel: (0796) 2484
Rannoch & District Angling Club	J. Brown, The Square, Kinloch Rannoch, Perthshire. Tel: (0882) 632268
River Almond Angling Association	H. Meikle, 23 Glen Terrace, Deans, Livingston, West Lothian.
St. Andrews Angling Club	Secretary, 54 St. Nicholas Street, St. Andrews, Fife. Tel: (0334) 76347
St. Marys Loch Angling Club	J. Miller, 25 Abbotsford Court, Colinton Road, Edinburgh EH10 5EH. Tel: 031-447 4187.
Selkirk & District Angling Association	A. Murray, 40 Raeburn Meadows, Selkirk. Tel: (0750) 21534
Stanley & District Angling Club	Stewart Grant, 12a Perth Road, Stanley, Perth PH1 4NQ. Tel: (0738) 828179.
Stormont Angling Club	The Factor, Scone Estates Office, Scone Palace, Perth.
Stranraer & District Angling Association	J. Nimmo, Inchparks Schoolhouse, Stranraer DG9 8RR. Tel: (0776) 4568
Strathmore Angling Improvement Association	Mrs. A. Henderson, 364 Blackness Road, Dundee DD2 1SF. Tel: (0382) 68062
Turriff Angling Association	I. Masson, 6 Castle Street, Turriff AB53 7BJ.
Upper Annandale Angling Association	A. Dickson, Braehead, Woodfoot, Beattock, Dumfriesshire DG10 9PL. Tel: (06833) 592.
Upper Nithsdale Angling Club	K. Mclean, Pollock & McLean, Solicitors, 61 High Street, Sanquhar DG4 6DT. Tel: (0659) 50241
Whiteadder Angling Association	R. Baker, Milburn House, Duns, Berwickshire. Tel: (0361) 83086

TURN TO PAGE 58 FOR GAME FISHING GAZETTEER

STATIC FLY FOR LOCH TROUT

by Alan Spence

Away back in the mists of time when my juvenile hand first cast a tentative fly upon the waters of the Borders, wet fly was the principle method used on Tweed and its tributaries. Gradually on Scottish lowland rivers dry fly has attracted an increasing number of adherents with, certainly on my home waters, this technique producing at least an equal number of trout and further more these are generally a better class of fish.

On lochs and reservoirs a cast of traditional wet flies, "suggestive" patterns, the materials and colours used in their dressing emphasised a point in an insect's life cycle as it emerged from water into the air. Fished from a drifting boat in a breeze the Butcher, Peter Ross and a host of other traditional patterns probably still account for the majority of trout caught from Scottish lochs. These of course depend upon not only the key factors in the dressing but the movement imparted upon them by the angler as he works them back towards the boat.

For the stillwater angler dry fly may be employed as a last ditch effort when a combination of calm and bright conditions make a team of traditional wet flies impractical. Yet there are many weather conditions when stillwater trout will take a static floating or sub-surface fly, even in circumstances which would suggest a different approach.

There is a vast difference, of course, between dry fly fishing on rivers to the same method employed on a stillwater. For the river angler dry fly means perpetual motion - a

trout rises - the artificial fly cast to cover it - the current carries the offering down - lift off and cast again. On stillwaters although this term is not completely accurate, patience is the watchword here. Depending upon the wind speed the fly or flies may either lie static or drift slowly round with the wind.

Static surface and sub-surface fishing on lochs is an excellent method for a number of reasons, not least for the fact that there are times when trout simply refuse to look at a moving fly. This usually occurs on waters rich in natural food when trout become focussed on one particular type of insect, on or near the surface. A bonus is that loch dry fly gives a break from casting and retrieving during a long day on the water. It is less tiring for the older or handicapped angler and it is eminently suitable for the bone idle lazy angler such as myself. It is even possible to sit down on the bank when dry fly fishing on stillwaters, a double bonus here in both resting one's legs and being less obvious to the quarry.

So what about tackle? Obviously, a floating line is essential and may be double or forward tapered, a braided tapered leader is useful while at times point material may need to be as light as 4lbs or even 3lbs b.s. Just about any rod will do the job provided it is of a reasonable light rating, not over AFTM 7, anything heavier means you are missing a lot of sport and risking broken leaders. My own preference is for an 11ft 6in butt actioned rod rated four to six. Disadvantages in being unable to cast half a mile with this outfit are far outweighed by the very small number of fish lost during playing. As yet I am unaware of any manufacturer building specialist rods for the stillwater and big river dry fly fisherman. Something medium to tip actioned between ten and eleven feet rated 4 to 6 would fill the bill for a smart lift off from the surface and a firm strike. So far it does not appear to exist but it is a poor worker who blames his tools. A selection of appropriate dry flies and nymphs plus line grease and degreaser completes the outfit.

When do you fish for loch trout with the floating fly or semi submerged fly? Well the answer is any time fish are seen moving on or near the surface. Not necessarily the classic ring when a surface insect is taken, but the boil or swirl or the dorsal fin breaking the surface as a trout takes an insect about to hatch. On waters where small midges hatch in prolific numbers trout may be seen actually swimming round in circles. Whether their intake is in the same manner as a feeding basking shark I am uncertain, but certainly at these times they cannot be distracted with a moving fly or lure - occasionally a pupae imitation is taken but with such a wide choice of food this can be something of a lucky dip.

Artificial imitative static flies used by the angler in stillwater should roughly match the size of the natural insects hatching at the time. This may range from tiny midges almost impossible to imitate, to large fluttering sedge flies which bring the trout boiling and slashing to the surface. Yet there are times, mainly in calms or light ripples, when fussy trout may take a smaller than the natural artificial. Or in a good breeze a larger pattern may prove more

visible to the trout, and certainly easier seen by the angler.

The size range therefore can be from a size 20 dry midge to a size 10 for a sedge. As discussed earlier many trout seen feeding near the surface are taking not the adult fly but the pupae as it nears the surface film in readiness to hatching. A selection of artificial flies should include pupae imitations in black, brown, green and red. A pheasant tail herl body seems to make an acceptable offering for a number of different natural midges. Add to this some adult dry flies and sedge pupae or where lake olives occur appropriate imitations.

All tackled up and ready to go! First of all the static fly is at its least effective from a drifting boat driving downwind before a steady breeze. Under these conditions a team of traditional loch wet flies worked back to the boat wins hands down every time. Otherwise from the bank or anchored boat I have found the static fly to work well in anything from flat calms to a fresh breeze - say something around Force 4.

Before starting there are several methods of rigging the leader to give the angler the best of both worlds. First, when fishing the static loch fly it is possible to hedge one's bets - in other words use two flies. It makes sense to have an imitation of the adult and hatching fly on the leader at the same time, brave souls may even try a three fly cast giving the option of a different colour also. When I try this on rivers, the rapid quick fire casting usually results in an almighty tangle, the slower pace of the game on stillwaters makes this a less regular occurence.

The leader may be made up in a number of ways, with the floating fly on the point or on the dropper, or again you can have a midge pupae suspended between two dry flies. In flat calms the leader must be degreased to sink it into the surface film. When a fresh breeze blows it must be treated with floatant to keep the flies on the surface. A number of permutations of degreasing say the droppers and treating intermediate sections with floatant - allows a variety of depths to be fished. Employing this method with say three flies on the cast allows the option of one fly on the surface, one just below, with the point fly six inches to a foot down.

When fishing with a mixture of floating and sub-surface flies the floater can act as a bite indicator to sunk flies and takes to these are not always readily visible. With a dry fly on the dropper, a take on the sunk point fly can be seen by the floater moving away. Somewhat disconcerting is, with the dry fly on the point in this instance, when a fish takes the sunk fly the former moves back towards the angler.

Whether fishing from bank or anchored boat my favourite method is to cast across the wind and allow the surface drift to swing the flies around which they do at a surprising speed. In bright conditions polarising glasses are essential to keep an eye on their progress - as they do so the line may be inclined to slacken but a very gentle retrieve keeps the angler in touch. It is in fact almost like wet fly river fishing, but in slow motion. Other than in flat calms the line can be recovered in the normal way before recasting, a steady figure of eight retrieve with the customary dropper dibble before lifting off.

The thing is, do you fish the water or cast to rising fish? A loch boiling with trout does not always guarantee success as I found out while compiling this piece in July 1993. On arrival at the waterside for an evening session, so dense were the number of newly hatched caneis transposing to the spinner stage on clothing, face and glasses that seeing to tie on the appropriate artificial was almost impossible.

Within a few minutes trout were rising everywhere, many right in the margins virtually below the rod tip. Conditions were virtually flat calm, the hatching caneis crawling into eyes and nostrils. The trout rose steadily and steadfastly ignored the cunningly tied and perfectly presented artificial caneis spinner. It was not until a cold northwest wind drove the majority of fish down, leaving only the occasional surface feeder, that contact was made with a trout.

During a heavy hatch with plenty of fish rising it is probably best to fish the water as sooner or later this will be seen and hopefully taken by a trout. The same applies when very few trout rise, cast out and let the wind carry the line and leader round. At times when trout are rising steadily the moving fish should be covered. For instance to see a fish rising steadily approaching up wind, it would be futile not to give it the opportunity to see the artificial.

Not all natural flies taken by stillwater trout are aquatic. Some of the best opportunities for the angler who wants to fish a static fly is when terrestrial flies are blown upon the water. Mainly this is a day time occurence which seldom fails to bring a response from the trout. Of all the insects blown on the water three can be figured out for special attention, the hawthorn fly, the heather fly and the gangling crane fly or as it is known in angling circles the Daddy Longlegs, in Scotland often termed simply Jennies.

Initially due to the size of the insect, trout seem to treat the appearance of Jennies with some suspicion, but once their apetite is whetted it can bring some of the larger fish on to feed making spectacular rises, slashing at the meaty mouthful or even at times apparently drowning the insect with a blow from the tail.

When terrestrials of any kind are on the water, fly identification is easier for the angler while furthermore there is only the need to imitate the adult fly. Even so there is some merit in fishing two flies, one floating the other soggy or awash. It usually takes a light breeze to bring a fall of terrestrials, which makes for an easy life for the bank angler who should head for the shore from which the wind is blowing. In these circumstances there is found invariably a stretch of calm water between the bank and where the ripple starts, an area well worth exploiting as fish seem to cruise the ripple edge looking for the next meal to be blown from the bank. Anglers without ethics may walk around kicking any bankside growth to encourage insects to emerge from hiding, a form of natural ground baiting which I have indulged in on occasions with varying degrees of success.

Unlike normal loch tactics when the fly or lure is being actively retrieved by the angler when the trout more or less hooks itself, the static fly angler must strike to set the hook. But when do you strike? Generally if the fly is sub-surface the strike should be made at the first sign of activity in the region of the fly or flies. It may be a slight disturbance on the surface, or a blink of silver as a fish turns, or the movement of a floating fly fished on the same cast as discussed earlier.

Other indications of fishy interest may be seen in any movement of the fly line, the red joint between fly line and braided leader is usually highly visible, or watch the loop of line between the rod tip and the water. A straightening of this usually means a bite.

When fishing a fly actually floating on the surface the strike must be more controlled, but to my mind there is no hard and fast rule such as counting to three. Each case must be treated on its merits, in some instances on a taught line the trout will actually hook itself. There are times when a fish drowns rather than takes the surface fly, nothing must be done but "feel" gently for the fish taking the fly which is now below the surface. In general the larger the fly the more leisurely the strike, but personally I find in most instances that by the time the rise has registered and the brain signals the arm to move, the majority of takers are hooked.

During the 1993 season I have been experimenting with a number of fly dressings in an attempt to make an all purpose static fly for stillwater fishing. The results have not been sensational, but on seven stillwater outings using these there has only been one blank and even so, on this occasion, two trout were lost, one in fact breaking the leader. The pattern has proved useful on rivers also, having accounted for brown trout up to 2lbs.

The dressings are designed to imitate an aquatic insect in the act of hatching, but also to give the impression of dry fly on the surface be it hatching or egg laying. The idea is by no means a new one, there are many emerger patterns available to meet this situation already. Where this differs is that it rides on the surface and protrudes below it also. It is in fact a "Paradox" a dry fly, nymph, pupae and even wet fly in one.

The tying is on long shank hooks such as Partridge Captain Hamilton, Nymph Hooks mainly in size 14 and 16. The Paradox fly can be adapted to a number of dressings but the materials must be chosen carefully to ensure buoyancy on the top half and weight or water absorbency on the lower. The bodies contain a large proportion of copper wire either as an underbody, or depending upon the contents of your local council domestic refuse skip, the finished body.

From the innards of old radios comes a soft port wine coloured copper wire, virtually the same colour as cock pheasant centre tail - this forms a finished body. Other dressings use gold or silver wire as an underbody, shining through the outer covering of soft mobile herl - dyed ostrich being the most suitable for this. For buoyancy a thorax of seals fur can be worked in and the flies float best with a double hackle.

Procedure for tying the wire only body is as follows:

Start behind the hook eye with the tying silk taking it down in loose turns to the bend of the hook. Here tie in the wine coloured copper wire then return the silk two thirds to threequarters way up the hook shank. Now in close touching turns from the body of copper wire tying the end off with the silk at a distance form the hook eye to leave room for a thorax and double hackle. Wax the thread and dub with thorax material before tying in two hackles, wind these on and tie off behind the eye.

For flies with a wire underbody the technique differs slightly:

Start behind the eye with the tying silk but this time tie in the wire at a distance from the eye to leave room for the thorax and hackles. Wind the wire in close touching turns to the bend and here secure the overbody material with a couple or so turns of wire. Wind the herl palmer fashion back towards the eye then rib with the silver or gold wire. Trim both off and complete with thorax and hackle as before. This gives a really translucent body, while the ostrich herl is extremely mobile and lifelike in the water.

Variations can be used by incorporating white breathing tubes as in midge pupae patterns, or a small tail can be added to complete the illusion of an insect emerging from it pupael shuck near the surface. Testing these dressings in a tumbler will show they hang truly vertical in the water, under fishing conditions this does not appear to be always so, rather the body may be at 45 degrees to the surface film but the important thing is that the hackle is maintained upon the surface while the body penetrates below.

When fishing apply floatant to the hackle but in the instance of the herl bodies degrease this for the best performance.

Proper dry fly patterns for loch fishing are numerous, many imitative dressings are available but something black and uncomplicated such as the Williams Favourite should not be ignored. For buoyancy a palmered pattern Zulu and such like, come in handy while the G & H deerhair sedge is practically unsinkable. I use this latter pattern often as a "float" for a team of pupae and trout persist in taking it. Some direct imitations, e.g. Adult Midge, Hawthorn Fly and Heather Fly do not go amiss but be aware of what is hatching from or being blown upon the water. In a similar vein there are many patterns for midge and sedge pupae which are suitable for static loch fishing, too numerous to list but again if in doubt black does not go amiss.

Dressings for Paradox.

The wire body version or Purple Paradox

Hook –	Partridge Captain Hamilton Nymph Hook 14 or 16
Tying Silk –	Maroon
Body –	Port wine coloured copper wire

Thorax –	Maroon seals fur
Hackle –	Dark red game

Dressing for herl body Paradox

Hook –	As above
Tying silk –	To match body colour
Body –	Green, black or buff ostrich herl
Thorax –	To match overbody
Underbody –	Silver or gold wire
Rib –	Same as underbody
Hackle –	Double badger

Do not wind on the herl body too tightly but ensure that the underbody shows through to maintain translucent effect.

Choosing a fly – Loch Hakel, Sutherland

CLOSE SEASON

The following are the statutory close season dates for trout and salmon fishing in Scotland.

TROUT

The close season for trout in Scotland is from 7 October to 14 March, both days inclusive, but many clubs extend this close season still further to allow the fish to reach better condition.

Fresh trout may not be sold between the end of August and the beginning of April, and not at any time if less than eight inches long.

SALMON

Net Fishing	Rod Fishing	River District
1 Sept-15 Feb	1 Nov-15 Feb	Add
27 Aug-10 Feb	1 Nov-10 Feb	Ailort
27 Aug-10 Feb	1 Nov-10 Feb	Aline
27 Aug-10 Feb	1 Nov-10 Feb	Alness
27 Aug-10 Feb	1 Nov-10 Feb	Applecross
27 Aug-10 Feb	1 Nov-10 Feb	Arnisdale (Loch Hourn)
27 Aug-10 Feb	16 Oct-10 Feb	Awe
27 Aug-10 Feb	1 Nov-10 Feb	Ayr
27 Aug-10 Feb	1 Nov-10 Feb	Baa & Goladoir
27 Aug-10 Feb	1 Nov-10 Feb	Badachro & Kerry (Gairloch)
27 Aug-10 Feb	1 Nov-10 Feb	Balgay & Shieldaig
27 Aug-10 Feb	16 Oct-10 Feb	Beauly
27 Aug-10 Feb	1 Nov-10 Feb	Berriedale
10 Sept-24 Feb	1 Nov-24 Feb	Bervie
27 Aug-10 Feb	1 Nov-10 Feb	Bladenoch
27 Aug-10 Feb	1 Nov-10 Feb	Broom
27 Aug-10 Feb	16 Oct-31 Jan	Brora
10 Sept-24 Feb	1 Nov-24 Feb	Carradale
27 Aug-10 Feb	1 Nov-10 Feb	Carron (W. Ross)
10 Sept-24 Feb	1 Nov-24 Feb	Clayburn (Isle of Harris (East))
27 Aug-10 Feb	1 Nov-10 Feb	Clyde & Leven
27 Aug-10 Feb	1 Oct-25 Jan	Conon
14 Sept-28 Feb	15 Oct-28 Feb	Cree
27 Aug-10 Feb	17 Oct-10 Feb	Creed or Stornoway and Laxay (Isle of Lewis)
27 Aug-10 Feb	1 Nov-10 Feb	Creran (Loch Creran)
27 Aug-10 Feb	1 Nov-10 Feb	Croe & Shiel
27 Aug-10 Feb	1 Oct-31 Jan	Dee (Aberdeenshire)
27 Aug-10 Feb	1 Nov-10 Feb	Dee (Kirkcudbrightshire)
27 Aug-10 Feb	1 Nov-10 Feb	Deveron
27 Aug-10 Feb	1 Nov-10 Feb	Don
27 Aug-10 Feb	1 Nov-10 Feb	Doon
1 Sept-15 Feb	16 Oct-15 Feb	Drummachloy or Glenmore (Isle of Bute)
27 Aug-10 Feb	16 Oct-10 Feb	Dunbeath
21 Aug- 4 Feb	1 Nov-31 Jan	Earn
1 Sept-15 Feb	1 Nov-15 Feb	Echaig
1 Sept-15 Feb	1 Nov-15 Feb	Esk, North
1 Sept-15 Feb	1 Nov-15 Feb	Esk, South
27 Aug-10 Feb	1 Nov-10 Feb	Ewe (Isle of Harris (West))
27 Aug-10 Feb	6 Oct-10 Feb	Findhorn
10 Sept-24 Feb	1 Nov-24 Feb	Fleet (Kirkcudbright)
10 Sept-24 Feb	1 Nov-24 Feb	Fleet (Sutherland)
27 Aug-10 Feb	1 Nov-10 Feb	Forss
27 Aug-10 Feb	1 Nov-31 Jan	Forth
1 Sept-15 Feb	1 Nov-15 Feb	Fyne, Shira & Aray (Loch Fyne)
10 Sept-24 Feb	1 Nov-24 Feb	Girvan
27 Aug-10 Feb	1 Nov-10 Feb	Glenelg
27 Aug-10 Feb	1 Nov-10 Feb	Gour
27 Aug-10 Feb	1 Nov-10 Feb	Greiss, Laxdale or Thunga
27 Aug-10 Feb	1 Nov-10 Feb	Grudie or Dionard
27 Aug-10 Feb	1 Nov-10 Feb	Gruinard and Little Gruinard
27 Aug-10 Feb	1 Oct-11 Jan	Halladale, Strathy, Naver & Borgie
27 Aug-10 Feb	1 Oct-10 Jan	Helmsdale
27 Aug-10 Feb	1 Oct-11 Jan	Hope and Polla or Strathbeg
10 Sept-24 Feb	1 Nov-24 Feb	Howmore
27 Aug-10 Feb	1 Nov-10 Feb	Inchard
10 Sept-24 Feb	1 Nov-24 Feb	Inner (on Jura)
27 Aug-10 Feb	1 Nov-10 Feb	Inver
10 Sept-24 Feb	1 Nov-24 Feb	Iora (on Arran)
10 Sept-24 Feb	1 Nov-24 Feb	Irvine & Garnock
27 Aug-10 Feb	1 Nov-10 Feb	Kannaird
27 Aug-10 Feb	1 Nov-10 Feb	Kilchoan
27 Aug-10 Feb	1 Nov-10 Feb	Kinloch (Kyle of Tongue)
27 Aug-10 Feb	1 Nov-10 Feb	Kirkaig
27 Aug-10 Feb	1 Nov-10 Feb	Kishorn
27 Aug-10 Feb	1 Oct-10 Jan	Kyle of Sutherland
10 Sept-24 Feb	1 Nov-10 Feb	Laggan & Sorn (Isle of Islay)
27 Aug-10 Feb	1 Nov-10 Feb	Laxford

Net Fishing	Rod Fishing	River District	Net Fishing	Rod Fishing	River District
27 Aug-10 Feb	1 Nov-10 Feb	Little Loch Broom	27 Aug-10 Feb	1 Nov-10 Feb	Pennygowan or
27 Aug-10 Feb	1 Nov-10 Feb	Loch Duich			Glenforsa & Aros
27 Aug-10 Feb	1 Nov-10 Feb	Loch Luing			
27 Aug-10 Feb	17 Oct-10 Feb	Loch Roag	27 Aug-10 Feb	1 Nov-10 Feb	Resort
27 Aug-10 Feb	1 Nov-10 Feb	Lochy	1 Sept-15 Feb	1 Nov-15 Feb	Ruel
27 Aug-10 Feb	16 Oct-10 Feb	Lossie			
10 Sept-24 Feb	1 Nov-24 Feb	Luce	27 Aug-10 Feb	1 Nov-10 Feb	Sanda
27 Aug-10 Feb	1 Nov-10 Feb	Lussa	27 Aug-10 Feb	1 Nov-10 Feb	Scaddle
		(Isle of Mull)	10 Sept-24 Feb	1 Nov-24 Feb	Shetland Isles
			27 Aug-10 Feb	1 Nov-10 Feb	Shiel
27 Aug-10 Feb	1 Nov-10 Feb	Moidart	27 Aug-10 Feb	1 Nov-10 Feb	Sligachan
27 Aug-10 Feb	1 Nov-10 Feb	Morar	27 Aug-10 Feb	1 Nov-10 Feb	Snizort
20 Sept-24 Feb	1 Nov-24 Feb	Mullangaren,	27 Aug-10 Feb	1 Oct-10 Feb	Spey
		Horasary and	10 Sept-24 Feb	1 Nov-24 Feb	Stinchar
		Lochnaciste	27 Aug-10 Feb	1 Nov-10 Feb	Sunart
		(Isle of North Uist)			(except Earn)
			21 Aug- 4 Feb	16 Oct-14 Jan	Tay
27 Aug-10 Feb	1 Oct-10 Feb	Nairn	27 Aug-10 Feb	6 Oct-10 Jan	Thurso
27 Aug-10 Feb	1 Nov-10 Feb	Nell, Feochan	27 Aug-10 Feb	1 Nov-10 Feb	Torridon
		and Euchar	15 Sept-14 Feb	1 Dec-31 Jan	Tweed
27 Aug-10 Feb	16 Oct-14 Jan	Ness			
10 Sept-24 Feb	1 Dec-24 Feb	Nith	10 Sept-24 Feb	1 Nov- 9 Feb	Ugie
			27 Aug-10 Feb	1 Nov-10 Feb	Ullapool
			10 Sept-24 Feb	1 Dec-24 Feb	Urr
10 Sept-24 Feb	1 Nov-24 Feb	Orkney Isles			
27 Aug-10 Feb	1 Nov-10 Feb	Ormsary (Loch	27 Aug-10 Feb	1 Nov-10 Feb	Wick
		Killisport), Loch			
		Head & Stornoway	10 Sept-24 Feb	1 Nov-10 Feb	Ythan

There is no close season for coarse fishing.

THE FORTH FISHERY CONSERVATION TRUST

The Trust was formed in August 1987, with the aim of improving all the fisheries within the Forth catchment area which extends from Fifeness to Balquidder in the north, and Loch Katrine to Torness in the south. The initial aim was to purchase a boat to assist the Forth District Salmon Fishery Board stop illegal netting of salmon on the Estuary.

Within twelve weeks two 18ft high speed launches were acquired for use by the new Superintendent Water Bailiff, Ian Baird, and the impact on the illegal netting operations has been dramatic. The River Teith and its tributaries experienced a good run of spring salmon and sea trout are running through almost unhindered.

The Trust has also stimulated discussions on salmon poaching and fish conservation at the highest legal and government levels and will continue that dialogue.

Although a number of enthusiastic clubs have worked hard to open up fisheries, to restock and protect them, the Forth catchment area remains a virtually untapped fishery. These could be developed to provide leisure, tourism and employment for the region.

There are three major tasks the Trust wishes to undertake.

1. To increase efforts to eliminate all illegal fishing both on the estuary and throughout the whole river system.
2. To identify ownership of all stretches of water and fisheries in the area so that more effective supervision may be introduced.
3. To review the existing population and habitat of all fish species and assess the potential for increasing their numbers throughout the area.

This information will help all clubs, landowners and local inhabitants to make the best possible use of available resources and improve the quality of salmon, sea trout and coarse fishing throughout the Forth catchment area.

Area Tourist Board
Scottish Borders Tourist Board

Director of Tourism
Scottish Borders Tourist Board
Municipal Buildings
High Street
Selkirk TD7 4JX.
Tel: Selkirk (0750) 20555

RIVER PURIFICATION BOARD
TWEED RIVER PURIFICATION BOARD

Burnbrae
Mossilee Road
Galashiels.
Tel: (0896) 2425

RIVERS

Water	Location	Species	Season	Permit available from	Other Information
Blackadder	Greenlaw	Brown Trout	1 Apr. to 6 Oct.	Greenlaw Angling Club J. Purves, 9 Wester Row, Greenlaw. All hotels.	No bait fishing till 15 Apr. Sunday fishing. No spinning. No Sunday competitions.
Bowmont Water	Morebattle	Trout Grayling	15 Mar. to 6 Oct.	D.Y. Gray, 17 Mainsfield Avenue, Morebattle.	No ground baiting, No Sunday fishing from Primeside Mill up.
Eden Water	Kelso	Brown Trout	1 Apr. to 30 Sept.	Forrest & Sons, 35 The Square, Kelso. Tel: (0573) 224687. Intersport, 43 The Square, Kelso. Tel: (0573) 223381. Border Hotel, Woodmarket, Kelso TD5 7AX. Tel: (0573) 224791.	Fly only. No spinning. Restricted to 3 rods.
	Gordon	Brown Trout	15 Mar. to 6 Oct.	J.H. Fairgrieve, Burnbrae, Gordon. Tel: (057 381) 357.	No Spinning. No Sunday fishing.
Ettrick & Yarrow	Bowhill	Salmon Trout	1 Feb.-30 Nov. 15 Mar.-30 Sep.	Buccleuch Estates Ltd., Estate Office, Bowhill, Selkirk. Tel: (0750) 20753.	Fly only.
	Selkirk	Brown Trout	1 Apr. to 30 Sept.	P. & E. Scott (Newsagents), 6 High Street, Selkirk. Tel: (0750) 20749.	Night fishing 15 May-14 Sept. Week ticket only. No minnows or spinning. No Sundays.
Ettrick	Ettrick Bridge	Brown Trout Salmon	1 Apr.-30 Sep. 1 Feb.-30 Nov.	Ettrickshaws Hotel, Tel: (0750) 52229.	Packed Lunches and flask for residents. Permits also available for other waters.
Kale Water	Eckford	Trout Grayling	1 Apr. to 30 Sept.	Mr. Graham, Eckford Cottage, Eckford, Kelso. Tel: (083-55) 255.	No Sundays.
	Morebattle	Trout Grayling	15 Mar. to 6 Oct.	D.Y. Gray, 17 Mainsfield Avenue, Morebattle. Templehall Hotel, Morebattle. Tel: (05734) 249.	No ground baiting. No Sunday fishing.

Water	Location	Species	Season	Permit available from	Other Information
Leader Water	Lauderdale	Trout	15 Mar. to 6 Oct.	R. & A. Dickson Newsagent, Lauder. J.S. Main, Saddler, 87 High Street, Haddington. Tel: (062 082) 2148. Lauder Post Office. Tower Hotel, Oxton, By Lauder. Tel: (05785) 235. Anglers Choice, 23 Market Square, Melrose TD6 9PL. Tel: (089 682) 3070.	No Spinning. Sunday fishing. No Grayling fishing.
Leader Water/ Tweed	Earlston	Trout	15 Mar. to 30 Sept.	Earlston Angling Association P. Hessett, 2 Arnot Place, Earlston. Tel: 577. E. & M. Browne, Newsagent, Earlston. L. & M. Pollard Newsagents, The Square, Earlston. Tel: (0896) 84330. Anglers Choice, 23 Market Square, Melrose. Tel: (089 682) 3070. Hotels & pubs.	No Sunday fishing. Other restrictions as per permit.
Liddle Water	Newcastle-ton	Sea Trout	1 May to 30 Sept.	J.D. Ewart, Fishing Tackle Shop, Newcastleton. Tel: (03873) 75257.	Day & weekly tickets available.
	South Roxburgh shire	Salmon Sea Trout Herling Brown Trout	1 Feb.-31 Oct. 1 May to 30 Sept. 15 Apr. to 30 Sept.	Esk & Liddle Fisheries, R.J.B. Hill, Bank of Scotland Buildings, Langholm. Tel: (03873) 80628. George Graham, Hagg-on-Esk, Old School, Canonbie. Tel: (03873) 71416. Peter Lillie, 19 Rowanburn, Canonbie. Tel: (03873) 71224.	Spinning allowed until 14 Apr. and otherwise only when water is above markers at Newcastleton, Kershopefoot and Penton Bridges. No Sunday fishing.
Liddle Water	Newcastleton	Sea Trout	1 May to 30 Sept.	J.D. Ewart, Fishing Tackle Shop, Newcastleton. Tel: (03873) 75257.	Day & weekly tickets available.
	South Roxburgh shire	Salmon Sea Trout Herling Brown Trout	1 Feb.-31 Oct. 1 May to 30 Sept. 15 Apr. to 30 Sept.	Esk & Liddle Fisheries, R.J.B. Hill, Bank of Scotland Buildings, Langholm. Tel: (03873) 80628. George Graham, Hagg-on-Esk, Old School, Canonbie. Tel: (03873) 71416. Peter Lillie, 19 Rowanburn, Canonbie. Tel: (03873) 71224	Spinning allowed until 14 Apr. and otherwise only when water is above markers at Newcastleton, Kershopefoot and Penton Bridges. No Sunday fishing.

Water	Location	Species	Season	Permit available from	Other Information
Lyne Water	Tweed Junction to Flemington Bridge	Trout Grayling	1 Apr. to 30 Sept.	Peeblesshire Trout Fishing Association D.G. Fyfe, 39 High Street, Peebles. Tel: (0721) 720131. Tweeddale Tackle Centre, 1 Bridgegate, Peebles EH45 8RZ. Tel: (0721) 720979. Sonny's Sports Shop, Innerleithen. Tel: (0896) 830806. Tweed Valley Hotel, Walkerburn. Tel: (089 687) 636. J. Dickson & Son, 21 Frederick Street, Edinburgh. Tel: 031-225 4218. Crook Inn, Tweedsmuir. Tel: (089 97) 272.	No Sundays. No spinning. No bait fishing April & Sept. Tickets also cover Tweed.
Oxnam Water	Morebattle	Trout Grayling	15 Mar. to 6 Oct.	D.Y. Gray, 17 Mainsfield Avenue, Morebattle.	No ground baiting, no Sunday fishing from Bloodylaws up.
Teviot	Kelso	Brown Trout Grayling	1 Apr. to 30 Sept.	Forrest & Sons, 35, The Square, Kelso. Tel: (0573) 224687. Intersport, 43, The Square, Kelso. Tel: (0573) 223381. Border Hotel, Woodmarket, Kelso TD5 7AX. Tel: (0573) 224791.	No Sundays. Restrictions on spinning. No maggots or ground bait. Size limit 10″.
	Eckford	Salmon Sea Trout Brown Trout	1 Feb.-30 Nov. 15 Mar. to 30 Sep.	Mr. Graham Eckford Cottage, Eckford, Kelso. Tel: (083-55) 255.	No Sundays. Limited to 4 day permits. Bait and spinning 15 Feb.-15 Sept., only. Spinning for Trout and Grayling prohibited.
	Jedforest	Salmon	1 Feb. to 31 Nov.	Jedforest Angling Association J.T. Renilson, 4 Canongate, Jedburgh.	No Sundays. Salmon: 4 rods per day. Spinning 15 Feb.-14 Sept. Fly only 15 Sept.-30 Nov.
		Trout	1 Apr. to 30 Sept.	Shaws (Newsagent), 10 Canongate, Jedburgh.	No Sundays, No spinning. Fly only until 1st May.
Teviot (and Ale Slitrig Borthwick Rule)	Hawick	Brown Trout	15 Mar. to 30 Sept.	Porteous & Newcombe, Howgate, Hawick. The Pet Store, 1 Union Street, Hawick. Tel: (0450) 73543.	All rules and regulations on ticket.
		Salmon	1 Feb. to 30 Nov.	The Pet Store, Union Street, Hawick. Tel: (0450) 73543.	
		Grayling	1 Jan. to 30 Sept.	The Pet Store, 1 Union Street, Hawick. Tel: (0450) 73543.	

Water	Location	Species	Season	Permit available from	Other Information
Teviot	Above Chesters	Salmon Sea Trout	1 Feb. to 30 Nov.	The Pet Store, Union Street, Hawick. Tel: (0450) 73543.	All rules and regulations on ticket. Limited to 9 rods on 3 beats per day. (9 day tickets Mon-Fri. 6 visitor season tickets only on application to:) Mr. R.A. Sutherland, Hawick Angling Club, 20 Longhope Drive, Hawick TD9 0DU. Tel: 0450 75150.
Tweed	Tweedsmuir	Brown Trout Grayling	1 Apr. to 30 Sept.	Crook Inn, Tweedsmuir. Tel: (08997) 272.	All rules and regulations on permits.
	Peeblesshire (substantial stretch of river)	Trout Grayling	1 Apr. to 30 Sept.	Tweed Valley Hotel, Walkerburn. Tel: (089 687) 636. F. & D. Simpson, 28/29 West Preston Street, Edinburgh EH8 9PZ. Tel: 031-667 3058. J. Dickson & Son, 21 Frederick Street, Edinburgh. Tel: 031-225 4218.	No spinning. No bait fishing, Apr. & Sept. No Sunday fishing. Tickets also cover Lyne Water. Waders desirable. Fly only on Tweed from Lynefoot upstream.
	Peebles (Wire Bridge Pool to Nutwood Pool - excluding Kailzie)	Salmon	21 Feb. to 30 Nov.	Peeblesshire Salmon Fishing Association Seasons: Blackwood & Smith, W.S., 39 High Street, Peebles. Tel: (0721) 720131. Day permits: Tweeddale Tackle Centre, 1 Bridgegate, Peebles EH45 8RZ. Tel: (0721) 720979.	Strictly fly fishing only. No Sunday fishing. Other regulations on tickets.
	Walkerburn	Salmon/ Sea Trout Trout	1 Feb to 30 Nov. 1 Apr.-30 Sep.	Tweed Valley Hotel, Walkerburn. Tel: (089 687) 636.	Salmon tickets for hotel guests only after 14 Sept. Special salmon and trout weeks, tuition. Trout and grayling permits available to all.
	Peel	Salmon Sea Trout	1 Feb. to 30 Nov.	Tweed Valley Hotel, Walkerburn. Tel: (089 687) 636.	Private 2-rod salmon beat on south bank. Week or day lets Spring/Summer. Week lets only October and November. Angling Course September.
	Nest	Salmon Sea Trout Trout	1 Feb.to 30 Nov. 1 Apr.-30 Sep.	Tweed Valley Hotel, Walkerburn. Tel: (089 687) 636.	Private salmon/sea trout beat approx. 1¾ miles, 4 rods. Fly only 15 Sept to 30 Nov. Trout and grayling permits available to all. Week or day lets Spring/Summer. Week lets only October and November. Angling Course September.

Water	Location	Species	Season	Permit available from	Other Information
Tweed cont.	Haystoun (Beat 1½ miles)	Salmon Sea Trout	1 Feb. to 30 Nov.	Fraser's Salmon Fishing & Hire Ltd., 16 Kingsmuir Crescent, Peebles. Tel: (0721) 22960.	No spinning in autumn - fly only. No Sunday fishing. Rods limited to 6 per day. Part-time ghillie included in permit price. 8 named salmon pools.
	Kingsmeadow (Beat ¾ mile)	Salmon Sea Trout	15 Feb. to 30 Nov.	Fraser's Salmon Fishing & Hire Ltd., 16 Kingsmuir Crescent, Peebles. Tel: (0721) 22960.	Spinning allowed 15 Feb to 14 Sept. Rods limited to 3 per day. Easy car access to beat. Part-time ghillie included in permit price. 5 named salmon pools.
	Glenormiston (Beat 1½ miles)	Salmon Sea Trout	15 Feb. to 30 Nov.	Fraser's Salmon Fishing & Hire Ltd., 16 Kingsmuir Crescent, Peebles. Tel: (0721) 22960.	Fly only. Rods limited to 7 per day. Easy car access to beat.
	Galashiels	Trout	1 Apr. to 30 Sept.	Messrs. J. & A. Turnbull, 30 Bank Street, Galashiels. Tel: (0896) 3191. Kingsknowes Hotel, Galashiels. Tel: (0896) 58375. Anglers Choice, 23 Market Square, Melrose TD6 9PL. Tel: (0896) 823070.	No Sundays. Day tickets available on Saturdays. No spinning.
	Melrose	Trout Grayling	1 Apr.to 6 Oct. 7 Oct.to 15 Mar.	Melrose & District Angling Association Anglers Choice, 23 Market Square, Melrose. Tel: (0896) 823070.	No spinning. No ground baiting. No Sundays. Minnow fishing not permitted. Spinning reels of all types prohibited.
	Melrose (Ravenswood Tweedswood)	Brown Trout	1 Apr. to 30 Sept.	Anglers Choice, 23 Market Square, Melrose. Tel: (0896) 823070.	
	Melrose (Pavilion)	Salmon Sea Trout	1 Feb. to 30 Nov.	Anglers Choice, 23 Market Square, Melrose. Tel: 3070.	Fly only - 1 to 15 Feb. and 15 Sept. to 30 Nov. Feb. 16 to Sept. 14 fly and spinning.
	St. Boswells	Brown Trout	1 Apr. to 30 Sept.	Dryburgh Abbey Hotel, St. Boswells. Tel: (0835) 22261. Anglers Choice, 23 Market Square, Melrose. Miss A. Laing, Newsagent, St. Boswells.	Fly only 1 Apr. to 1 May. No ground baiting. No bait fishing until May 1. No Sundays. No spinning tackle. No coarse fishing allowed outside season. Access to restricted beats by special permits only. Full details shown on permit.
Tweed (and Teviot)	Kelso	Grayling	1 May-31 Aug. 1 Dec.-31 Jan.	Forrest & Sons, 35, The Square, Kelso. Tel: (0573) 224687. Intersport, 43, The Square, Kelso. Tel: (0573) 223381. Border Hotel, Woodmarket, Kelso. Tel: (0573) 224791.	Spinning restrictions. No maggots or ground bait. No fishing above Roxburgh Viaduct between 15 & 30 Sept. incl.

Water	Location	Species	Season	Permit available from	Other Information
Tweed (and Teviot) cont.				Tweedside Tackle, 36-38 Bridge Street, Kelso. Tel: (0573) 225306.	Day/week/season. Tweedside Tackle have a computerised salmon letting facility on various beats on the Tweed.
	Kelso	Brown Trout Coarse Fish	1 Apr. to 30 Sept.	Forrest & Sons, 35, The Square, Kelso. Tel: (0573) 224687.	
Tweed	Cornhill	Salmon Sea Trout Brown Trout	Salmon 1 Feb. to 30 Nov.	Tillmouth Park Hotel, Cornhill-on-Tweed, Northumberland TD12 4UU. Tel: (0890) 2255.	No Sundays. No worming. Boats and ghillies available. Special terms for residents.
	Ladykirk	Brown Trout	19 Mar. to 8 Oct.	Victoria Hotel, Norham, Tel: (0289) 82237.	No spinning. No ground baiting. Fly only above Norham Bridge to West Ford. No Sundays.
	Horncliffe (Tidal)	Trout, Grayling, Roach, Dace and Eel.		No permit required.	
Whiteadder & Dye & Tributaries	30 miles	Brown/ Rainbow Trout	15 Mar. to 30 Sept.	Whiteadder Angling Association Mr. Cowan, Crumstane, Duns. (Bailiff). Tel: (0361) 83235.	No Sundays. Fly only before 15 Apr. Worm from 15 Apr. only. Minnow from 1 May only. Tickets in advance. Size limit 8 inches. River stocked annually.
Whiteadder & Dye & Tributaries	30 miles	Brown/ Rainbow Trout	15 Mar. to 30 Sept.	Whiteadder Angling Association Mr. Cowan, Crumstane, Duns. (Bailiff). Tel: (0361) 83235.	No Sundays. Fly only before 15 Apr. Worm from 15 Apr. only. Minnow from 1 May only. Tickets in advance. Size limit 8 inches. River stocked annually.

LOCHS & RESERVOIRS

Water	Location	Species	Season	Permit available from	Other Information
Acreknowe Reservoir	Hawick	Brown/ Rainbow Trout	15 Mar. to end Sept.	Porteous & Newoomo, Howgate, Hawick. The Pet Shop, 1 Union Street, Hawick. Tel: (0450) 73543. Mr. R.A. Sutherland, 20 Longhope Drive, Hawick. Tel: (0450) 75150.	Ticket covers all other trout waters managed by Hawick Angling Club. Boat available from Pet Shop. Fly fishing only.
Alemoor Loch	Hawick	Brown Trout Perch Pike		As Acreknowe	Bank fishing only.
Fruid Reservoir	Tweedsmuir	Brown Trout	1 Apr. to 30 Sept.	Waterkeeper, Victoria Lodge, Talla Reservoir. Tel: (08997) 2098 (8am to 8pm).	Fly fishing. Spinning and worm fishing. Sunday fishing. 2 boats and bank fishing.

Water	Location	Species	Season	Permit available from	Other Information
Hellmoor Loch	Hawick	Brown Trout		As Acreknowe	No Boat. No competitions. Limit 6 trout.
Loch Lindean	Selkirk	Brown Trout	Apr. to Oct.	P. & E. Scott (Newsagent), 6 High Street, Selkirk TD7 4DA. Tel: (0750) 20749.	2 boats available.
Loch of the Lowes and St. Mary's Loch	Selkirk	Brown Trout Pike Perch Eels	1 Apr-30 Sept 1 May to 30 Sept	St. Mary's A.C. per Sec. J. Miller, 25 Abbotsford Court, Colinton Road, Edinburgh. Gordon Arms Hotel, Yarrow. Countrylife, 229 Balgreen Road, Edinburgh. F. & D. Simpson, 28 West Preston Street, Edinburgh. Hook, Line & Sinker, 20 Morningside Road, Edinburgh. Sonny's Tackle Shop, Innerleithen. Tibbie Shiels Inn, St. Mary's Loch, Yarrow, Selkirk. Tel: (0750) 42231. Anglers Choice, 23 Market Square, Melrose. Glen Cafe (Loch side). Tweeddale Tackle Centre, North Gate, Peebles.	Fly fishing only, until 30th April thereafter spinning and bait allowed. Club fishing apply Secretary or keeper. Sunday fishing. Weekly permits & rowing boats from keeper, Mr. Brown (0750) 42243. Outboard engines of upto 5H.P. may be used, but none available for hire. No float fishing. Loch of the Lowes is bank fishing only. River Tweed Protection order applies. Club memberships available.
Megget Reservoir	Megget Valley	Trout	1 Apr. to 30 Sept.	Tibbie Shiels Inn, St. Mary's Loch, Yarrow, Selkirk. Tel: (0750) 42231	No bait fishing. 6 boats available. Max. bag limit 10 fish.
Peeblesshire Lochs	Tweed Valley	Brown/ Rainbow Trout	Apr. to Oct.	Tweed Valley Hotel, Walkerburn. Tel: (089 687) 636.	Stocked private lochans. Wild brown trout loch.
Portmore Game Fisheries	Peebles-Eddleston	Wild Brown Trout Rainbow Trout	1 Apr. to 31 Oct.	Portmore Game Fisheries at the Loch. Tel: (0968) 675684.	Average weight of fish caught: 2lbs. Popular flies: Lures at beginning; from May - dry & wet. Boats are available - contact: Steve McGeachie at above number.
Synton Loch	Hawick	Brown Trout		As Acreknowe Reservoir.	Boats available From Pet Store, 1 Union Street, Hawick. Fly only.
Talla Reservoir	Tweedsmuir	Brown Trout	1 Apr. to 30 Sept.	Waterkeeper, Victoria Lodge, Talla Reservoir. Tel: (08997) 2098 (8am to 8pm).	Fly fishing only.

Water	Location	Species	Season	Permit available from	Other Information
Upper Loch	Bowhill	Brown/ Rainbow Trout	1 Apr. to 28 Sept.	Buccleuch Estate Ltd., Estate Office, Bowhill, Selkirk. Tel: (0750) 20753.	Fly only. 2 rods per boat and limit of 8 fish per boat. Boat available on: Tues & Thurs all season, Mondays during June, July & Aug.
Watch Reservoir	Longformacus	Brown Trout Rainbow Trout	15 Mar.-30 Sept. All year	W.F. Renton, The Watch Fly Reservoir, Tel: (03617) 331 & (0289) 306028.	Sunday fishing. Fly only. Strictly no use of bait/maggots etc.
Whiteadder Reservoir	nr. Gifford	Brown Trout	1 Apr to 30 Sept.	Waterkeeper, Hungry Snout, Whiteadder Reservoir. Tel: (03617) 362 (8am to 8pm).	Bank fishing 1 June to 30 Sept. Sunday fishing. Fly fishing only. 4 boats are available.
Williestruther Loch	Hawick	Brown/ Rainbow Trout		As Acreknowe Reservoir.	Any legal method.
Wooden Loch	Eckford	Rainbow Trout	1 Apr.-31 Oct.	Mr. Graham Eckford Cottage, Eckford, Kelso. Tel: (083-55) 255.	1 boat. No bank fishing. Only rainbow trout after 30 Sept. Only 2 rods at any time. Advance booking necessary. No Sundays.

Area Tourist Board
Dumfries and Galloway Tourist Board

Director of Tourism,
Dumfries and Galloway Tourist Board
Douglas House,
Newton Stewart,
Wigtownshire DG8 6DQ.
Tel: Newton Stewart (0671) 2549

RIVER PURIFICATION BOARD
SOLWAY RIVER PURIFICATION BOARD

River's House, Irongray Road,
Dumfries DG2 0JE.
Tel: (0387) 720502.

RIVERS

Water	Location	Species	Season	Permit available from	Other information
Annan	Hoddom & Kinmount Estates Ecclefechan	Salmon Sea Trout Brown Trout	25 Feb. to 15 Nov.	Miss Marsh, 1 Bridge End Cottage, Hoddom, Lockerbie DG11 1BE. Tel: (05763) 488.	No Sunday fishing. Fly water unless the spinning mark is covered.
	Halleaths Estate Lockerbie	Salmon Sea Trout	25 Feb. to 15 Nov.	Messrs. McJerrow & Stevenson, Solicitors, 55 High Street, Lockerbie, Dumfriesshire. Tel: (05762) 2123.	Limited number of tickets.
	Royal Four Towns Water Lockerbie	Salmon Sea Trout Brown Trout Herling Chub Grilse	25 Feb. to 15 Nov.	Clerk to the Commissioners, of Royal Four Towns Fishing Mrs. K. Ratcliffe, Clerk, 'Jay-Ar', Preston House Road, Hightae, Lockerbie. Tel: 0387 810220. Castle Milk Estates Office, Norwood, Lockerbie. Tel: 057 65 203.	Boats prohibited. No shrimps, prawns or maggots. No Sunday fishing.
	St. Mungo Parish	Salmon Sea Trout Brown Trout	15 Mar. to 6 Oct. 25 Feb. to 15 Nov.	Castle Milk Estates Office, Norwood, Lockerbie. Tel: 057 65 203.	Fly fishing only. No Sunday fishing.
	Warmanbie Estate	Salmon Sea Trout Brown Trout	25 Feb. to 15 Nov.	Warmanbie Hotel & Restaurant, Annan DG12 5LL. Tel: (0461) 204015.	Fly, spinning, worm all season. Access to many other stretches.
Bladnoch	Newton Stewart	Salmon	1 Mar. to 31 Oct.	Newton Stewart Angling Association Galloway Guns & Tackle, 36 Arthur Street, Newton Stewart. Tel: (0671) 3404 Palakona Guest House, Queen Street, Newton Stewart DG8 6JL. Tel: (0671) 402323	
Cairn	Dumfries	Brown Trout Salmon Sea Trout	15 Mar.-31 Aug.	Dumfries & Galloway Angling Association, Secretary: D. Byers, 4 Bloomfield Edinburgh Road, Dumfries DG1 1SG. Tel: (0387) 53850.	Limited number of permits. No Sunday fishing. Restrictions depend on water level. Visitors Mon.-Fri. only.

Water	Location	Species	Season	Permit available from	Other Information
Cree (and Pencill Burn)	Drum-lamford Estate	Salmon Trout	April to October	The Keeper, The Kennels, Drumlamford Estate, Barrhill. Tel: (046 582) 256.	No Sunday fishing.
	Newton Stewart	Salmon Sea Trout	1 Mar. to 14 Oct.	Newton Stewart Angling Association Galloway Guns & Tackle, 36 Arthur Street, Newton Stewart. Tel: (0671) 3404.	No Sunday fishing.
Cross Waters of Luce	New Luce	Salmon Sea Trout	1 May to 31 Oct.	Stranraer & District Angling Association. The Sports Shop, 90 George Street, Stranraer. Tel: (0776) 2705.	No Sunday fishing. Live lobworm, branderings & magggots; fresh water baits. Day permits available for Piltanton Burn from Dunragit Angling Club.
Dee	Aboyne	Salmon Sea Trout	1 Feb. to 30 Sep.	Brooks House, Glen Tanar, Aboyne. Tel: (03398) 86451.	No Sunday fishing on Dee. Permits available for August only on Waterside & Ferrar Beats.
Black Water of Dee	Mossdale	Trout Pike Perch Salmon	15 Mar. to 30 Sept. 11 Feb. to 31 Oct.	Local Hotels & Shops.	
Esk	East Dumfries-shire	Salmon Sea Trout/ Herling Brown Trout	1 Feb.to 31 Oct. 1 May to 30 Sept. 15 Apr. to 30 Sept.	Esk & Liddle Fisheries R.J.B. Hill, Bank of Scotland Buildings, Langholm. Tel: (03873) 80628. George Graham, Hagg-on-Esk, Old School, Canonbie. Tel: (03873) 71416. Mrs. Pauline Wylie, Byreburnfoot, Canonbie. Tel: (03873) 71279.	Spinning allowed until 14 April and otherwise only when water is above markers at Skippers Bridge, Canonbie Bridge & Willow Pool. No Sunday fishing.
Kelhead Quarry	Dalry	Brown Trout	1 Apr. to 30 Sept.	Ken Bridge Hotel, New Galloway. Tel: (064-42) 211.	No Sunday fishing on Dalry A.A. waters. Fly only to 1 June.
Ken	New Galloway	Salmon Brown/ Rainbow Trout Perch Pike Roach	15 Mar. to 30 Sept.	Mr. Swain, Kenmure Arms Hotel, High Street, New Galloway. Tel: (06442) 240 or 360.	Boats available from hotel.
Liddle	Newcastleton Ticket	Salmon Sea Trout Brown Trout	15 Apr.-31 Oct. 1 May-30 Sept. 15 Apr.-30 Sept.	J.D. Ewart, Tackle Agent, Newcastleton. Tel: (03873) 75257. R.J.B. Hill, Bank of Scotland Buildings, Langholm. Tel: (03873) 80628.	Spinning allowed when water is above markers at Newcastleton and Kershopelfoot Bridges. No Sunday fishing. Day tickets available.
Milk	Scroggs Bridge	Sea Trout Brown Trout	1 Apr. to 30 Sept.	Mr. Anthony Steel, Kirkwood, Lockerbie. Tel: (057 65) 212/200.	Fly fishing only. No Sunday fishing.

Water	Location	Species	Season	Permit available from	Other Information
Minnoch	Newton Stewart	Salmon	1 Mar. to 30 Sept.	Galloway Guns & Tackle, 36 Arthur Street, Newton Stewart. Tel: (0671) 3404.	
Nith	Dumfries	Salmon Sea Trout Brown Trout	25 Feb. to 30 Nov. 15 Mar. to 6 Oct.	Director of Finance, Nithsdale District Council, Municipal Chambers, Dumfries. Tel: (0387) 53166, ext. 230.	No Sunday fishing. Visitors fishing Mon. to Fri. only. Advance booking.
				Dumfries & Galloway Angling Association Secretary, D. Byers, 4 Bloomfield Edinburgh Road, Dumfries DG1 1SG. Tel: (0387) 53850	Limited number of permits. Weekly permits from Mon.-Fri. Advance booking possible. Spinning restrictions.
	Thornhill	Salmon Sea Trout Brown Trout Grayling	25 Feb. to 30 Nov. 1 Apr.-31 Sept. No close season	The Drumlanrig Castle Fishings, The Buccleuch Estates Ltd., Drumlanrig Mains, Thornhill DG3 4AG. Tel: (08486) 283.	Lower, Middle & Upper beats. Average weight of fish caught: Salmon - 9lbs 8oz, Grilse - 6lbs, Sea Trout - 2lbs, Brown Trout - 8oz, Grayling 8oz. Popular flies: Stoats Tail, General Practitioner, Silver Doctor, Flying C, Silver Toby. Spinning. Worming (until 31 Aug, in Yellow Spate) Weekly and daily lets up to 3 rods/beat.
		Salmon Sea Trout Brown Trout Grayling	25 Feb. to 30 Nov. 1 Apr.-31 Sept. No close season	The Drumlanrig Castle Fishings, The Buccleuch Estates Ltd., Drumlanrig Mains, Thornhill DG3 4AG. Tel: (08486) 283.	Nith Linns Average weight of fish caught: Salmon - 9lbs 8oz, Grilse - 6lbs, Sea Trout - 2lbs, Brown Trout - 8oz, Grayling - 8oz. Popular flies: Stoats Tail, General Practitioner, Silver Doctor, Flying C, Silver Toby. Spinning. Worming (until 31 Aug.) Weekly and daily lets up to 4 rods.
		Salmon Sea Trout Brown Trout	25 Feb.-30 Nov. 1 Apr. to 30 Sept.	Mid Nithsdale Angling Assoc., Secretary, Mr. I.R. Milligan, 37 Drumlanrig Street, Thornhill DG3 5LS. Tel: (0848) 30555.	No day permits on Saturdays. Spinning & worming allowed, only in flood conditions. Advisable to book for autumn fishing.
Nith (and Tributaries Kello Crawick Euchan Mennock)	Sanquhar	Salmon Sea Trout Brown Trout Grayling	15 Mar. to 30 Nov. Jan., Feb.	Upper Nithsdale Angling Club. Pollock & McLean, Solicitors, 61 High Street, Sanquhar. Tel: (0659) 50241.	No Saturday/Sunday fishing. Visitors and residents. Day tickets - limit of 20 per day during months: Sept., Oct. & Nov. Week tickets - limit of 10 per week during season.
Tarf	Kirkcowan	Sea Trout Brown Trout	Easter - 30 Sept.	A. Brown, Three Lochs Caravan Park, Kirkcowan, Newton Stewart, Wigtownshire. Tel: (067183) 304.	
Upper Tarf	Nr. Newton Stewart	Salmon Trout	1 Mar.-14 Oct. 15 Mar.-6 Oct.	Palakona Guest House, Queen Street, Newton Stewart DG8 6JL. Tel: (0670) 402323.	Fly, spin or worm.

Water	Location	Species	Season	Permit available from	Other Information
Urr	Castle Douglas	Salmon Sea Trout Brown Trout	25 Feb. to 30 Nov. 15 Mar. to 6 Oct.	Castle Douglas and District Angling Association Tommy's Sport Shop, King Street, Castle Douglas. Tel: (0556) 2851. Dalbeattie Angling Association Ticket Sec., M. McCowan & Son, 43 High Street, Dalbeattie. Tel: (0556) 610270.	
White Esk	Eskdalemuir	Salmon Sea Trout	15 Apr.-30 Oct 15 Apr.-30 Sept.	Hart Manor Hotel, Eskdalemuir, by Langholm. Tel: (03873) 73217.	Fly and spinner only.

LOCHS & RESERVOIRS

Water	Location	Species	Season	Permit available from	Other Information
Barend Loch	Sandyhills	Rainbow Trout	No close season	Barend Properties, Reception, Sandyhills, Dalbeattie. Tel: (038778) 663.	
Barscobe Loch	Balmaclellan	Brown Trout	15 Mar. to 6 Oct.	Sir Hugh Wontner, Barscobe, Balmaclellan, Castle Douglas. Tel: (064 42) 245/294.	Fly fishing only. Obtain permit first.
Black Esk Reservoir	Eskdalemuir	Brown Trout	1 Apr. to 30 Sept.	Hart Manor Hotel, Eskdalemuir, by Langholm. Tel: (03873) 73217.	Fly and spinner only.
Black Loch	Newton Stewart	Stocked Brown Trout	15 Mar.-30 Sept.	Forestry Commission, Creebridge. Tel: (0671) 2420. Clatteringshaws Wildlife Visitors Centre, New Galloway. Tel: (064 42) 285.	Fly only until 1 July. Sunday fishing.
Black Loch	Nr. Kirkcowan	(Stocked) Brown Trout Pike	15 Mar.-6 Oct. No close season	Palakona Guest House, Queen Street, Newton Stewart. Tel: (0671) 402323.	Any legal method permitted.
Bruntis Loch	Newton Stewart	Brown/ Rainbow Trout	15 Mar. to 30 Sept.	Newton Stewart Angling Association. Galloway Guns & Tackle, 36 Arthur Street, Newton Stewart. Tel: (0671) 3404.	Fly fishing only (fly & worm from June 1). Bank fishing only. Sunday fishing.
Carsfad Loch	Dalry	Brown Trout	1 April to 30 Sept.	P.O. Shop, Carsphairn. Tel: (06446) 283.	Obtain permit before fishing.
Clatteringshaws Loch	6 miles west of New Galloway	Brown Trout Pike Perch	Open all year for coarse fish	Clatteringshaws Wildlife Visitors Centre, New Galloway. Tel: (064 42) 285. Galloway Guns & Tackle, 36 Arthur Street, Newton Stewart. Tel: (0671) 3404. Konmure Arms Hotel, High Street, New Galloway. Tel: (06442) 240.	Fly fishing, spinning or worm fishing permitted.

Water	Location	Species	Season	Permit available from	Other Information
Dalbeattie Reservoir	Dalbeattie	Brown/ Rainbow Trout	15 Apr. to 30 Sept.	Dalbeattie Angling Association M. McCowan & Son, 43 High Street, Dalbeattie. Tel: (0556) 610270.	Bank fishing. Fly only. Boats for hire.
Loch Dee	Castle Douglas	Brown Trout	15 Mar. to 6 Oct.	Forestry Commission, Creebridge. Tel: (0671) 2420. Forest Enterprise, 21 King Street, Castle Douglas. Tel: (0556) 3626. Clatteringshaws Wildlife Visitors Centre, New Galloway. Tel: (064 42) 285.	Fly fishing only, sunrise to sunset. Bank fishing only. Sunday fishing. Annual fly fishing competition in August.
Dindinnie Reservoir	Stranraer	Brown Trout	15 Mar. to 30 Sept.	Stranraer & District Angling Association. The Sports Shop, 90 George Street, Stranraer. Tel: (0776) 2705. Local hotels.	Fly fishing only. Sunday fishing.
Loch Dornal	Drumlamford Estate,	Coarse Stocked Trout	Apr. to Oct.	The Keeper, The Kennels, Drumlamford Estate, Barrhill. Tel: (046 582) 256.	Spinning allowed. Boats available. Fly fishing.
Loch Drumlamford	Drumlamford Estate	Stocked Trout	April to October	The Keeper, The Kennels, Drumlamford Estate, Barrhill. Tel: (046 582) 256.	Fly fishing only. Boats available.
Loch Dunskey	Portpatrick	Brown Trout	1 Apr. to 15 Sept.	Keeper, Dunskey Estate, Portpatrick. Tel: (077681) 364/211.	Fly only. Boat available.
Loch Ettrick	Closeburn	Rainbow Trout (stocked) Brown Trout	No close season 15 Mar to 30 Sept.	Gilchristland, Closeburn, Thornhill DG3 5HN. Tel: (0848) 30827/31204/ 31364.	Average weight of fish: 12 oz to 1lb. Popular flies: Nymphs. Fly fishing only. 2 boats available.
Glenkiln Reservoir	Dumfries	Brown Trout (stocked) Rainbow Trout	1 Apr. to 30 Sept.	Dumfries & Galloway Regional Council, Director of Water & Sewerage, Marchmount House, Dumfries DG1 1PW. Tel: (0387) 60756.	Enquiries to Mr. Ling at No. opposite.
Jericho Loch	Dumfries	Brown Trout Rainbow Trout Brook Trout	1 Apr. to 31 Oct.	Mouswald Caravan Park, Mouswald, by Dumfries. Tel: (038 783) 226. McMillan's Tackle Shop, Friars Vennel, Dumfries. Pattie's Tackle Shop, Queensberry Street, Dumfries. Thistle Stores, Locharbriggs, Dumfries. Club Bookings - contact: Jimmy Younger, Tel: (0387) 75247. Sunday tickets from:- Tourist Information Centre, Dumfries, Tel: (0387) 53862.	Bank fishing only. Fly fishing only. Popular flies: Lures, Nymphs, Traditionals. Sunday fishing.

Water	Location	Species	Season	Permit available from	Other Information
Loch Ken	West Bank Lochside Aird's (Viaduct)	Salmon Trout and coarse fish	Open all year for coarse fish	Shops, hotels in New Galloway	Surcharged if permits bought from bailiffs.
	New Galloway	Brown Trout Salmon Pike Perch Roach	15 Mar. to 30 Sept. All year round	Kenmure Arms Hotel, High Street, New Galloway. Tel: (06442) 240. Local shops.	Sunday fishing allowed except for Salmon. Worm & spinning permitted. Boats available.
Kettleton Reservoir	by Thornhill	Brown/ Rainbow Trout	1 Apr. to 30 Sept.	I.R. Milligan, 37 Drumlanrig Street, Thornhill.	Fly fishing only. Popular flies: Muddler, Black Pennel.
Kirriereoch Loch	Newton Stewart	Brown Trout (stocked)	15 Mar. to 6 Oct.	Newton Stewart Angling Association. Galloway Guns & Tackle, 36 Arthur Street, Newton Stewart. Tel: (0671) 3404. Merrick Caravan Park, Glentrool. Tel: (0671) 84 280.	Fly fishing only (fly & worm after June 1). Bank fishing only. Sunday fishing.
Knockquassan Reservoir	Stranraer	Brown Trout	15 Mar. to 30 Sept.	Stranraer & District Angling Association. The Sports Shop, 90 George Street, Stranraer. Tel: (0776) 2705. Local hotels.	Bank fishing only. Fly and spinner. Sunday fishing.
Lairdmannoch Loch	Twynholm	Wild Brown Trout	1 Apr. to 30 Sept.	G.M. Thomson, & Co. Ltd., 27 King Street, Castle Douglas. Tel: (0556) 2701/2973.	Boat fishing only. Limited rods. Limited days. Self-catering Accom. Available.
Lillies Loch	Castle Douglas	Brown Trout	15 Mar. to 6 Oct.	Forestry Commission, Creebridge. Tel: (0671) 2420. Forest Enterprise, 21 King Street, Castle Douglas. Tel: (0556) 3626.	Bank fishing only. Any legal method. Sunday fishing.
Lochenbreck Loch	Lauriston	Brown/ Rainbow Trout	1 Apr. to 30 Sept.	Watson McKinnel, 15 St. Cuthbert Street, Kirkcudbright. Tel: (0557) 30693. M. & E. Brown, 52 High Street, Gatehouse of Fleet. Tel: (0557) 814222. (shop hours: 6.30am-5pm).	8.30 am to 10 pm. Bank and fly fishing. Five boats. Sunday fishing.
Loch of the Lowes	Newton Stewart	Brown trout (stocked)	15 Mar. to 6 Oct.	Forestry Commission Creebridge. Tel: (0671) 2420. Clatteringshaws Wildlife Visitors Centre, New Galloway. Tel: (064 42) 285.	Fly only. Sunday fishing.

Water	Location	Species	Season	Permit available from	Other Information
Morton Castle Loch	Thornhill	Stocked Brown/ Rainbow Trout	1 Apr. to 30 Sept.	The Buccleuch Estates Ltd., Drumlanrig Mains, Thornhill DG3 4AG. Tel: (08486) 283.	Average weight of fish: 2.25lbs Popular flies: Montanna, Damsel, P/T Nymph, Aces of Spades, Coachman (dry). Fly fishing only. Bank and boat fishing. Let on a daily basis for up to 3 rods.
Mossdale Loch	Mossdale Nr. New Galloway	Stocked Rainbow Trout Wild Brown Trout	15 Mar. to 30 Sept.	Mossdale Post Office, Mossdale, Castle Douglas DG7 2NF. Tel: (06445) 281.	Fly fishing only from boat. Boats available from Post Office. Sunday fishing.
Loch Nahinie	Drum- lamford Estate	Stocked Trout	April to October	The Keeper, The Kennels, Drumlamford Estate, Barrhill. Tel: (046 582) 256.	Fly fishing only. Boats available.
Penwhirn Reservoir	Stranraer	Brown Trout	15 Mar. to 30 Sept.	Stranraer & District Angling Association. The Sports Shop, 90 George Street, Stranraer. Tel: (0776) 2705. Local hotels.	Fly fishing and spinning. Bank fishing. Sunday fishing.
Purdom Stone Reservoir	Hoddom & Kinmount Estates, Lockerbie	Brown Trout	1 Apr. to 15 Sept.	The Water Bailiff, 1 Bridge End Cottage, Hoddom, Lockerbie. Tel: Ecclefechan 488.	Fly fishing only.
Loch Roan	Castle Douglas	Brown/ Rainbow Trout	1 Apr. to 6 Oct.	Tommy's Sports Shop, King Street, Castle Douglas. Tel: (0556) 2851.	Fly fishing only. Four boats.
Soulseat Loch	Stranraer	Brown/ Rainbow Trout	15 Mar. to 30 Sept.	Stranraer & District Angling Association. The Sports Shop, 90 George Street, Stranraer. Tel: (0776) 2705. Local hotels.	Fly, spinning and bait. Bank fishing and two boats. Sunday fishing.
Spa-wood Loch	Nr. Newton Stewart	Wild Brown Trout	15 Mar. to 30 Sept.	Palakona Guest House, Queen Street, Newton Stewart DG8 6JL. Tel: (0671) 402323.	Average weight of fish: 1lb 8oz. Fly only - guests only.
Starburn Loch	Thornhill	Stocked Brown/ Rainbow Trout	1 Apr. to 31 Aug.	The Buccleuch Estates Ltd., Drumlanrig Mains, Thornhill DG3 4AG. Tel: (08486) 283.	Average weight of fish: 2.2lbs. Popular flies: Montanna, Damsel, P/T Nymph, Ace of Spades, Coachman (dry). Fly fishing only. Bank and boat fishing available. Let on a daily basis for up to 3 rods.
Loch Whinyeon	Gatehouse of Fleet	Brown Trout	1 Apr. to 30 Sept.	M. & E. Brown, 52 High Street, Gatehouse of Fleet. Tel: 0557 814 222. Watson McKinnel, 15 St. Cuthbert Street, Kirkcudbright. Tel: (0557) 30693.	8 am to 10 pm. Bank and fly fishing only.

Constituent Area Tourist Boards

Ayrshire and Burns Country Tourist Board
Director of Tourism,
Ayrshire & Burns Country Tourist Board,
39 Sandgate, Ayr KA7 1BG.
Tel: Ayr (0292) 284196.

Ayrshire Valleys Tourist Board
Tourist Officer,
Ayrshire Valleys Tourist Board,
62 Bank Street,
Kilmarnock,
Ayrshire KA1 1ER.
Tel: (0563) 39090.

Clyde Valley Tourist Board
Tourism Officer,
Clyde Valley Tourist Board,
Horsemarket,
Ladyacre Road,
Lanark ML11 7LQ.
Tel: (0555) 2544

Tourist Information Centre
Tourist Officer,
Tourist Information Centre,
Promenade, Largs,
Ayrshire KA30 8BG.
Tel: Largs (0475) 673765

Isle of Arran Tourist Board
Area Tourist Officer,
Isle of Arran Tourist Board,
Information Centre, The Pier,
Brodick, Isle of Arran KA27 8AU.
Tel: Brodick (0770) 2140.

Greater Glasgow Tourist Board
Chief Executive,
Greater Glasgow Tourist Board,
39 St. Vincent Place,
Glasgow G1 2ER.
Tel: 041-227 4885/4880.

Other Tourist Organisations

CUMBERNAULD AND KILSYTH
INVERCLYDE
MONKLANDS
EAST KILBRIDE
EASTWOOD

RIVER PURIFICATION BOARD
CLYDE RIVER PURIFICATION BOARD
River House, Murray Road, East Kilbride, Tel:
East Kilbride 38181.

RIVERS

Water	Location	Species	Season	Permit available from	Other information
Annick	Irvine	Salmon Sea Trout Brown Trout	15 Mar. to 31 Oct. 15 Mar. to 6 Oct.	Dreghorn Angling Club, Mr. S. Wallace, 14 Lismore Way, Dreghorn. Mr. R.W. Gillespie, 16 Marble Avenue, Dreghorn.	
Annick (and Glazert)	Kilmaurs	Salmon Sea Trout Brown Trout	15 Mar. to 31 Oct. 15 Mar. to 6 Oct.	Kilmaurs Angling Club, T.C. McCabe, 8 East Park Crescent, Kilmaurs. Mr. D. Dunn, 22 Habbieauld Road, Kilmaurs. Tel: (0563) 23846.	
Avon	Strathaven	Brown Trout Grayling	15 Mar.-6 Oct. No Close Season	Country Lines, 29 Main Street, The Village, East Kilbride. Tel: (03552) 28952. Sportsman Emporium, Hamilton. Tel: (0698) 283903. P. & R. Torbet, 15 Strand Street, Kilmarnock. Tel: (0563) 41734.	Any legal method.

Water	Location	Species	Season	Permit available from	Other Information
Ayr	Craigie Park	Salmon Sea Trout Trout	10 Feb. to 31 Oct.	Gamesport (Ayr) Ltd., 60 Sandgate, Ayr. Tel: (0292) 263822.	No bait restriction. Fly, spin or worm.
	Failford	Salmon Sea Trout Trout	10 Feb. to 31 Oct.	Gamesport (Ayr) Ltd., 60 Sandgate, Ayr. Tel: (0292) 263822.	No Saturday or Sunday visitor permits.
	Mauchline	Salmon Sea Trout Brown Trout	15 Mar. to 31 Oct. 15 Mar. to 15 Sept.	Linwood & Johnstone Newsagent, The Cross, Mauchline. Tel: (0290) 50219.	
Ayr (Cessnock Lugar)	Mauchline	Salmon Sea Trout Brown Trout	11 Feb. to 31 Oct. 15 May-6 Oct.	Linwood & Johnstone Newsagents, The Cross, Mauchline. Tel: (0290) 50219.	
Ayr (Lugar)	Mauchline	Salmon Sea Trout Brown Trout	15 Mar. to 30 Oct. 15 Mar.-15 Sept.	Linwood & Johnstone Newsagents, The Cross, Mauchline. Tel: (0290) 50219.	
Cart	Busby	Brown Trout	15 Mar to 6 Oct.	Tackle & Guns, 920 Pollokshaws Road, Glasgow G41 2ET. Tel: 041-632 2005.	Average weight of fish caught: 8oz-10oz Popular flies: small spider flies. Bait fishing allowed, no spinning.
Cessnock	Mauchline	Brown Trout	15 Mar. to 15 Sept.	Linwood & Johnstone, Newsagents, The Cross, Mauchline. Tel: (0290) 50219.	
Clyde	Motherwell, Lanark, Carstairs, Roberton & Crawford	Brown Trout Grayling Coarse	15 Mar. to 30 Sept. All year.	Country Lines, 29 Main Street, The Village, East Kilbride. Tel: (03552) 28952.	
Clyde	Thankerton & Roberton	Brown Trout Grayling	15 Mar. to 6 Oct. 7 Oct.-14 Mar.	B.F. Dexter, Secretary, Lamington & District Angling Improvement Association, 18 Boghall Park, Biggar. Waterbailiffs: Mr. McMahon at Wolfclyde Bridge & Mr. J. Grierson at Symington. W.P. Bryden, Newsagent, 153 High Street, Biggar. Tel: (0899) 20069. O'Hara Grocers, Thankerton. Wyndales Hotel, Symington.	Spinning with legal lures allowed from 1st May. Fly fishing at all times. Flies in normal use size 14. Ground baiting and keep nets are not allowed. No Sunday fishing.
Douglas (and Clyde)	Douglas Water	Brown Trout Grayling	15 Mar.-30 Sep. All year.	Permits widely available in tackle shops in Glasgow and Lanarkshire.	
Garnock	Kilbirnie	Brown Trout Salmon Sea Trout	15 Mar. to 6 Oct. 15 Mar.-31 Oct.	Kilbirnie Angling Club I. Johnstone, 12 Grahamston Avenue, Glengarnock, KA14 3AF. Tel: (0505) 682154. R.T. Cycles, Glengarnock. Tel: (0505) 682191.	No Sunday fishing after July 1.

Water	Location	Species	Season	Permit available from	Other Information
Garnock (and Lugton)	Kilwinning	Salmon Sea Trout Brown Trout	15 Mar. to 31 Oct. 15 Mar.-6 Oct.	The Craft Shop, 42 Main Street, Kilwinning. Tel: (0294) 58559.	No Saturday or Sunday fishing. No permits Friday, 14th August.
Gryfe	Bridge of Weir	Brown Trout Salmon Sea Trout	15 Mar.-6 Oct. 15 Mar.-31 Oct.	M. Duncan, Newsagent, Main Street, Bridge of Weir. Tel: (0505) 612477.	No Saturday or Sunday fishing.
Iorsa	Isle of Arran	Salmon Sea Trout	1 June to 15 Oct.	The Estate Office, Dougarie, Isle of Arran. Tel: (077084) 259.	
Irvine	Hurlford and Crookedholm	Salmon Sea Trout Brown Trout	15 Mar. to 31 Oct. 15 Mar. to 6 Oct.	P. & R. Torbet, 15 Strand Street, Kilmarnock. Tel: (0563) 41734.	
	Kilmarnock	Salmon Sea trout Brown Trout	15 Mar. to 31 Oct. 15 Mar.-6 Oct.	McCririck & Sons, 38 John Finnie Street, Kilmarnock. Tel: (0563) 25577.	No Sunday fishing after 31st July.
Irvine (and Annick)	Dreghorn	Salmon Sea Trout Brown Trout	15 Mar. to 31 Oct. 15 Mar.-6 Oct.	Dreghorn Angling Club. Mr. S. Wallace, 14 Lismore Way, Dreghorn. Mr. R.W. Gillespie, 16 Marble Avenue, Dreghorn.	River Irvine only, extension of season for salmon and sea trout - 1 to 15 November. Fly only.
Irvine (and Cessnock)	Galston	Salmon Sea Trout Brown Trout	15 Mar. to 30 Nov. 15 Mar.-6 Oct.	Galston Angling Club, Sec. J. Steven, 12 Millands Road, Galston. Tel: Galston 820344. P. & R. Torbet, 15 Strand Street, Kilmarnock. Tel: (0563) 41734. Mr. MacRoberts (Newsagents), Wallace Street, Galston.	
Kelvin	Glasgow-Strathkelvin	Salmon Sea Trout	11 Feb. to 31 Oct.	Lawrence Angling, 268 Dumbarton Road, Glasgow G11 6TU. Tel: 041-339 1085.	Any legal bait permitted.
Machrie	Arran	Salmon Sea Trout	1 June to 15 Oct.	Margo M. Wilson, Boltachan House, Aberfeldy PH15 2LA. Tel: (0887) 820496.	No Sunday fishing. Booking: Nov.-Oct.
Rotten Calder	E. Kilbride	Brown Trout	15 Mar. to 6 Oct.	Country Lines, 29 Main Street, The Village, East Kilbride. Tel: (03552) 28952.	Any legal method.
Stinchar	Colmonell	Salmon Sea Trout	25 Feb. to 31 Oct.	Queen's Hotel, Colmonell. Tel: (046 588) 213.	No Sunday fishing.
White Cart	Waterfoot (Upstream)	Brown Trout	15 Mar. to 6 Oct.	Country Lines, 29 Main Street, The Village, East Kilbride. Tel: (03552) 28952.	

Water	Location	Species	Season	Permit available from	Other Information

LOCHS & RESERVOIRS

Water	Location	Species	Season	Permit available from	Other Information
Loch Arklet	Stirling & Trossachs	Brown Trout	30 Mar. to 28 Sept.	Strathclyde Reg. Council, Water Department, 419 Balmore Road, Glasgow, Tel: 041-355 5333. Or on location.	Fly fishing by rowing boat only. No live bait/spinning. Rowing boats supplied. 7 days fishing.
Loch Belston	Sinclairston	Brown Trout Rainbow Trout	15 Mar. to 15 Sept.	Linwood & Johnstone, Newsagents, The Cross, Mauchline. Tel: (0290) 50219.	Boats available.
		Rainbow Trout	No close season	Gamesport (Ayr) Ltd., 60 Sandgate, Ayr. Tel: (0292) 263822.	
Loch Bradan	Straiton	Brown Trout (Stocked)	15 Mar. to 30 Sept.	Forestry Commission, Straiton. Tel: (065 57) 637. Mr. R. Heaney, Tallaminnoch, Straiton. Tel: (065 57) 617.	Five Boats. Sunday fishing.
Loch Brecbowie	Straiton	Brown Trout	15 Mar. to 30 Sept.	Forestry Commission, Straiton. Tel: (065 57) 637. Mr. R. Heaney, Tallaminnoch, Straiton. Tel: (065 57) 617.	Fly fishing advised. Sunday fishing.
Burnfoot Reservoir	Nr. Fenwick	Brown/ Rainbow Trout	15 Mar. to 6 Oct.	Kilmaurs A.C., Mr. T.C. McCabe, 8 East Park Crescent, Kilmaurs. Mr. D. Dunn, 22 Habbieauld Road, Kilmaurs. Tel: (0563) 23846. Pages Newsagent, Main Street, Kilmaurs.	Average weight of fish caught: 1lb-5lbs. Popular flies: Butcher, Montanna, Nymph, Viva, Soldier Palmer. Any legal method - no swim feeders or floats.
Busbie Muir Reservoir	Ardrossan	Brown Trout	1 Apr. to 6 Oct.	Ardrossan Eglinton A.C., Alpine Stores, Dalry Road, Ardrossan.	Obtain permits before fishing. Average weight of fish caught: 8-12oz. Popular flies: Wickhams, Kate McLaren, Soldier Palmer, Grouse & Claret, Invicta, Blae & Black. Two boats, keys available from Alpine Store.
Camphill Reservoir	Kilbirnie	Brown Trout	1 Apr. to 6 Oct.	Kilbirnie A.C., I. Johnstone, 12 Grahamstone Avenue, Glengarnock KA14 3AF. Tel: (0505) 682154. R.T. Cycles, Glengarnock. Tel: (0505) 682191.	Fly only. Boat only.
Dhu Loch	Straiton	Brown Trout	15 Mar. to 30 Sept.	Mr. R. Heaney, Tallaminnoch, Straiton. Tel: (065-57) 617.	Fly only.
Glen Finglas	Stirling & Trossachs	Brown Trout	30 Mar. to 28 Sept.	Strathclyde Reg. Council, Water Department, 419 Balmore Road, Glasgow, Tel: 041-355 5333. Or on location.	Fly fishing by rowing boat only. No live bait/spinning. Rowing boats supplied. 7 days fishing.

Water	Location	Species	Season	Permit available from	Other Information
Loch Goin (between orange markers)	Nr. Eaglesham	Brown Trout	15 Mar. to 6 Oct.	Kilmaurs A.C., Mr. T.C. McCabe, 8 East Park Crescent, Kilmaurs. Mr. D. Dunn, 22 Habbieauld Road, Kilmaurs. Tel: (0563) 23846.	Average weight of fish caught: 8oz to 3lbs. Popular flies: traditional small flies. No other baits - fly only.
Craigendunton Reservoir	Nr. Kilmarnock	Rainbow/ Brown Trout	15 Mar. to 6 Oct.	Kilmarnock A.C., McCririck & Sons, 38 John Finnie Street, Kilmarnock. Tel: (0563) 25577.	Average weight of fish caught: Rainbow - 1lb 8oz. Brown - 12oz. Fly and spinning only; no live bait. Obtain permits before fishing.
Harelaw Dam	Neilston	Brown Trout	15 Mar. to 6 Oct.	Doug Brown, 10 Garrioch Drive, Glasgow. Tel: 041 946 6060. Tackle & Guns, 920 Pollokshaws Road, Glasgow. Tel: 041-632 2005. Lawrence Angling, 268 Dumbarton Road, Glasgow G11 6TU. Tel: 041-339 1085.	Average weight of fish caught: 1lb 2oz. Popular flies: Black Pennel, Soldier Palmer, Sedges, and Dry Fly. Boats day or evening.
Loch Katrine	Stirling & Trossachs	Brown Trout	30 Mar. to 28 Sept.	Strathclyde Reg. Council, Water Department, 419 Balmore Road, Glasgow, Tel: 041-355 5333. Or on location.	Fly fishing by rowing boat only. No live bait/spinning. Rowing boats supplied. 7 days fishing.
Kilbirnie Loch	Kilbirnie	Brown/ Rainbow Trout	15 Mar. to 6 Oct.	Kilbirnie Angling Club, I. Johnstone, 12 Grahamston Avenue, Glengarnock KA14 3AF. Tel: (0505) 682154. R.T. Cycles, Glengarnock. Tel: (0505) 682191.	All legal methods. Boats available.
Mill Glen Reservoir	Ardrossan	Brown Trout	15 Mar. to 6 Oct.	Ardrossan Eglinton A.C., Alpine Stores, Dalry Road, Ardrossan.	Obtain permits before fishing. Average weight of fish caught: 8-12oz. Popular flies: Wickhams, Kate McLaren, Soldier Palmer, Grouse & Claret, Invicta, Blae & Black. Fly fishing only.
North Craig Reservoir	Kilmaurs	Brown/ Rainbow Trout	15 Mar. to 6 Oct.	Kilmaurs A.C., T.C. McCabe, 8 East Park Crescent, Kilmaurs. Mr. D. Dunn, 22 Habbieauld Road, Kilmaurs. Tel: (0563) 23846. Pages Newsagent, Main Street, Kilmaurs.	Average weight of fish caught: 1-5lbs. Popular flies: Butcher, Soldier Palmer, Blue Zulu, Baby Doll, Viva. Any legal method - no swim feeders or floats.
Penwhapple Reservoir	Nr. Girvan	Stocked Brown Trout Rainbow Trout	1 Apr. to 15 Sept.	Mrs. Stewart, Wee Lames Farm, Nr. Girvan. (¼ mile from reservoir).	Fly fishing only. Average weight of fish caught: 12oz. Popular flies: Kate McLaren, Zulu, Invicta; traditional patterns. 4 boats available.

Water	Location	Species	Season	Permit available from	Other Information
Prestwick Reservoir	Monkton	Rainbow Trout	15 Mar to 15 Nov.	Gamesport, Ayr. Kirk, Ayr. Newhall's Newsagent, Monkton. Wheatsheaf Inn, Monkton.	Average weight of fish caught: 1-4lbs. Popular flies: Butcher, Greenwell Glory. Worm fishing.
Raith Reservoir (Prestwick)	Monkton by Ayr	Rainbow Trout	15 Mar. to 15 Nov.	Gamesport (Ayr) Ltd., 60 Sandgate, Ayr. Tel: (0292) 263822.	
Loch Skelloch	Straiton	Brown Trout (Stocked)	15 Mar. to 30 Sept.	Mr. R. Heaney, Tallaminnoch, Straiton. Tel: (065 57) 617.	Fly fishing only. Boats available. Sunday fishing.
Strathclyde Country Park Loch (and adjacent River Clyde)	Motherwell	Grayling Trout	15 Mar. to 29 Sept.	Booking Office, Strathclyde Country Park, 366 Hamilton Road, Motherwell. Tel: Motherwell 66155.	
Loch Thom and compensations 6,7 & 8	Greenock	Brown Trout	15 Mar. to 6 Oct.	John M. Clark, Cornalees Farm, Greenock.	Fly and bank fishing only.

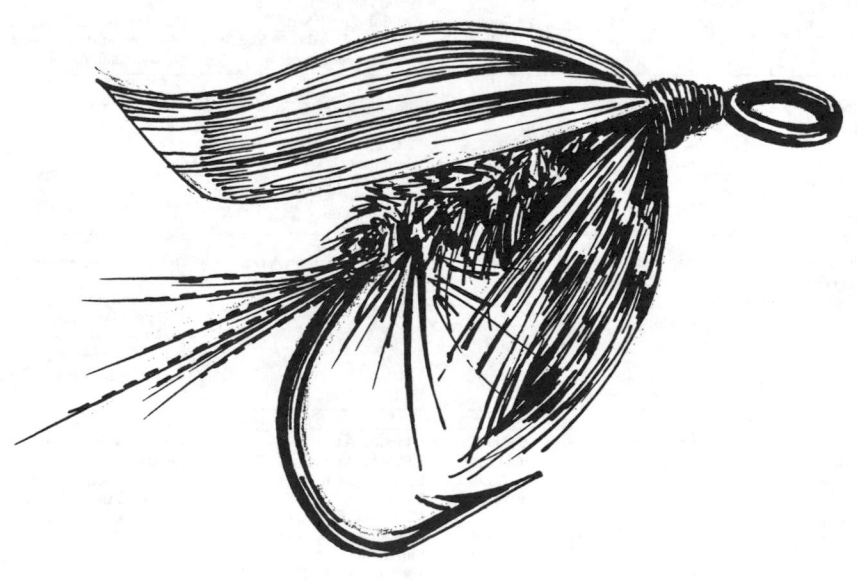

STRATHCLYDE (NORTH)

Constituent Area Tourist Boards

Dunoon and Cowal Tourist Board
Area Tourist Officer,
Dunoon and Cowal Tourist Board,
Information Centre,
7 Alexandra Parade,
Dunoon, Argyll PA23 8AB.
Tel: Dunoon (0369) 3785.

West Highlands & Islands of Argyll Tourist Board,
Area Tourist Officer,
West Highlands & Islands of Argyll Tourist board,
Albany Street, Oban,
Argyll PA34 1RN.
Tel: (0631) 63059.

Isle of Bute Tourist Board
Area Tourist Officer,
Isle of Bute Tourist Board,
15 Victoria Street, Rothesay,
Isle of Bute PA20 0AJ.
Tel: Rothesay (0700) 502151.

RIVER PURIFICATION BOARD
CLYDE RIVER PURIFICATION BOARD
Rivers House,
Murray Road,
East Kilbride G75 0LA.
Tel: East Kilbride 03552 38181.

RIVERS

Water	Location	Species	Season	Permit available from	Other information
Aros	Mull	Salmon Sea Trout	End June to Mid Oct.	Tackle and Books, Main Street, Tobermory, Isle of Mull. Tel: (0688) 2336.	
Bellart	Mull	Salmon Sea Trout	June to End Oct.	Tackle & Books, Main Street, Tobermory, Isle of Mull. Tel: (0688) 2336.	No Sunday fishing.
Cur	13 miles from Dunoon	Salmon Sea Trout Brown Trout	1 Apr. to 31 Oct.	Purdies of Argyll, 112 Argyll Street, Dunoon. Tel: Dunoon 3232. Dunoon & District Angling Club.	Fishing all legal methods. Bookings, Hon. Sec., D. & D.A.C., "Ashgrove", 28 Royal Crescent, Dunoon PA23 7AH. Tel: (0369) 5732.
Douglas	Inveraray	Salmon Sea Trout	May to Mid-Oct.	Argyll Caravan Park, Inveraray, Argyll. Tel: (0499) 2285.	No Sunday fishing. Fly fishing only.
Euchar	Kilninver	Salmon Sea Trout Brown Trout	1 June to 15 Oct.	Mrs. Mary McCorkindale, 'Glenann' Kilninver, by Oban, Argyll. Tel: (085 26) 282.	No Sunday fishing.
		Salmon Sea Trout	Mid-July to Mid-Oct.	I T P. Mellor, Barncromin Farm, Knipoch, by Oban, Argyll. Tel: (085 26) 273.	(Tues, Wed & Thurs.)
	Kilninver (Lagganmore)	Salmon Sea Trout Brown Trout	June to 14 Oct.	Lt. Col. P.S. Sandilands, Lagganmore, Kilninver, by Oban. Tel: (085 26) 200.	Not more than 3 rods per day. Fly fishing only. No Sunday fishing.
Finnart	12 miles from Dunoon	Salmon Sea Trout Brown Trout	1 Apr. to 15 Oct.	Dunoon & District Angling Club. Purdie's of Argyll, 112 Argyll Street, Dunoon. Tel: Dunoon 3232.	Fishing all legal methods. Advanced bookings Hon. Sec., D.& D.A.C., "Ashgrove", 28 Royal Crescent, Dunoon PA23 7AH. Tel: (0369) 5732.
Forsa	Mull	Salmon Sea Trout	Mid-June to Mid-Oct.	Tackle and Books, Main Street, Tobermory. Tel: (0688) 2336.	No Sunday fishing.

Water	Location	Species	Season	Permit available from	Other Information
Grey	Islay	Salmon Sea Trout	July to October	Brian Wiles, Head Gamekeeper's House, Islay House Square, Bridgend. Tel: (049 681) 293.	Fly only. No night fishing.
Laggan	Islay	Salmon Sea Trout	July to October	Brian Wiles, Head Gamekeeper's House, Isle House Square, Bridgend. Tel: (049 681) 293.	Fly fishing only. No night fishing.
Machrie	Islay	Salmon Sea Trout Brown Trout	25 Feb. to 31 Oct.	Machrie Hotel, Port Ellen, Islay, Argyll PA42 7AN. Tel: (0496) 2310.	Own river. Loch by Arrangement.
Massan	6 miles from Dunoon	Salmon Sea Trout Brown Trout	1 Apr. to 31 Oct.	Dunoon & District Angling Club. Purdies of Argyll, 112 Argyll Street, Dunoon. Tel: Dunoon 3232.	All legal methods. Advanced booking Hon. Sec., D. & D.A.C., "Ashgrove", 28 Royal Crescent, Dunoon PA23 7AH. Tel: (0369) 5732.
Orchy	Dalmally	Salmon	11 Feb. to 15 Oct.	W.A. Church, Croggan Crafts, Dalmally, Argyll. Tel: (083 82) 201.	
Ruel	Glendaruel	Salmon Sea Trout	16 Feb. to 31 Oct.	Glendaruel Hotel, Clachan of Glendaruel, Argyll PA22 3AA. Tel: (036982) 274.	No Sunday fishing.
Sorn	Islay	Salmon Sea Trout	October	Brian Wiles, Head Gamekeeper's House, Islay House Square, Bridgend. Tel: (049 681) 293.	Fly fishing only. No night fishing.

LOCHS & RESERVOIRS

Water	Location	Species	Season	Permit available from	Other Information
Loch A'Bharrain	Nr. Oban	Brown Trout	15 Mar. to 6 Oct.	D. Graham, Combe Street, Oban. Tack & Tackle Shop, Oban. Sports Centre, Oban. Anglers' Corner, Oban. Post Office, Kilmelford. Trading Post, Kilchrenan. Mr. Morrison, Ledaig Motors, Benderloch.	Standard trout flies wet or dry (12 & 14). Peaty loch with small fish.
Loch a'Chaorainn	Nr. Kilmelford	Brown Trout	15 Mar. to 6 Oct.	D. Graham, Combe Street, Oban. Tack & Tackle Shop, Oban. Sports Centre, Oban. Anglers' Corner, Oban. Post Office, Kilmelford. Trading Post, Kilchrenan. Mr. Morrison, Ledaig Motors, Benderloch.	Popular flies: imitations of natural flies. The loch contains trout up to 2lbs.

Water	Location	Species	Season	Permit available from	Other Information
Loch a'Cheigin	Nr. Kilmelford	Brown Trout	15 Mar. to 6 Oct.	D. Graham, Combe Street, Oban. Tack & Tackle Shop, Oban. Sports Centre, Oban. Anglers' Corner, Oban. Post Office, Kilmelford. Trading Post, Kilchrenan. Mr. Morrison, Ledaig Motors, Benderloch.	Popular flies: standard trout patterns, size 14.
Loch a'Chlachain	Nr. Kilmelford	Brown Trout	15 Mar. to 6 Oct.	D. Graham, Combe Street, Oban. Tack & Tackle Shop, Oban. Sports Centre, Oban. Anglers' Corner, Oban. Post Office, Kilmelford. Trading Post, Kilchrenan. Mr. Morrison, Ledaig Motors, Benderloch.	Popular flies: standard trout flies, wet or dry (12 & 14).
Loch a'Chreachain	Nr. Kilmelford	Brown Trout	15 Mar. to 6 Oct.	D. Graham, Combe Street, Oban. Tack & Tackle Shop, Oban. Sports Centre, Oban. Anglers' Corner, Oban. Post Office, Kilmelford. Trading Post, Kilchrenan. Mr. Morrison, Ledaig Motors, Benderloch.	Popular flies: standard pattern trout flies sizes 12 & 14 also big lure type flies for the bigger trout.
Loch a'Cruaiche	Nr. Kilmelford	Brown Trout	15 Mar. to 6 Oct.	D. Graham, Combe Street, Oban. Tack & Tackle Shop, Oban. Sports Centre, Oban. Anglers' Corner, Oban. Post Office, Kilmelford. Trading Post, Kilchrenan. Mr. Morrison, Ledaig Motors, Benderloch	Small weedy loch with small trout.
Loch a'Mhinn	Nr. Kilmelford	Brown Trout	15 Mar. to 6 Oct.	D. Graham, Combe Street, Oban. Tack & Tackle Shop, Oban. Sports Centre, Oban. Anglers' Corner, Oban. Post Office, Kilmelford. Trading Post, Kilchrenan. Mr. Morrison, Ledaig Motors, Benderloch.	Popular flies: standard trout flies, wet or dry (12 & 14). The loch contains small fat trout, frequently difficult to catch.
Loch a'Phearsain	Nr. Kilmelford	Brown Trout	15 Mar. to 6 Oct.	D. Graham, Combe Street, Oban. Tack & Tackle Shop, Oban. Sports Centre, Oban. Anglers' Corner, Oban. Post Office, Kilmelford. Trading Post, Kilchrenan. Mr. Morrison, Ledaig Motors, Benderloch.	Average weight of fish: 8oz to 1lb. Popular flies: standard patterns, sizes 12 & 14.
Loch an Daimh	Nr. Kilmelford	Brown Trout	15 Mar. to 6 Oct.	D. Graham, Combe Street, Oban. Tack & Tackle Shop, Oban. Sports Centre, Oban. Anglers' Corner, Oban. Post Office, Kilmelford. Trading Post, Kilchrenan. Mr. Morrison, Ledaig Motors, Benderloch.	The loch contains trout up to 6oz, but they are difficult to catch. Popular flies: standard trout flies, wet or dry (10 &14).

Water	Location	Species	Season	Permit available from	Other Information
Loch an Losgainn Beag	Nr. Kilmelford	Brown Trout	15 Mar. to 6 Oct.	D. Graham, Combe Street, Oban. Tack & Tackle Shop, Oban. Sports Centre, Oban. Anglers' Corner, Oban. Post Office, Kilmelford. Treading Post, Kilchrenan. Mr. Morrison, Ledaig Motors, Benderloch.	Popular flies: standard trout flies, wet or dry (10 to 14). The loch contains very large trout that are difficult to catch. Reputed to fish best in the evening during June.
Loch an Losgainn Mor	Nr. Kilmelford	Brown Trout	15 Mar. to 6 Oct.	D. Graham, Combe Street, Oban. Tack & Tackle Shop, Oban. Sports Centre, Oban. Anglers' Corner, Oban Post Office, Kilmelford. Trading Post, Kilchrenan. Mr. Morrison, Ledaig Motors, Benderloch.	Popular flies: standard trout flies, wet or dry (10 to 14). The loch contains trout of 6oz. but they are difficult to catch.
Loch Airigh-Shamhraidh	Musdale	Brown Trout	15 Mar. to 6 Oct.	D. Graham, Combe Street, Oban. Tack & Tackle Shop, Oban. Sports Centre, Oban. Anglers' Corner, Oban. Post Office, Kilmelford. Trading Post, Kilchrenan. Mr. Morrison, Ledaig Motors, Benderloch.	Popular flies: standard trout flies wet or dry (12 & 14). Loch is full of easily caught trout.
Ardlussa Home Loch	Ardlussa	Salmon Sea Trout Brown Trout	20 July to 5 Oct.	C. Fletcher, Ardlussa, Isle of Jura. Tel: 049-682 323.	Fly only. 2 boats for 2 rods each.
Loch Aros Lake	Aros	Rainbow Trout	1 Apr. to 30 Nov.	Brown's Shop, Tobermory. Tel: (0688) 2020.	Popular flies: Butcher, Teal & Green, Soldier Palmer, Grouse & Claret (size 10 & 12). Bank fishing only. No spinning.
Loch Ascog	Argyll	Brown/ Rainbow Trout	15 Mar. to 5 Oct.	Kyles of Bute Angling Club. Several shops in Kames and Tighnabruaich.	Fly only.
Loch Assopol	Mull	Salmon Sea Trout Brown Trout	April to beg. Oct.	Argyll Arms Hotel, Bunessan, Isle of Mull. Tel: Fionnphort 240.	Fly and spinner only. No Sunday fishing.
Glen Astil Lochs (2)	Isle of Islay	Brown Trout	1 Apr. to 15 Oct.	I.G. Laurie, Newsagent, 19 Charlotte Street, Port Ellen, Isle of Islay. Tel: (0496) 2264.	£2.50 per rod per day. Fly only. No Sunday fishing. No catch limit. Permit covers all 5 lochs of Port Ellen Angling Club (see Loch Kinnabus).
Loch Avich	Taynuilt	Brown Trout Rainbow Trout	15 Mar. to 6 Oct.	Mr. N.D. Clark, 11, Dalavich, By Taynuilt, Argyll PA35 1HN. Tel: Lochavich 209. W.A. Church, Croggan Crafts, Dalmally, Argyll. Tel: (083 82) 201.	5 boats available.

Water	Location	Species	Season	Permit available from	Other Information
Loch Avich cont.	Argyll	Brown/ Rainbow Trout	15 Mar. to 6 Oct.	Lochgilphead Tourist Office, Lochnell Street, Lochgilphead. Tel: (0546) 602344. Oban Tourist Office, Boswell House, Argyll Square, Oban. Tel: (0631) 63122.	Permits also available for pike fishing (no close season).
	Nr. Kilmelford	Brown Trout	15 Mar. to 6 Oct.	D.Graham, Combe Street, Oban. Tack & Tackle Shop, Oban. Sports Centre, Oban. Angler's Corner, Oban. Post Office, Kilmelford. Trading Post, Kilchrenan. Mr. Morrison, Ledaig Motors, Benderloch.	Popular flies: standard patterns, sizes 12 & 14.
Loch Awe	South Lochaweside by Dalmally	Salmon Sea Trout Brown Trout Rainbow Trout Perch Char Pike	11 Feb. to 15 Oct. 15 Mar. to 6 Oct. All year	Ardbrecknish House, by Dalmally, Argyll. Tel: (08663) 223/256.	Boats, tackle and permits available. Clubs welcome.
		Salmon Sea Trout Brown Trout Rainbow Trout Perch Char Pike	15 Mar. to 15 Oct. 15 Mar. to 6 Oct. All year	The Portsonachan Hotel, Nr.Dalmally, Argyll PA33 1BL. Tel: (086 63) 224/225/356/328.	
		Brown/ Rainbow Trout Salmon	15 Mar. to 15 Oct.	Ford Hotel, Ford. Tel: (054 681) 273.	
	Taynuilt	Salmon Sea Trout Brown Trout Rainbow Trout	12 Feb. to 15 Oct. 15 Mar. to 6 Oct.	Mr. N.D. Clark, 11, Dalavich, By Taynuilt, Argyll PA35 1HN Tel: Lochavich 209. D. Graham, Combe Street, Oban. Tack & Tackle Shop, Oban. Sports Centre, Oban. Anglers' Corner, Oban. Post Office, Kilmelford. Trading Post, Kilchrenan. Mr. Morrison, Ledaig Motors, Benderloch.	Boats available.
		Salmon Brown Trout Sea Trout Rainbow Trout Char Perch Pike	16 Mar. to 6 Oct. (No close season Pike)	Country Lines, 29 Main Street, The Village, East Kilbride. Tel: (03552) 28952.	Separate Pike permit available. Restrictions detailed on permit.
	Argyll	Brown/ Rainbow Trout	15 Mar. to 6 Oct.	Lochgilphead Tourist Office, Lochnell Street, Lochgilphead. Tel: (0546) 602344. Oban Tourist Office, Boswell House, Argyll Square, Oban. Tel: (0631) 63122. W.A. Church, Croggan Crafts, Dalmally, Argyll. Tel: (083 82) 201.	Permits also available for Pike fishing (no close season).
Ballygrant Loch	Ballygrant	Brown Trout	15 Mar. to 6 Oct.	Port Askaig Stores, Port Askaig, Isle of Islay. Tel: (049684) 245.	Average weight of fish caught: 8-16oz. Boats are available.

Water	Location	Species	Season	Permit available from	Other Information
Barnluasgan Loch	Loch-gilphead	Brown Trout	15 Mar. to 6 Oct.	Mr. A. MacVicar, Gartnagrenach, Achnamara.	Boat available.
Loch Bealach Ghearran	Nr. Minard Village	Brown Trout	15 Mar. to 6 Oct.	Mr. R. Hardie, No. 1, Nursery Cottages, Birdfield, Minard, Argyll. Mr. D. McNeil, Hydro Cottage, Lochgair. Forest District Office, Whitegates, Lochgilphead.	Average weight of fish caught: 8oz. Popular flies: most dark flies.
Big Feinn Loch	Nr. Kilmelford	Brown Trout	15 Mar. to 6 Oct.	D. Graham, Combe Street, Oban. Tack & Tackle Shop, Oban. Sports Centre, Oban. Anglers' Corner, Oban. Post Office, Kilmelford. Trading Post, Kilchrenan. Mr. Morrison, Ledaig Motors, Benderloch.	The loch contains very large trout which are very difficult to catch. It fishes best at the beginning of the season in windy conditions. Popular flies: large salmon flies - Demons or Terrors.
Blackmill Loch	Nr. Minard Village	Brown Trout	15 Mar. to 6 Oct.	Mr. R. Hardie, No. 1, Nursery Cottages, Birdfield, Minard, Argyll. Mr. D. McNeil, Hyrdo Cottage, Lochgair. Forest District Office, Whitegates, Lochgilphead.	Average weight of fish caught:8oz. Popular flies: most dark flies.
Cam Loch	Nr. Ford	Brown Trout	15 Mar. to 6 Oct.	Ford Hotel, Ford. Tel: Ford 273.	Average weight of fish caught: 8oz. Popular flies: most dark flies.
Coille Bhar	Lochgilphead	Brown Trout	1 Apr. to 6 Oct.	Mr. A. MacVicar, Gartnagrenach, Achnamara.	Two boats
Loch Crauch Maolachy	Nr. Kilmelford	Brown Trout	15 Mar. to 6 Oct.	D. Graham, Combe Street, Oban. Tack & Tackle Shop, Oban. Sports Centre, Oban. Anglers' Corner, Oban. Post Office, Kilmelford. Trading Post, Kilchrenan. Mr. Morrison, Ledaig Motors, Benderloch.	Stocked trout reach 2lbs or more. Standard patterns, sizes 12 & 14.
Dubh Loch	Kilninver	Loch Leven Trout Brown Trout	April to Mid-Oct.	J.T.P. Mellor, Barndromin Farm, Knipoch, by Oban. Tel: (085 26) 273.	Boat on loch.
Loch Dubh-Bheag	Nr. Kilmelford	Brown Trout	15 Mar. to 6 Oct.	D. Graham, Combe Street, Oban. Tack & Tackle Shop, Oban. Sports Centre, Oban. Post Office, Kilmelford. Trading Post, Kilchrenan. Mr. Morrison, Ledaig Motors, Benderloch.	Popular flies: standard trout patterns, sizes 12 & 14
Loch Dubh-Mor	Nr. Kilmelford	Brown Trout	15 Mar. to 6 Oct.	D. Graham, Combe Street, Oban. Tack & Tackle Shop, Oban. Sports Centre, Oban. Anglers' Corner, Oban. Post Office, Kilmelford. Trading Post, Kilchrenan. Mr. Morrison, Ledaig Motors, Benderloch.	Average weight of fish caught: 4oz. Popular flies: standard patterns, 10 & 12.

Water	Location	Species	Season	Permit available from	Other Information
Dunoon Reservoir	Dunoon	Rainbow & Brook Trout	1 Mar. to 31 Nov.	Dunoon & District Angling Club. Purdies of Argyll, 112 Argyll Street, Dunoon. Tel: Dunoon 3232.	Fly fishing only.
Ederline Lochs 18 hill lochs	Ford	Wild Brown Trout	May to 6 Oct.	The Keeper, Keepers Cottage, Ederline, Ford, Lochgilphead. Tel: (054 681) 215.	Average weight of fish caught: 8oz. Fly only. Boats available on 5 lochs.
Loch Ederline (& 3 smaller lochs)	Ford	Pike Perch	No close season	The Keeper, Keepers Cottage, Ederline, Ford, Lochgilphead. Tel: (054 681) 215.	All baits allowed. 3 boats available.
Loch Fad	Bute	Brown Trout Rainbow Trout	15 Mar. to 6 Oct.	Bailiff at Loch. Tel: (0700) 504871.	Boats available. Whole day and evening tickets. No night fishing.
		Rainbow Trout Brown Trout	March to October	Carleol Enterprises Angling Holidays, 3 Alma Terrace, Rothesay. Tel: (0700) 503716.	Accommodation and permits are available.
Loch Fada	Isle of Colonsey	Brown Trout	15 Mar. to 30 Sept.	The Hotel, Isle of Colonsey, Argyll.	Fly fishing only. Boats are available.
Loch Finlaggan	Islay	Brown Trout	15 Mar. to 30 Sept.	Brian Wiles, Islay House Square, Bridgend, Isle of Islay, Argyll PA44 7NZ. Tel: (049 681) 293.	Two boats.
Forestry Hill Lochs	Ford	Brown Trout	15 Mar. to 6 Oct.	Ford Hotel, Ford, Argyll. Tel: (054-681) 273.	
Loch Frisa	North end of Mull	Brown Trout Sea Trout	Apr. to Oct.	Tackle and Books, Main Street, Tobermory, Mull. Tel: (0688) 2336.	1 Boat.
Loch Glashan	Nr. Lochgair Village	Brown Trout	15 Mar. to 6 Oct.	Mr. R. Hardie, No. 1, Nursery Cottages, Birdfield, Minard, Argyll. Mr. D. McNeil, Hydro Cottage, Lochgair. Forest District Office, Whitegates, Lochgilphead.	Average weight of fish caught: 12oz. Popular flies: most dark flies. One boat is available.
Loch Gleann A'Bhearraidh	Lerags by Oban	Brown Trout	15 Mar. to 6 Oct.	Cologin Homes Ltd., Lerags, by Oban, Argyll. Tel: (0631) 64501. The Barn Bar, Cologin, Lerags, by Oban.	One boat available.
Loch Gorm	Islay	Brown Trout	15 Mar. to 30 Sept.	Brian Wiles, Islay House Square, Bridgend, Isle of Islay, Argyll PA44 7NZ. Tel: (049 681) 293.	3 Boats available.

Water	Location	Species	Season	Permit available from	Other Information
Loch Gully	Nr. Kilmelford	Brown Trout	15 Mar. to 6 Oct.	D. Graham, Combe Street, Oban. Tack & Tackle Shop, Oban. Sports Centre, Oban. Anglers' Corner, Oban. Post Office, Kilmelford. Trading Post, Kilchrenan. Mr. Morrison, Ledaig Motors, Benderloch.	The loch contains some good fat trout. Popular flies: standard patterns, 12 & 14.
Iasg Loch	Nr. Kilmelford	Brown Trout	15 Mar. to 6 Oct.	D. Graham, Combe Street, Oban. Tack & Tackle Shop, Oban. Sports Centre, Oban. Anglers' Corner, Oban. Post Office, Kilmelford. Trading Post, Kilchrenan. Mr. Morrison, Ledaig Motors, Benderloch.	Popular flies: standard patterns, 10 & 12.
Inverawe Fisheries	Taynuilt	Rainbow Trout	Mar. to Dec.	Inverawe Fisheries, Taynuilt, Argyll. Tel: (08662) 446.	
Kinnabus Lochs (3)	Islay	Brown Trout Arctic Char	1 Apr. to 15 Oct.	I.G. Laurie, Newsagent, 19 Charlotte Street, Port Ellen, Isle of Islay. Tel: (0496) 2264.	£2.50 per rod per day. Fly only. No Sunday fishing. No catch limit. Ticket covers all five lochs (see Glen Astil).
Lochgilphead Lochs	Loch-gilphead	Brown Trout	15 Mar. to 6 Oct.	Lochgilphead and District A.C. c/o The Sports Shop, 31 Lochnell Street, Lochgilphead PA31 8JL. Tel: (0546) 602390.	10 lochs. Fly only. No Sunday fishing.
Loch Loskin	1 mile from Dunoon	Brown/ Sea Trout	1 Apr. to 30 Sept.	Dunoon & District Angling Club. Purdies of Argyll, 112 Argyll Street, Dunoon. Tel: Dunoon 3232.	Fly only. Boat only.
Loch Lossit	Ballygrant	Brown Trout	15 Mar. to 6 Oct.	Port Askaig Stores, Port Askaig, Isle of Islay. Tel: (049684) 245.	Average weight of fish caught: 8-16oz. Boats are available.
Loch Lussa	Campbel-town	Brown Trout	15 Mar. to 6 Oct.	MacGrory & Co., 16/20 Main Street, Campbeltown. Tel: (0586) 552132.	
Mishnish & Aros Lochs	Mull	Brown Trout	15 Mar. to 30 Sept.	Tobermory A.A., c/o Brown's Shop, Tobermory. Tel: (0688) 2020.	Average weight of fish caught: 12oz. Popular flies: Soldier Palmer, Teal & Green. No Spinners. 3 boats available. No Sunday fishing.
Loch na Curraigh	Nr. Kilmelford	Brown Trout	15 Mar. to 6 Oct.	D. Graham, Combe Street, Oban. Tack & Tackle Shop, Oban. Sports Centre, Oban. Anglers' Corner, Oban. Post Office, Kilmelford. Trading Post, Kilchrenan. Mr. Morrison, Ledaig Motors, Benderloch.	The loch has some fat 8oz-1lb trout that sometimes rise freely. The south-end is floating bog and fishing from this bank is not advised. Popular flies: standard trout flies, wet or dry (12 & 14).

Water	Location	Species	Season	Permit available from	Other Information
Loch nam Ban	Nr. Kilmelford	Brown Trout	15 Mar. to 6 Oct.	D. Graham, Combe Street, Oban. Tack & Tackle Shop, Oban. Sports Centre, Oban. Anglers' Corner, Oban. Post Office, Kilmelford. Trading Post, Kilchrenan. Mr. Morrison, Ledaig Motors, Benderloch.	Fish upto 2lbs have been caught on occasion. Popular flies: standard trout flies, wet or dry (12 & 14).
Loch na Sailm	Nr. Kilmelford	Brown Trout	15 Mar. to 6 Oct.	D. Graham, Combe Street, Oban. Tack & Tackle Shop, Oban. Sports Centre, Oban. Anglers' Corner, Oban. Post Office, Kilmelford. Trading Post, Kilchrenan. Mr. Morrison, Ledaig Motors, Benderloch.	The loch has been damned to improve fishing. Popular flies: Standard trout pattern, sizes 12 & 14.
Loch Nell	Nr. Oban	Salmon, Sea Trout Brown Trout Char	15 Mar. to 6 Oct. (Brown Trout)	D. Graham, Combe Street, Oban. Tack & Tackle Shop, Oban. Sports Centre, Oban. Anglers' Corner, Oban. Post Office, Kilmelford. Trading Post, Kilchrenan. Mr. Morrison, Ledaig Motors, Benderloch.	Popular flies: standard patterns Salmon and Sea Trout flies (8 &10). Fly, spinning and Bubble & fly are permitted. Boat available.
Oude Reservoir	14 miles from Oban	Brown Trout	15 Mar. to 6 Oct.	D. Graham, Combe Street, Oban. Tack & Tackle Shop, Oban. Sports Centre, Oban. Anglers' Corner, Oban. Post Office, Kilmelford. Trading Post, Kilchrenan. Mr. Morrison, Ledaig Motors, Benderloch.	Bank fishing can be difficult because of the fluctuating water level. Popular flies: standard trout flies, wet or dry (12 & 14). A boat is often located on this loch for periods.
Paperworks Reservoir	Argyll	Brown/ Rainbow Trout	15 Mar. to 5 Oct.	Kyles of Bute A.C., c/o Kames Hotel. Tel: (0700) 811489. Several shops in Kames and Tighnabruaich.	Fly and bait only, no spinning.
Loch Quien	Bute	Brown Trout	1 Apr. to 4 Oct.	Bute Estate Office, Rothesay, Isle of Bute. Tel: (0700) 502627.	Fly only. Salmon and trout fishing in sea around Bute.
Loch Scammadale	Kilninver	Salmon Sea Trout Brown Trout	1 June to 15 Oct. 15 Mar.-6 Oct.	Mrs. McCorkindale 'Glenann', Kilninver, by Oban, Argyll. Tel: (085 26) 282.	No Sunday fishing.
Loch Seil	Kilninver	Sea Trout Brown Trout	Apr. to Mid-Oct.	J.T.P. Mellor, Barndromin Farm, Knipoch, by Oban, Argyll. Tel: (085 26) 273.	Boat on Loch.
Sior Lochs	Nr. Oban	Brown Trout	15 Mar. to 6 Oct.	D. Graham, Combe Street, Oban. Tack & Tackle Shop, Oban. Sports Centre, Oban. Anglers' Corner, Oban. Post Office, Kilmelford. Trading Post, Kilchrenan. Mr. Morrison, Ledaig Motors, Benderloch.	Popular flies: standard trout flies, wet or dry (12 & 14). The lochs fish best in April & May.

Water	Location	Species	Season	Permit available from	Other Information
Loch Squabain	Mull	Salmon Sea Trout Brown Trout		Tackle & Books, Main Street, Tobermory, Mull. Tel: (0688) 2336.	Boat fishing only.
Loch Tarsan	8 miles from Dunoon	Brown Trout	1 Apr. to 30 Sept.	Dunoon & District Angling Club. Purdies of Argyll, 112 Argyll Street, Dunoon. Tel: Dunoon 3232.	Fly only
Tighnabruaich Reservoir (2 other lochs)	Tighnabruaich	Brown/ Rainbow Trout	15 Mar. to 5 Oct.	Kyles of Bute Angling Club. Several shops in Kames and Tighnabruaich, Argyll. Kames Hotel. Tel: (0700) 811489.	Motor boat available for sea fishing.
Torr Loch	North end of Mull	Wild Brown Trout Sea Trout Some Rainbow	April to Oct.	Tackle and Books, Main Street, Tobermory, Mull. Tel: (0688) 2336.	No Sunday fishing. 2 boats. Banks clear.
Loch Turamin	Isle of Colonsey	Brown Trout	15 Mar. to 30 Sept.	The Hotel, Isle of Colonsey, Argyll.	Fly fishing only. Boats are available.
Wee Feinn Loch	Nr. Kilmelford	Brown Trout	15 Mar. to 6 Oct.	D. Graham, Combe Street, Oban. Tack & Tackle Shop, Oban. Sports Centre, Oban. Anglers' Corner, Oban. Post Office, Kilmelford. Trading Post, Kilchrenan. Mr. Morrison, Ledaig Motors, Benderloch.	A small loch that contains trout up to 2lbs. Popular flies: standard trout patterns, sizes 10 & 12.

The Effects of POLLUTION may take years to disappear from a river

REPORT ALL CASES IMMEDIATELY

Keep samples of dead fish
Please telephone

Forth River Purification Board
031-441 1674 (24 hours) or 0786 51741
or **Forth District Salmon Fishery Board 0836 722 647**
or your local **Police Office**

Constituent Area Tourist Boards

Edinburgh Marketing
Waverley Market,
3 Princes Street,
Edinburgh EH2 2QP.
Tel: 031-557 2727.

Forth Valley Tourist Board
Tourist Officer,
Forth Valley Tourist Board,
Burgh Hall, The Cross,
Linlithgow,
West Lothian EH49 7AH.
Tel: (0506) 84 3306.

**Loch Lomond, Stirling and Trossachs
Tourist Board**
Tourism Manager,
Loch Lomond, Stirling and Trossachs
Tourist Board,
41 Dumbarton Road,
Stirling FK8 2LQ.
Tel: Stirling (0786) 75019.

St. Andrews and North East Fife Tourist Board
Tourism Manager,
St. Andrews and North East Fife Tourist Board,
2 Queens Gardens, St. Andrews,
Fife KY16 9TE.
Tel: St. Andrews (0334) 74609.

Kirkcaldy District Council
Tourist Officer,
Kirkcaldy District Council,
Information Centre,
South Street, Leven,
Fife KY8 4NT.
Tel: Leven (0333) 29464.

East Lothian Tourist Board
Tourism Director,
East Lothian Tourist Board,
Brunton Hall,
Musselburgh, EH21 6AE.
Tel: 031-665 3711.

**Other Tourist Organisations
MIDLOTHIAN**

**RIVER PURIFICATION BOARD
FORTH RIVER PURIFICATION BOARD**
Colinton Dell House,
West Mill Road, Colinton,
Edinburgh EH11 0PH.
Tel: 031-441 4691.

RIVERS

Water	Location	Species	Season	Permit available from	Other information
Allan	Bridge of Allan	Salmon Sea Trout Brown Trout	15 Mar. to 31 Oct. 15 Mar. to 6 Oct.	Country Pursuits, 46 Henderson Street, Bridge of Allan. Tel: (0786) 834495.	
Almond	Cramond	Salmon Sea Trout Brown Trout	1 Feb. to 31 Oct. 15 Mar. to 6 Oct.	Country Life, Balgreen Road, Edinburgh. Tel: 031-337 6230. Post Office, Davidsons Mains, Edinburgh.	Mouth to Old Cramond Brig. East bank only.
	West Lothian	Salmon Sea Trout Brown Trout	1 Feb. to 31 Oct. 15 Mar. to 6 Oct.	Livingston Sports, Almondvale Centre, Livingston. Country Life, Balgreen Road, Edinburgh. Tel: 031-337 6230.	20 miles of river.
Balvaig	Strathyre	Brown Trout Salmon	15 Mar. to 6 Oct.	Munro Hotel, Strathyre.	Average weight of fish caught: Trout - 1lb, Salmon - 8lbs Popular flies: Peter Ross, Blue Zulu. Worm fishing allowed.

Water	Location	Species	Season	Permit available from	Other Information
Devon	Dollar	Salmon Sea Trout Brown Trout	15 Mar. to 30 Oct. 15 Mar. to 5 Oct.	Devon Angling Association, R. Breingan, 33 Redwell Pl., Alloa. Tel: Alloa 215185. Scobbie Sports, 2/4 Primrose Street, Alloa. Tel: (0259) 722661. D.W. Black, The Hobby & Model Shop, 10-12 New Row, Dunfermline. Tel: (0383) 722582. D. Crockart & Son, 47 King Street, Stirling. Tel: (0786) 734433.	No Sunday fishing. Devonside Bridge upstream with excluded stretches. Fly fishing only from 15 Mar.-12 Apr.
	Hillfoots	Salmon Sea Trout Brown Trout	15 Mar. to 31 Oct. 15 Mar. to 6 Oct.	Country Pursuits, 46 Henderson Street, Bridge of Allan. Tel: (0786) 834495.	No Sunday fishing.
Eden	Cupar Area	Brown Trout Sea Trout Salmon	15 Mar.to 5 Oct. 15 Feb. to 31 Oct.	J. Caldwell, Newsagent & Fishing Tackle, Main Street, Methilhill, Fife.	All legal methods permitted.
Endrick	Drymen	Salmon Sea Trout Brown Trout	11 Feb. to 31 Oct. 15 Mar. to 6 Oct.	Loch Lomond Angling Improvement Association. R.A. Clement & Co. C.A., 29 St. Vincent Place, Glasgow. Tel: 041-221-0068.	Members only. No Sunday fishing. No worm fishing. Spinning restricted.
Esk	Musselburgh (Estuary to Buccleuch Estate both banks)	Salmon Sea Trout Brown Trout	15 Mar.to 31 Oct. 15 Mar. to 6 Oct.	Givan Shop, 67 Eskside West, Musselburgh. Tel: 031-665 3371.	No Sunday fishing. A max. of 6 fish per day. Spinning reels are prohibited. Further regulations on permit.
Esk	(North and South) Midlothian	Brown/ Rainbow Trout Grayling	15 Mar to 6 Oct. 7 Oct.-14 Mar. special winter permit.	Esk Valley Angling Improvement Association. Kevin Burns, 53 Fernieside Crescent, Edinburgh. Tel: 031-664 4685. F. & D. Simpson, 28/29 West Preston Street, Edinburgh EH8 9PZ. Tel: 031-667 3058. Country Life, Balgreen Road, Edinburgh. Tel: 031-337 6230. Laird & Dog Hotel, High Street, Lasswade. Bailiffs at water.	Fly rod and reel only to be used. Stocked at beginning of every month. Reductions for disabled, children and OAP's. Platform at Lasswade for disabled. Regulations on permit. Sunday fishing.
Forth	Stirling	Salmon Sea Trout Brown Trout	1 Feb.to 31 Oct. 15 Mar. to 6 Oct.	D. Crockart & Son, 47 King Street, Stirling. Tel: (0786) 73443. Mitchell's Tackle, 13 Bannockburn Road, Stirling. Country Pursuits, 45 Henderson Street, Bridge of Allan. Tel: (0786) 834495.	Information leaflet, maps, prices, rules, permits - Tel: (0786) 50403. No bait fishing before 1 Apr. or after 1 Sept.
	Gartmore Bridge- Buchlyvie (6½m beat)	Salmon Sea Trout Brown Trout	1 Feb.-31 Oct.	Lawrence Angling, 268 Dumbarton Road, Glasgow G11 6TU. Tel: 041-339 1085.	Fishing by any legal method permitted.

Water	Location	Species	Season	Permit available from	Other Information
Fruin	Helensburgh	Salmon Sea Trout Brown Trout	11 Feb. to 31 Oct. 1 Mar. to 6 Oct.	Loch Lomond Angling Improvement Association. R.A. Clement & Co. C.A., 29 St. Vincent Place, Glasgow. Tel: 041-221-0068.	Members only. Fly fishing only.
Water of Leith	Edinburgh	Brown Trout	1 Apr. to 30 Sept.	Lothian Regional Council, Reception, George IV Bridge, Edinburgh. Tel: 031-229 9292, ext. 3286. Post Office, 36 Main Street, Balerno. Post Office, Bridge Road, Colinton, Edinburgh. Tel: 031-441 1003.	Fly fishing above Slateford Road Bridge. No spinning. Regulations on permit.
Leven	Dumbarton	Salmon Sea Trout Brown Trout	11 Feb. to 31 Oct. 15 Mar. to 6 Oct.	Loch Lomond Angling Improvement Association. R.A. Clement & Co. C.A., 29 St. Vincent Place, Glasgow. Tel: 041-221-0068. Various local tackle shops. Country Lines, 29 Main Street, The Village, East Kilbride. Tel: (03552) 28952.	Members may fish all Association waters. No Sunday fishing. Day tickets available.
	Markinch to Leven	Brown Trout Salmon Sea Trout	15 Mar. to 30 Sept. 11 Feb. to 15 Oct.	J. Caldwell, Newsagent & Fishing Tackle, Main Street, Methilhill, Fife.	
Teith	Callander	Salmon Sea trout Brown Trout	1 Feb. to 31 Oct.	J. Bayne, Main Street, Callander. Tel: (0877) 30218.	Information leaflet, maps, prices, rules, permits: Tel: (0786) 50403. No Sunday fishing.
				Country Pursuits, 46 Henderson Street, Bridge of Allan. Tel: (0786) 834495.	Season permits only.
	Stirling (Blue Banks)	Salmon Sea Trout	1 Feb. to 31 Oct.	D. Crockart & Son, 47 King Street, Stirling. Tel: (0786) 73443.	
	Gart Farm by Callander	Salmon Sea Trout 1 Feb. to 31 Oct.		Country Pursuits, 46 Henderson Street, Bridge of Allan. Tel: (0786) 834495.	Season permits only.
Tyne	Haddington	Brown Trout Rainbow/ Sea Trout	15 Mar. to 6 Oct.	East Lothian Angling Association. J.S. Main, Saddlers, 87 High Street, Haddington. Tel: (062 082) 2148. John Dickson & Son Ltd., 21 Frederick Street, Edinburgh EH2 2NE. Tel: 031-225 4218. Country Life, Balgreen Road, Edinburgh. Tel: 031-337 6230.	Twenty miles of river. No Sunday fishing. No threadlines. No spinning.

LOCHS & RESERVOIRS

Water	Location	Species	Season	Permit available from	Other information
Loch Achray	By Callander	Brown Trout Perch Pike	15 Mar. to 6 Oct.	Forestry Commission, Queen Elizabeth Forest Park Visitor Centre, Aberfoyle. Loch Achray Hotel, Trossachs. Tel: (08776) 229/240. Bayne's Fishing Tackle Shop, Callander.	Bank fishing only.
Loch Ard	Kinlochard	Brown Trout	15 Mar. to 6 Oct.	Altskeith Hotel, Kinlochard FK8 3TL. Tel: (08777) 266.	Average weight of fish caught: 12oz. Popular flies: Silver Butcher, Kate McLaren, Alexandra. Fly fishing only. Boats are available.
Loch Arklet	By Inversnaid	Brown Trout	15 Mar. to 27 Sept.	Strathclyde Water, 419 Balmore Road, Glasgow G22 6NU or at Loch Arklet.	Average weight of fish caught: 8 to 12oz. Popular flies: Silver Butcher, Grouse & Claret, Black Pennel, Greenwell's Glory. No live bait allowed. Rowing boats only are available.
Beecraigs Loch	Linlithgow	Brown Trout Rainbow Trout Brook Trout	1 Mar. to 31 Oct.	Beecraigs Country Park. Tel: Linlithgow 844516.	Fly fishing only. Boat fishing only.
Bonaly Reservoir	Edinburgh	Brown/ Rainbow Trout	1 Apr. to 30 Sept.	None Required.	
Bowden Springs	Linlithgow	Rainbow/ Brown Trout	3 Jan. to 23 Dec.	W. Martin, Bowden Springs Fishery, Linlithgow. Tel: Linlithgow 847269.	Bank and boat fishing. Fly fishing only. Minimum size 1 lb. Corporate days.
Cameron Reservoir	St. Andrews	Brown Trout	Mid-Apr. to End-Sept.	St. Andrews Angling Club, Secretary, Mr. P. Malcolm, 54 St. Nicholas Street, St. Andrews. Tel: (0334) 76347. The bailiff at the fishing hut on Cameron Reservoir.	Average weight of fish caught: 1lb. Fly fishing only. 6 boats are available.
Upper Carriston Reservoir	Nr. Markinch	Brown Trout	1 Apr. to 30 Sept.	J. Caldwell Newsagent & Fishing Tackle, Main Street, Methilhill, Fife.	Average weight of fish caught: 1lb to 1lb 8oz. Fly fishing only. Bank fishing only - maximum 20 anglers.
Carron Valley Reservoir	Denny	Brown Trout	13 Apr. to 19 Sept.	Director of Finance, Central Regional Council, Viewforth, Stirling. Tel: (0786) 442000.	Boat fishing only.
Clubbiedean Reservoir	Edinburgh	Brown/ Rainbow Trout	1 Apr. to 30 Sept.	Lothian Regional Council, Pentland Hills Regional Park H.Q., Boghall Farm, Biggar Road, Edinburgh. Tel: 031-445 5969.	Three boats. Bag limit 6 trout. Fly fishing only. Sessions: May to August.

Water	Location	Species	Season	Permit available from	Other information
Cocksburn Loch	Bridge of Allan	Brown Trout	1 Apr. to 6 Oct.	Country Pursuits, 46 Henderson Street, Bridge of Allan. Tel: (0786) 834495.	Average weight of fish caught: 8-12oz. Boat fishing only. Popular flies: small dark flies.
Crosswood Reservoir	West Calder	Brown Trout Brook Trout Rainbow Trout	1 Apr. to 30 Sept.	Lothian Regional Council, Pentland Hills Regional Park H.Q., Boghall Farm, Biggar Road, Edinburgh. Tel: 031-445 5969. Dept. of Water & Drainage, Lomond House, Beveridge Square, Livingston Tel: (0506) 414004.	Three boats available. 1 boat available - Boghall Farm. 2 boats available - Livingston. Fly fishing only.
Loch Drunkie	Aberfoyle	Brown Trout	15 Mar. to 6 Oct.	Forestry Commission Queen Elizabeth Forest Park Visitor Centre, Aberfoyle.	Bank fishing only.
Loch Fitty	Kingseat, Dunfermline	Salmon Brown/ Rainbow Trout	1 Mar. to Xmas	The Fishing Lodge, Loch Fitty, Dunfermline, Fife. Tel: (0383) 620666.	Boat and Bank fly fishing. Day - 10am-5pm. Evenings - 5.30pm-dark. Reductions for single anglers, and 'Father & schoolboy Son'. Boats.
Gartmorn Dam Fishery	Nr. Alloa	Brown Trout	1 Apr. to 30 Sept.	Sept to April: Speirs Centre, 29 Primrose Street, Alloa FK10 1JJ. Tel: (0259) 213131. April to Sept: Visitor Centre, Gartmorn Dam Country Park, by Sauchie FK10 3AZ. Tel: (0259) 214319.	Average weight of fish caught: 1lb 4oz. Popular flies: Nymphs, Buzzers, Olives, Wickhams. Restricted bank spinning first six weeks 9 boats available. Disabled anglers' wheelyboat. 2 sessions: 9am-5pm & 5pm-Dusk.
Gladhouse Reservoir	Midlothian	Brown Trout	1 Apr. to 30 Sept.	Lothian Regional Council, Pentland Hills Regional Park H.Q., Boghall Farm, Biggar Road, Edinburgh. Tel: 031-445 5969. Mrs. E. Kirk, Toxsidehill, Gorebridge. Tel: (087530) 262.	Average weight of fish caught: 1 to 2lbs. Local Nature Reserve. Double-sessions: May-August Day: 8am 4.30pm. Evening: 5pm Sunset, plus 1 hour. Sunday fishing. Fly fishing only.
Glencorse Reservoir	Penicuik	Brown Trout Brook Trout Rainbow Trout	1 Apr. to 30 Sept.	Lothian Regional Council, Pentland Hills Regional Park H.Q., Boghall Farm, Biggar Road, Edinburgh. Tel: 031-445 5969.	Fly fishing only. 4 boats. Sessions: May to Aug.
Glen Finglas Reservoir	By Callander	Brown Trout	15 Mar. to 27 Sept.	Strathclyde Water, 419 Balmore Road, Glasgow G22 6NU or at Glen Finglas.	Average weight of fish caught: 8 to 12oz. Popular flies: Silver Butcher, Grouse & Claret, Black Pennel, Greenwell's Glory. No live bait allowed. Rowing boat only, are available.

Please mention this Pastime Publications guide   93

Water	Location	Species	Season	Permit available from	Other information
Loch Glow	Cleish Hills, Nr. Kelty	Brown Trout	15 Mar. to 6 Oct.	Tackle shops in Dunfermline, Cowdenbeath, Kelty & Kinross.	Fly, bait & spinning. Regularly stocked with brown trout; some tagged fish. Further information Mr. J.W. Mill, Tel: (0383) 722128.
Harlaw Reservoir	Balerno	Brown/ Rainbow Trout	1 Apr. to 30 Sept.	Day tickets: Fleming's Grocery Shop, 42 Main Street, Balerno. Tel: 031-449 3833. Season Permits: Dalmeny Estate Office, South Queensferry, West Lothian.	Average weight of fish caught: 1-2lbs. Fly fishing only. Bank fishing only. Season tickets issued by ballot - applications must be in by 1st March.
Harperrig Reservoir	West Calder	Brown Trout	1 Apr. to 30 Sept.	Dept. of Water & Drainage, Lomond House, Beveridge Square, Livingston. Tel: (0506) 414004. Bank fishing permits from machine at reservoir.	Correct coins required for machine, 50p 10p 5p denominations. Four boats and bank fishing. No Sunday fishing. Fly fishing only.
Hopes Reservoir	Gifford	Brown Trout	1 Apr. to 30 Sept.	Lothian Regional Council, Dept. of Water & Drainage, Alderston House, Haddington. Tel: (062 082) 4131, ext. 217.	2 boats.
Loch Katrine	Stronachlachar	Brown Trout	15 Mar. to 27 Sept.	Strathclyde Water, 419 Balmore Road, Glasgow G22 6NU or at Stronachlachar.	Average weight of fish caught: 8 to 12oz. Popular flies: Silver Butcher, Grouse & Claret, Black Pennel, Greenwell's Glory. No live bait allowed. Rowing boats only are available.
Lake of Menteith	Port of Menteith	Rainbow Trout	4 Apr. to 30 Oct.	Lake of Menteith Fisheries Ltd., Port of Menteith, Perthshire. Tel: (08775) 664.	28 boats are available. No bank fishing.
Lindores Loch	Newburgh	Brown/ Rainbow Trout	15 Mar. to 30 Nov.	F.G.A. Hamilton, The Byre, Kindrochet, St. Fillans PH6 2JZ. Tel: (076 485) 337.	Two sessions. 9 am - 5 pm 5 pm - 10 pm
Linlithgow Loch	Linlithgow	Brown/ Rainbow Trout	15 Mar. to 6 Oct.	Tel: (0831) 288921.	Average weight of fish caught: 1lb 8oz. Popular flies: black lures, Green Peter, Grouse & Claret, Buzzers. Fly fishing only. 12 boats are available.
Lochore	Ballingry	Brown/ Rainbow Trout	15 Mar. to 6 Oct.	Hobby & Model Shop, Dunfermline. Lochore Meadows Country Park, Crosshill, Lochgelly, Fife. Tel: (0592) 860086.	Reductions for clubs and groups. Sessions: Day - 9 am-5 pm. Evening - 5 pm-dusk. Fly fishing and spinning. Bait fishing from bank from 1 July.

Water	Location	Species	Season	Permit available from	Other information
Loch Lomond	Balloch to Ardlui	Salmon Sea Trout Brown Trout Pike Roach Perch	11 Feb. to 31 Oct. 15 Mar.-6 Oct. No close season	Loch Lomond Angling Improvement Association R.A. Clement & Co, C.A., 29 St. Vincent Place, Glasgow. Tel: 041-221-0068. Country Lines, 29 Main Street, The Village, East Kilbride. Tel: (03552) 28952. Local hotels, shops & tackle dealers.	Boats for hire locally. No Sunday fishing. Day permits available.
	Ardlui	Salmon Sea Trout Brown Trout Pike	11 Feb. to 31 Oct. 15 Mar. to 6 Oct.	Ardlui Hotel, Loch Lomond. Tel: 030 14 243.	Popular flies: Silver Victor, Mallard, Claret. Other baits: Toby, Rapala, Sprat. Boats are available.
	Balmaha	Salmon Sea Trout Pike	Mar to Oct. All year.	MacFarlane & Son, The Boatyard, Balmaha. Tel: 036 087 214.	Boats and outboard motors are available.
	By Drymen	Salmon Sea Trout Brown Trout	11 Feb. to 31 Oct. 15 Mar. to 6 Oct.	Rowardennan Hotel, Rowardennan.	Average weight of fish caught: Salmon - 9lbs, Sea Trout - 3 lbs, Brown Trout - 1lb 12oz. Other baits: Toby for trawling.
	Inverbeg	Salmon Sea Trout Brown Trout Pike Perch	11 Feb. to 31 Oct. 15 Mar. to 6 Oct. All Year.	Inverbeg Caravan Park, Inverbeg. Tel: 043 686 267.	Popular flies: March Brown, Peter Ross. Live bait allowed.
Maltings Fishery	West Barns, Dunbar EH42 1RG.	Brown/ Rainbow Trout	All year for Rainbow.	Dunbar Trout Farm, Tel: (0368) 63244. (Or at the fishery).	Fly only. Maximum fly size no. 10 long shank.
Morton Fishery	Mid Calder	Brown/ Rainbow Trout	6 Mar. to 30 Oct.	Morton Fishery, Morton Reservoir, Mid Calder, W. Lothian. Tel: (0506) 882293.	Fly fishing only. Advance bookings. Double sessions May-Aug, 9 am-5 pm, 5pm-dusk. Bag limits 3-6 fish per rod.
North Third	By Cambusbarron	Rainbow/ Brown Trout	15 Mar. to 31 Oct.	North Third Trout Fishery, "Greathill", Cambusbarron, Stirling. Tel: Stirling (0786) 71967.	Fly fishing only. Boat and bank. Day/season permits available. Advance bookings advisable. Fishery record for rainbow trout 19lbs. Loch stocked in 1992 with American brook trout.
Loch Ore	Ballingry	Brown/ Rainbow Trout	15 Mar. to 6 Oct.	Lochore Meadows Country Park, Crosshill, Lochgelly, Fife. Tel: (0592) 860086.	Average weight of fish caught: 1lb 4oz. Spinning and bait from bank (check of dates). Boats are available.
Lochan Reoidhe	Aberfoyle	Brown Trout	16 Mar. to 6 Oct.	Forestry Commission Queen Elizabeth Forest Park Visitor Centre, Aberfoyle.	Fly fishing only. Limited rods. Boat available. Advance bookings accepted.

Water	Location	Species	Season	Permit available from	Other information
Selm Muir Loch	Nr. Livingston	Rainbow Trout	All year	Selm Muir Loch.	Average weight of fish caught: 1lb 4oz. Popular flies: Montana Nymph, small black lures. Other baits: maggots, sweetcorn, no spinning.
Swan's Water Fishery	Stirling	Rainbow/ Brown Trout	All year for Rainbow	Swan's Water Fishery.	Average weight of fish caught: 1lb 12oz. Popular flies: Viva, Black Pennel. Fly fishing only. 2 boats are available.
Threipmuir Reservoir	Balerno	Brown/ Rainbow Trout	1 Apr. to 30 Sept.	Day tickets: Flemings, Grocer, 42 Main Street, Balerno. Tel: 031-449 3833. Season permits: Dalmeny Estate Office, South Queensferry, West Lothian.	Average weight of fish caught: 1-2lbs. Fly fishing only. Bank fishing only. Season tickets issued by ballot - applications must be in by 1st March.
Loch Venachar	Callander	Brown Trout	15 Mar. to 6 Oct.	J. Bayne, Main Street, Callander. Tel: (0877) 30218.	Boats for hire.
		Salmon Sea Trout Brown Trout	1 Feb. to 31 Oct. 15 Mar. to 6 Oct.	Country Pursuits, 46 Henderson Street, Bridge of Allan. Tel: (0786) 834495.	Season permits only.
Loch Voil	Balquhidder	Brown Trout Salmon Sea Trout Char	15 Mar. to 6 Oct.	Stronvar Country House Hotel, Balquhidder FK19 8PB. Tel: (08774) 688.	Hotel Guests only. Advanced bookings necessary.
				C.M. Oldham & I.T. Emslie, Muirlaggan, Balquidder, Lochearnhead FK19 8PB. Tel: (08774) 219.	Popular flies: Blae & Black, Kate McLaren, Grouse & Claret, Black Spider, Greenwell's Glory, Butcher, Professor (size 12). Other baits: spinners, rapala, toby, kynoch killer for salmon. 5 boats are available.

Constituent Area Tourist Boards

City of Dundee Tourist Board
Director,
City of Dundee Tourist Board,
Tourism Information Department,
4 City Square,
Dundee DD1 3BA.
Tel: Dundee (0382) 23141, ext. 4384

Perthshire Tourist Board
Director of Tourism,
Perthshire Tourist Board,
45 High Street, Perth PH1 5TJ.
Tel: Perth (0738) 27958.

Angus Tourist Board
Tourist Manager,
Angus Tourist Board,
Market Place, Arbroath,
Angus DD11 1HR.
Tel: Arbroath (0241) 76680.

RIVER PURIFICATION BOARD
TAY RIVER PURIFICATION BOARD
1 South Street,
Perth PH2 8NJ.
Tel: Perth (0738) 27989.

RIVERS

Water	Location	Species	Season	Permit available from	Other information
Braan	Amulree	Brown Trout	15 Mar. to 6 Oct.	Post Office, Amulree.	Fly fishing only.
	Cochill Burn	Brown Trout	15 Mar to 6 Oct.	Kettles of Dunkeld, Atholl Street, Dunkeld. Tel: (0350) 727556.	Fly fishing only.
Dean	Strathmore	Brown Trout	15 Mar. to 6 Oct.	Strathmore Angling Improvement Association, Mrs. A.J. Henderson, 364 Blackness Road, Dundee. Tel: (0382) 68062.	
	Devon Hillfoots, Tillicoultry to Crook of Devon	Salmon Sea Trout Brown Trout	15 Mar. to 31 Oct. 15 Mar.-6 Oct.	Country Pursuits, 46 Henderson Street, Bridge of Allan. Tel: (0786) 834495.	Fly fishing only from: 15 March to 12 April.
Dochart	Killin	Brown Trout	15 Mar. to 6 Oct.	J. Lewis, Tackle Dealer, Killin, Perthshire. Tel: (056 72) 362.	All legal lures permitted. Fly only on lower beat.
Earn	Crieff	Salmon Sea Trout Brown Trout	1 Feb. to 15 Oct. 15 Mar.-6 Oct.	Crieff Angling Club. Mr. R. Kelly, 39 King Street, Crieff. Tel: (0764) 3871.	No shrimp, prawn, diving minnow or floats. No bait before 1st May.
Earn	By Crieff	Salmon Sea Trout Brown Trout	1 Feb. to 31 Oct. 15 Mar.-6 Oct.	Country Pursuits, 46 Henderson Street, Bridge of Allan. Tel: (0786) 834495.	(Lower Strowan Beat) Permit available for season only (day per week throughout season).
Ericht	Bridge of Cally	Salmon Brown Trout	1 Jan.-15 Oct. 15 Mar. to 6 Oct.	Bridge of Cally Hotel, Blairgowrie, Perthshire. Tel: (025 086) 231.	Fly fishing only after 15 April.
	Craighall	Salmon Brown Trout	15 Jan.-15 Oct. 15 Mar to 6 Oct.	A.L. Rattray, Craighall, Blairgowrie PH10 7JB. Tel: (0250) 874749 or (0738) 30926.	Subject to availability.

Water	Location	Species	Season	Permit available from	Other information
Garry	Blair Atholl	Brown Trout	15 Mar. to 6 Oct.	Highland Shop, Blair Atholl. Tel: (0796) 481303.	Any legal method permitted.
Isla	Strathmore	Brown Trout	15 Mar. to 6 Oct.	Strathmore Angling Improvement Association, Mrs. A.J. Henderson, 364 Blackness Road, Dundee. Tel: (0382) 68062.	
Lochay	Killin	Brown Trout Pike Perch	15 Mar. to 6 Oct.	J. Lewis, Tackle Dealers, Main Street, Killin, Perthshire. Tel: (056 72) 362.	Fly only on upper beat.
Lunan	Arbroath	Sea/ Brown Trout	15 Mar. to 6 Oct.	Arbroath Cycle and Tackle Centre, 274 High Street, Arbroath. Tel: (0241) 73467.	Fly, bait or spinning.
Lyon	Aberfeldy	Salmon	15 Jan. to 15 Oct.	Fortingall Hotel, Fortingall, by Aberfeldy. Tel: (0887) 830367.	No Sunday fishing. Max. 5 rods on each of 2 beats. Maps, tackle etc. available. (6 miles single bank).
	Tirinie Fishings	Salmon Brown Trout	15 Jan.-15 Oct. 15 Mar.-6 Oct.	Coshieville Hotel, By Aberfeldy PH15 2NE.	Max. 4 rods. No bait fishing. No Sunday fishing. Boat & ghillie available for hire.
South Esk	Kirriemuir	Salmon Sea Trout	16 Feb. to 31 Oct.	H. Burness, Kirriemuir Angling Club, 13 Clova Road, Kirriemuir. Tel: (0575) 73456.	No permits on Saturdays. No Sunday fishing. Fly only in parts in low water. Booking advisable.
Tay	Aberfeldy	Brown Trout Grayling	15 Mar. to 6 Oct.	Jamiesons Sports Shop, 41 Dunkeld Street, Aberfeldy. Tel: (0887) 20385.	Fly only until 1st May.
		Salmon Brown Trout	15 Jan.-15 Oct. 15 Mar. to 6 Oct.	Weem Hotel, Weem, by Aberfeldy. Tel: (0887) 820381.	Salmon - any legal means. Trout - fly or small mepps only.
		Salmon Sea Trout	15 Jan. to 15 Oct.	Country Pursuits, 46 Henderson Street, Bridge of Allan. Tel: (0786) 834495.	(Killiechassie Beat) 4 rods maximum. Ghillie available. No prawns/shrimps after 1 Sept.
		Salmon Sea Trout	15 Jan. to 15 Oct.	Country Pursuits, 46 Henderson Street, Bridge of Allan. Tel: (0786) 834495.	(Derculich Beat) Maximum 3 rods. Ghillie available. No bait.
		Salmon Sea Trout	15 Jan. to 15 Oct.	Country Pursuits, 46 Henderson Street, Bridge of Allan. Tel: (0786) 834495.	(Lower Farleyer) 4 rods maximum. Ghillie Available. No Prawns/ shrimps after 1 Sept.
		Salmon Sea Trout	15 Jan. to 15 Oct.	Country Pursuits, 46 Henderson Street, Bridge of Allan. Tel: (0786) 834495.	(Moness Beat) Maximum 3 rods. Boat & ghillie available. No prawns/shrimps after 1 Sept.
	Grandtully	Salmon Brown Trout Grayling	15 Jan.-15 Oct. 15 Mar. to 6 Oct.	Grantully Hotel, Strathtay, Perthshire. Tel: (0887) 840207.	Fly or spinning. Boat & ghillie available. Booking advisable. Rod hire and tackle. 5-rod beat.

Water	Location	Species	Season	Permit available from	Other information
Tay cont.		Salmon Sea Trout	15 Jan. to 15 Oct.	Country Pursuits, 46 Henderson Street, Bridge of Allan. Tel: (0786) 834495.	(Findyate Beat) Maximum 3 rods. Boat & ghillie available. No prawns/shrimps after 1 Sept. Good Spring beat.
		Salmon Sea Trout	15 Jan. to 15 Oct.	Country Pursuits, 46 Henderson Street, Bridge of Allan. Tel: (0786) 834495.	(Clochfoldich Beat) Maximum 3 rods. Boat & ghillie available. No prawns/shrimps after 1 Sept. Good Spring beat.
	Dalguise	Salmon	15 Jan. to 15 Oct.	The Manager, Burnside, Dalguise, by Dunkeld. Tel: (0350) 727593.	1½ miles both banks.
	Dunkeld	Salmon Brown Trout	15 Jan.-15 Oct. 15 Mar.-6 Oct.	Stakis Hotels Ltd., Dunkeld House Hotel, Dunkeld. Tel: (0350) 727771.	Two boats with two rods. Experienced ghillies. 8 bank rods. Tuition. No salmon fishing on Sundays. Booking advisable.
		Brown Trout Grayling	15 Mar. to 6 Oct.	Kettles of Dunkeld, Atholl Street, Dunkeld. Tel: (0350) 727556.	Fly fishing only. Tackle hire.
		Salmon Sea Trout	15 Jan. to 15 Oct.	Country Pursuits, 46 Henderson Street, Bridge of Allan. Tel: (0786) 834495.	(Upper Newtyle Beat) Maximum 5 rods. Boat and ghillie available. No prawns/shrimps after 1 Sept.
		Salmon Sea Trout	15 Jan. to 15 Oct.	Country Pursuits, 46 Henderson Street, Bridge of Allan. Tel: (0786) 834495.	(Lower Newtyle Beat) Maximum 5 rods. Boat & ghillie available. No prawns/shrimps after 1 Sept.
	Stanley	Salmon Sea Trout Brown Trout	15 Jan.- 13 Oct. 12 Mar.- 6 Oct.	Tayside Hotel, Stanley, Nr. Perth. Tel: (0738) 828249.	Day permits available May-July. Ghillies by arrangement. Advisable to book in advance.
	Perth	Salmon Sea Trout Flounder Roach	15 Jan. to 15 Oct.	Director of Leisure & Recreation, Perth & Kinross District Council, 3 High Street, Perth. Tel: (0738) 39911, (Monday to Friday). Tourist Information Centre, 45 High Street, Perth PH1 5TJ. Tel: (0738) 38353 Weekends & public holidays.	Advisable to book in advance. Only 20 permits per day. Only 2 permits in advance by any one person. No weekly permits.
	Ballinluig	Salmon	15 Jan. to 15 Oct.	Jim Trittow, Port of Tay Cottage, Ballinluig.	(Upper Kinnaird Beat) Average weight of fish caught: 12lbs. Other baits: prawns, worms. Boats are available.
Tilt	Blair Atholl	Salmon	End-May to 15 Oct.	The Highland Shop, Blair Atholl. Tel: (0796) 481303.	(Private Beat, 3 miles) Booking advised. Fly or spinning only.
Tummel	Pitlochry	Salmon Sea Trout	15 Jan. to 15 Oct.	Pitlochry Angling Club c/o Tourist Office, Pitlochry. Tel: Mr. Gardiner, (0796) 472157 (eve./weekends).	Permits available Monday to Saturday.

Water	Location	Species	Season	Permit available from	Other information
Tummel cont.	Pitlochry to Ballinluig	Brown Trout Grayling	15 Mar. to 6 Oct.	Pitlochry Angling Club c/o Tourist Office, Pitlochry Tel: Mr. Gardiner (0796) 472157 (eve./weekends). Ballinluig Service Station. Milton of Fonab Caravan Site. Atholl Sports, Atholl Road, Pitlochry. Mitchells of Pitlochry, 23 Atholl Road, Pitlochry.	Five miles of river, both banks. Map and rules on permits.
	Moulinearn to Ballinluig	Salmon Sea Trout	15 Jan. to 15 Oct.	Pitlochry Angling Club c/o Tourist Office, Pitlochry. Tel: Mr. Gardiner (0796) 472157 (eve./weekends).	Only available July & August.
	Tummel (Upper) Kinloch Rannoch	Brown Trout	15 Mar. to 6 Oct.	E.M. Beattie (Sec.), 2 Schiehallion Place, Kinloch Rannoch. Tel: (0882) 632261. Local shops & hotels.	Average weight of fish caught: 12oz. Other baits: spinning and live.

LOCHS & RESERVOIRS

Water	Location	Species	Season	Permit available from	Other information
Loch Bainnie	Spittal of Glenshee	Brown Trout	18 Mar. to 11 Aug.	Invercauld Estates Office, Braemar AB35 5XQ. Tel: Braemar 41224.	Boat available from: Mr. R. Hepburn, Gamekeeper, Wester Binzean, Glenshee. Tel: Glenshee 206. No spinning or use of live bait.
Ben Vrackie Loch	By Pitlochry	Brown Trout	15 Mar. to 30 Sept.	Mr. Seaton, Gamekeeper's House, Baledmund Estate, Pitlochry.	Average weight of fish caught: 8oz. Any legal method permitted.
Blair Walker Pond	Blair Atholl	(Stocked) Brown/ Rainbow Trout	15 Mar. to 6 Oct.	The Highland Shop, Blair Atholl. Tel: (0796) 481303.	Fly only.
Butterstone Loch	Dunkeld	Rainbow/ Brown Trout	1 Apr. to 31 Oct.	The Bailiff, Lochend Cottage, Butterstone, by Dunkeld. Tel: (0350) 724238.	Fly fishing only. 15 Boats. Day Session: 9 am-5 pm. Evening: 5.30 pm-dusk.
Castlehill Reservoir	Glendevon	Brown Trout	1 Apr. to 30 Sept.	Fife Reg. Council, Craig Mitchell House. Flemington Road, Glenrothes. Tel: (0592) 754411). Glendevon Treatment Works. Tel: (0259) 781453.	Fly fishing only. Boat, 2 rods. Bank.
Loch Dochart	by Crianlarich	Salmon Brown Trout	1 Feb. to 6 Oct.	Portnellan House, by Crianlarich FK20 8QS. Tel: (08383) 284.	Popular flies: Black Pennel, Black & Peacock, Mullard, Claret. Any legal method permitted. Boats available.
Dunalastair Loch	Kinloch Rannoch	Brown Trout	15 Mar. to 6 Oct.	Lassintullich Fisheries. Tel: (0882) 632238.	Five boats. No bank fishing. Fly fishing only.

Water	Location	Species	Season	Permit available from	Other information
Loch Earn	Lochearnhead	Brown Trout	15 Mar. to 6 Oct.	Clachan Cottage Hotel, Lochside, Lochearnhead. Tel: (05673) 247. Lochearnhead Holiday Centre. Tel: (05673) 221.	Fishing Mon. to Sun. Fly rod, Fly reel and any legal method, max. B.S. 4lbs. Min. taking size 8" Prohibited baits: diving minnow.
		Brown/ Rainbow Trout	Mar. to Oct.	St. Fillans Post Office, St. Fillans.	Average weight of fish caught: 12oz-2lbs. The loch is regularly stocked.
Loch Eigheach	Moor of Rannoch	Brown Trout	15 Mar. to 6 Oct.	Rannoch & District Angling Club, John Brown, The Square, Kinloch Rannoch. Tel: (0882) 632268.	Bank fishing only.
Errochty Dam	Nr. Blair Atholl	Brown Trout Pike	15 Mar. to 6 Oct. No close season	The Highland Shop, Blair Atholl. Tel: (0796) 481303.	Any legal method permitted.
Loch Faskally	Pitlochry	Salmon	Mar., May to Oct.	Mr. D. McLaren, Pitlochry Boating Station, Loch Faskally, Pitlochry. Tel: (0796) 472919/472759	Any legal lure for salmon Boats available. Cafe facilities.
		Brown Trout Pike Perch	Mar. to Sept.		
Glendevon (Lower Reservoir)	Glendevon	Brown Trout	1 Apr. to 30 Sept.	Fife Regional Council, Craig Mitchell House. Flemington Road, Glenrothes. Tel: (0592) 754411. Glendevon Treatment Works. Tel: (025981) 453.	Fly fishing only. No Sunday fishing. Bank fishing allowed on Lower Glendevon. Boat 2 rods. Bank.
Glenfarg	Glenfarg	Brown Trout	1 Apr. to 30 Sept.	Fife Regional Council, Craig Mitchell House, Flemington Road, Glenrothes. Tel: (0592) 754411. Glenfarg Treatment Works. Tel: (05773) 561.	Fly fishing only. No Sunday fishing. Boat available.
Heatherytord	Just off Junction 6 on M90 at Kinross.	Brown/ Rainbow Trout	Mid-March to Dec.	Kinross Trout Fishery, office on site. Tel: (05778) 64212	All bank fishing, top quality trout. Trout master water. Fly fishing only.
Holl	Lomond Hills	Brown Trout	1 Apr. to 30 Sept.	Fife Regional Council, Craig Mitchell House, Flemington Road, Glenrothes. Tel: (0592) 754411.	Fly fishing only. No Sunday fishing. Boat available.
Loch lubhair	Nr. Crianlarich	Salmon Brown Trout	1 Feb. to 6 Oct.	Portnellan House, by Crianlarich FK20 8QS. Tel: (08383) 284.	Popular flies: Black Pennel, Black & Peacock, Mullard, Claret. Any legal method permitted. Boats are available.
Loch Kinardochy	Tummel bridge	Brown Trout	15 Mar. to 6 Oct.	Mitchells of Pitlochry, 23 Atholl Road, Pitlochry PH16 5BX. Tel: (0796) 472613.	Fly fishing from boat only. Advance booking recommended.

Please mention this Pastime Publications guide

Water	Location	Species	Season	Permit available from	Other information
Lochan-na-Laraig	Killin	Trout	15 Mar. to 6 Oct.	J. Lewis, Tackle Dealers, Main Street, Killin. Tel: (056 72) 362.	All legal lures.
Loch Lee	Glen Esk	Brown Trout Arctic Char	1 May to 12 Aug.	Head Keeper, Invermark, Glenesk, by Brechin DD9 7YZ. Tel: (0356) 670208.	Average weight of fish caught: 8oz to 12oz. Popular flies: any small dark flies. 3 boats - 3 rods per boat. No Sunday fishing. No bank fishing.
Loch Leven	Kinross	Brown Trout (Loch Leven strain)	2nd Apr. to 6th Oct.	Lochleven Fisheries, The Pier, Kinross. Tel: (0577) 863407.	Fly and boat fishing only.
Lintrathen Reservoir	Kirriemuir	Brown Trout	1 Apr. to 6 Oct.	Lintrathen Angling Club Jack Yule, 61 Hillrise, Kirriemuir, Angus DD8 4JS. Tel: (05756) 327. Club bookings: Dr. Parratt, 91 Strathearn Road, Broughty Ferry, Dundee. Tel: (0382) 77305. (Not after start of season).	18 boats. Sunday fishing. Max. catch 24 fish per boat. Tel. for details of sessions and backwater dam. Bank fishing only.
Monikie	Monikie	Brown Trout	Beg. Apr. to 6 Oct.	Tel: Newbigging 300.	Average weight of fish caught: 1lb 4oz. Popular flies: Bibio, Kate McLaren, Ace of Spades. Boats: (10) Island Pond, (4) North Pond, (4) Crombie. Fly only. Boat only.
Loch Nan Ean	Dalmunzie	Brown Trout	18 Mar. to 11 Aug.	Invercauld Estates Office, Braemar AB35 5XQ. Tel: Braemar 41224.	No spinning or use of live bait permitted.
Loch Rannoch	Kinloch Rannoch	Brown Trout	15 Mar. to 6 Oct.	Loch Rannoch Conservation Association, Cuilmore Cottage, Kinloch Rannoch. Loch Rannoch Hotel. Tel: (0882) 632201. Bunrannoch Hotel, Tel: (0882) 632367.	Fly fishing only. 6 am - 10 pm. 15 foot open boats. No live bait. Ghillie service. Rod hire. Small tackle shop.
		Brown Trout Pike Perch	15 Mar. to 6 Oct.	E.M. Beattie (Sec.), 2 Schiehallion Place, Kinloch Rannoch. Tel: (0882) 632261. Local shops and hotels.	Average weight of fish caught: 8oz to 1lb. No live bait allowed. Boats are available from: Dunalastair or Loch Rannoch hotels.
Rescobie Loch	Forfar	Brown/ Rainbow Trout	15 Mar. to 31 Oct.	Bailiff, Rescobie Loch, South Lodge, Reswallie, By Forfar DD8 2SA. Tel: (030781) 384.	Fly fishing only. Bank & Boat.
Sandy-knowes Fishery	Bridge of Earn	Rainbow Trout	1 Mar. to 30 Nov.	E. Christie, The Fishery Office, Sandyknowe Fishery, Bridge of Earn. Tel: (0738) 813033.	Bank fly fishing only. Session times 10 am-2 pm, 2 pm-6 pm, 6 pm-10 pm. Bag limit - 4 trout per session. Open 7 days. No Sunday evenings.
Loch Tay	Killin	Brown Trout	15 Mar. to 5 Oct.	J. Lewis, Tackle Dealers, Main Street, Killin. Tel: (056 72) 362.	All legal lures permitted.

Water	Location	Species	Season	Permit available from	Other information
Loch Tay cont.		Salmon	15 Jan.-15 Oct.	Clachaig Hotel, Killin. Tel: (056 72) 270.	3 boats available with outboards.
	Milton Morenish	Salmon Trout	15 Jan.-15 Oct. 15 Mar.-6 Oct.	Loch Tay Highland Lodges, Milton Morenish, by Killin. Tel: (056 72) 323.	Sixteen boats available. Ghillie and rod hire. Special offers for mid-week fishing.
	Kenmore	Salmon Brown Trout Rainbow Trout	15 Jan.-15 Oct. 15 Mar. to 15 Oct.	Kenmore Hotel, Kenmore, by Aberfeldy. Tel: (0887) 830205.	Boats available on Loch Tay. Ghillie service, rod hire to residents. Fishing for two miles on River Tay.
Loch Tummel	West of Pitlochry	Trout Pike Perch	Apr. to Oct.	Queen's View Visitor Centre Strathtummel, by Pitlochry PH16 5NR.	
Loch Turret	Crieff	Brown Trout	1 Apr. to 30 Sept.	The Director, Central Scotland Water Development Board, Balmore, Torrance, Glasgow G64 4AJ. Tel: (0360) 205. Mr. R. Kelly, 39 King Street, Crieff. Tel: (0764) 3871.	Four boats with outboards. Fly only.

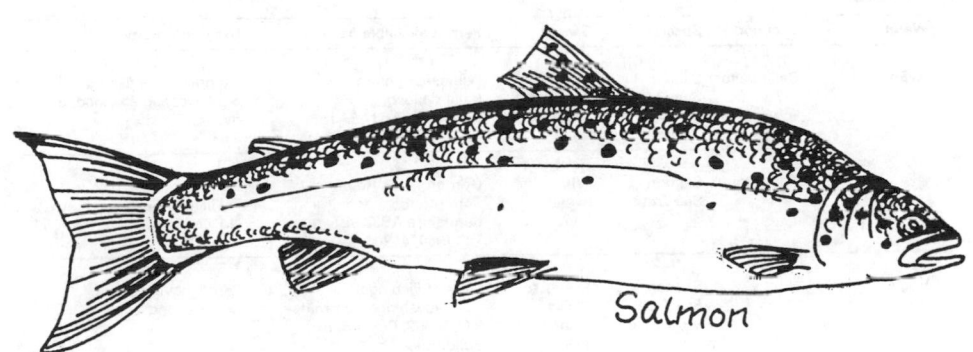

Salmon

Constituent Area Tourist Boards

Aviemore and Spey Valley Tourist Board
Area Tourist Officer,
Aviemore and Spey Valley Tourist Board,
Grampian Road, Aviemore,
Inverness-shire PH22 1PP.
Tel: Aviemore (0479) 810363.

Banff and Buchan Tourist Board
Tourism Manager,
Banff and Buchan Tourist Board,
Collie Lodge,
Banff AB4 1AU.
Tel: Banff (026 12) 2789.

Kincardine and Deeside Tourist Board
Tourist Officer,
Kincardine and Deeside Tourist Board,
45 Station Road, Banchory,
Kincardineshire AB31 3XX.
Tel: Banchory (033 02) 2066.

City of Aberdeen Tourist Board
Director,
City of Aberdeen Tourist Board,
St. Nicholas House, Broad Street,
Aberdeen AB9 1DE.
Tel: Aberdeen (0224) 632727.

Gordon District Tourist Board
Director,
Gordon District Tourist Board,
St. Nicholas House, Broad Street,
Aberdeen AB9 1DE.
Tel: Aberdeen (0224) 632727.

Moray District Council
Chief Tourist Officer,
Moray District Council,
17 High Street, Elgin,
Morayshire IV30 1EG.
Tel: Elgin (0343) 542666.

RIVER PURIFICATION BOARD
NORTH EAST RIVER PURIFICATION BOARD
Greyhope House,
Greyhope Road, Torry,
Aberdeen AB1 3RD.
Tel: Aberdeen (0224) 248338.

RIVERS

Water	Location	Species	Season	Permit available from	Other information
Avon	Ballindalloch	Salmon, Sea Trout	11 Feb. to 30 Sept.	Delnashaugh Inn, Ballindalloch, Banffshire AB37 9AJ. Tel: Ballindalloch 255.	No prawn. Fly fishing Sept. No lead attached to fly.
	Tomintoul	Salmon, Sea Trout	Feb. to end Sept.	Gordon Arms Hotel, Tomintoul, Banffshire AB37 9ET. Tel: (08074) 206.	No prawn. Fly fishing Sept. No lead attached to fly.
Bogie	Huntly	Salmon, Sea Trout, Brown Trout	11 Feb. to 31 Oct. 1 Apr. to 6 Oct.	Clerk of Fishings, Huntly Fishings Committee, P.O. Box 2, Royal Bank Buildings, 27/29 Duke Street, Huntly. Tel: (0466) 792291.	Permit covers Bogie, Deveron and Isla.
Carron	Stonehaven	Brown Trout, Sea Trout, Salmon	1 May to 31 Aug.	Davids Sports Shop, 31 Market Square, Stonehaven. Tel: Stonehaven 62239.	Visitors permits for Sea pool to railway viaduct. For further information: Mr. D. MacDonald, 93 Forest Park, Stonehaven AB3 2GF. Tel: (0569) 64717.
Clunie	Braemar	Brown Trout	15 Mar. to 20 Sept.	Invercauld Estates Office, Braemar AB35 5XQ. Tel: Braemar 41224. Tourist Information Centre, Braemar.	Fly fishing only.

Water	Location	Species	Season	Permit available from	Other information
Cowie	Stonehaven	Salmon Sea Trout Brown Trout	1 May to 31 Aug.	Davids Sports Shop, 31 Market Square, Stonehaven. Tel: Stonehaven 62239.	Visitors permits for Sea pool to railway viaduct. For further information: Mr. D. MacDonald, 93 Forest Park, Stonehaven AB3 2GF. Tel: (0569) 64717.
Dee	Aboyne	Salmon Sea Trout	1 Feb. to 30 Sept.	Brooks House, Glen Tanar, Aboyne. Tel: (03398) 86451.	No Sunday fishing. Permits available from Aug. only on Waterside & Ferrar beats.
Deveron	Huntly	Salmon Sea Trout Brown Trout	11 Feb. to 31 Oct. 1 Apr. to 6 Oct.	Clerk of Fishings, Huntly Fishings Committee, P.O. Box 2, Royal Bank Buildings, 27/29 Duke Street, Huntly. Tel: (0466) 792291.	Permits cover Deveron, Bogie and Isla.
		Salmon Sea Trout Brown Trout	11 Feb. to 31 Oct.	Castle Hotel, Huntly AB54 4SH. Tel: (046679) 2696.	Fishing on other private beats on Deveron & Don.
	Turriff	Salmon Sea Trout Brown Trout	11 Feb. to 31 Oct.	Turriff Ang. Assoc., I. Masson, The Cross, 6 Castle Street, Turriff. Tel: (0888) 62428.	No day tickets. Six weekly available to visitors. Restrictions on spinning.
Don	Glenkindie	Salmon Brown Trout	11 Feb.-31 Oct. 15 Mar.-1 Oct.	Glenkindie Arms Hotel, Glenkindie, by Alford. Tel: Glenkindie 41288.	May to Sept. fly only.
	Manar Fishings	Salmon Sea Trout Brown Trout	11 Feb. to 31 Oct. 1 Apr.-30 Sept.	J.J. Watson 44 Market Place, Inverurie. Tel: (0467) 20321.	No worm, shrimp or prawn. Limit of 8 rods per day.
	Kemnay	Salmon Brown Trout	11 Feb. to 31 Oct.	F.J. & S.L. Milton, Kemnay House, Kemnay, Aberdeenshire AB51 9LH. Tel: Kemnay 42220	Advance booking essential. Fly or spinning only.
	Strathdon	Salmon Brown Trout	11 Feb. to 31 Oct.	Bellabeg Shop, Strathdon. Tel: (09756) 51211.	Fly & spinning only.
	Kintore	Salmon Sea Trout Brown Trout	11 Feb. to 31 Oct.	Kintore Arms Inn, Kintore. Tel: (0467) 32216. J.A. Copland, Newsagent, 2 Northern Road, Kintore. Tel: (0467) 32210.	No worm till 1 Apr. No natural minnow. No shrimp or prawn. Reductions for school children and OAP's.
	Inverurie	Salmon Sea Trout Brown Trout	11 Feb. to 31 Oct. 1 Apr.-30 Sept.	J.J. Watson, 44 Market Place, Inverurie. Tel: (0467) 20321.	No worm till 1 Apr. No natural minnow. No shrimp or prawn. Reductions for school children and OAP's.
Dulnain	Grantown- on-Spey	Salmon Sea Trout Brown Trout	11 Feb. to 30 Sept. 16 Mar.-30 Sept.	Strathspey Angling Assoc., Mortimer's, 3 High Street, Grantown-on-Spey. Tel: (0479) 2684.	Visitors resident in Grantown, Cromdale, Duthill, Carrbridge, Dulnain Bridge and Nethy Bridge areas. 12 miles of river.

Please mention this Pastime Publications guide

Water	Location	Species	Season	Permit available from	Other information
Findhorn	Forres	Salmon Sea Trout	11 Feb. to 30 Sept.	J. Mitchell, Tackle Shop, 97D High Street, Forres. Tel: (0309) 672936.	Popular flies: all shrimp, Stoats Tail, Dunkeld, Munro Killer. Spinning or worming allowed. Some private beats available.
Gairn	Nr. Ballater	Brown Trout	15 Mar. to 20 Sept.	Invercauld Estates Office, Braemar AB35 5XQ. Tel: Braemar 41224. Countrywear, Bridge Street, Ballater.	Fly fishing only.
Isla	Huntly	Salmon Sea Trout Brown Trout	11 Feb. to 31 Oct. 1 Apr. to 6 Oct.	Clerk of Fishings, Huntly Fishings Committee, P.O. Box 2, Royal Bank Buildings, 27/29 Duke Street, Huntly. Tel: (0466) 792291.	Permit covers Isla, Deveron and Bogie.
Muckle burn	By Forres	Salmon Sea Trout	11 Feb. to 30 Sept.	J. Mitchell, Tackle Shop, 97D High Street, Forres. Tel: (0309) 672936.	Reductions for juniors
Spey	Aberlour	Salmon Sea Trout Brown Trout	11 Feb. to 30 Sept.	J.A.J. Munro, 93-95 High Street, Aberlour. Tel: Aberlour 871428	3 tickets per hotel, (Aberlour, Lour & Dowans or 6 day tickets, first come first served.) One fish above bridge (9 am-5 pm), one fish below bridge (9 am-midnight), other fish sold for club funds. No day tickets on Saturday or local holidays.
	Grantown on-Spey	Salmon Sea Trout Brown Trout	11 Feb. to 30 Sept. 15 Mar.-30 Sept.	Strathspey Angling Assoc., Mortimer's 3 High Street, Grantown-on-Spey. Tel: (0479) 2684.	7 miles both banks. No prawn. No Sunday fishing. Visitors must reside in Grantown, Cromdale, Duthil, Carrbridge, Dulnain Bridge and Nethy Bridge.
	Nethy Bridge Boat of Garten	Salmon Sea Trout Brown Trout	11 Feb. to 30 Sept.	Abernethy Angling Improvement Assoc. Boat of Garten. Allen's, Deshar Road, Boat of Garten. Tel: 372.	
	Boat of Garten	Salmon Sea Trout Brown Trout	11 Feb. to 30 Sept. 15 Mar.-30 Sept.	Abernethy Angling Improvement Assoc. Craigard Hotel, Boat of Garten. Tel: Boat of Garten 206. Allen's, Deshar Road, Boat of Garten. Tel: 372.	
	Aviemore	Salmon Sea Trout Brown Trout	11 Feb. to 30 Sept.	Rothiemurchus Estate, Inverdruie, Aviemore PH22 1QH. Tel: (0479) 810703. Kinrara Estate Office, Aviemore. Tel: (0479) 810240/811252. Lynwilg Hotel. Tel: (0479) 810207.	3 beats plus Lochan Mor.

Water	Location	Species	Season	Permit available from	Other information
Spey cont.	Aviemore	Salmon Sea Trout Brown Trout	11 Feb. to 30 Sept.	Abernethy Angling Improvement Assoc., Speyside Sports, 64 Grampian Road, Aviemore. Tel: (0479) 810656.	
	Kincraig	Brown Trout Salmon Sea Trout	11 Feb. to 30 Sept.	Alvie Estate Office, Kincraig, by Kingussie. Tel: (0540) 651255/651249. Dalraddy Caravan Park, Aviemore. Tel: (0479) 810330.	Fly fishing or spinning.
Ugie	Peter-head	Salmon Sea Trout Brown Trout	11 Feb. to 31 Oct.	Dicks Sports, 54 Broad Street, Fraserburgh. Tel: (0346) 24124. Robertson Sports, 1-3 Kirk Street, Peterhead AB4 6RT. Tel: (0779) 72584.	Bag limit - 8 fish per day. Fly, spinning or worm entire season. No shrimps, prawns or illegal baits.
Ury	Inverurie	Salmon Sea Trout Brown Trout	11 Feb. to 31 Oct. 1 Apr.-30 Sept.	J.J. Watson, 44 Market Place, Inverurie AB5 9XN. Tel: (0467) 20321.	No worm till 1 Apr. No natural minnow. No shrimp or prawn. Reductions for school children and OAP's. Sunday fishing - trout only.
Ythan	(Estuary) Newburgh	Salmon Sea Trout	11 Feb. to 31 Oct.	The Ythan Fishery, Mrs. Forbes, 3 Lea Cottages, Newburgh, Ellon, Aberdeenshire AB41 0BN. Tel: (03586) 89297.	Limited fishing available. Details from Mrs. Forbes.
	Fyvie	Salmon Sea Trout	11 Feb. to 31 Oct.	Fyvie Angling Assoc., Local shop, hotel, cafe, bank.	No shrimps or prawns. No worming May to August

LOCHS & RESERVOIRS

Water	Location	Species	Season	Permit available from	Other information
Aboyne Loch	Aboyne	Pike Perch		The Warden, Aboyne Loch, Holiday Park. Tel: (03398) 86244.	Fishing parties restricted on Sat. and Sun. afternoons.
Loch Alvie	Aviemore	Brown Trout Pike	15 Mar. to 6 Oct.	Alvie Estate Office, Kincraig, by Kingussie. Tel: (0540) 651255/651249. Dalraddy Caravan Park, Aviemore. Tel: (0479) 810330.	1 Boat. Fly fishing or spinning only.
Avielochan	Aviemore	Rainbow/ Brown Trout	1 Apr. to 30 Sept.	Mortimer's, 3 High Street, Grantown-on-Spey. Tel: (0479) 2684. Mrs. MacDonald, Avielochan, Aviemore. Tel: (0479) 810847.	Bank fishing only. Spinning area designated. No Sunday fishing. 10am-6pm & 6pm-10pm.
Loch of Blairs	Forres	Brown/ Rainbow Trout	30 Mar. to 30 Sept.	J. Mitchell, Tackle Shop, 97D High Street, Forres. Tel: (0309) 672936.	Average weight of fish caught: 1lb 8oz. Popular flies: lures, conventional wet flies, dry flies. Two sessions. Boat fishing. Fly only. Sunday fishing. 3 boats available.

Water	Location	Species	Season	Permit available from	Other information
Loch Dallas	Boat of Garten	Brown/ Rainbow Trout	1 Apr. to 30 Sept.	Mortimer's 3 High Street, Grantown-on-Spey. Tel: (0479) 2684. Allan's Store, Boat of Garten. Tel: (0479) 83 372.	Fly fishing only (10am-6pm). Boat fishing. No Sunday fishing. 1 boat (2 rods).
Loch Ericht	Dalwhinnie	Brown Trout	15 Mar. to 6 Oct.	Badenoch Angling Association, Loch Ericht Hotel, Dalwhinnie. Tel: (05282) 257.	Boat & bank fishing.
Glenlatterach Reservoir	By Elgin	Stocked Brown Trout	1 May to 30 Sept.	Warden at Millbuies, Tel: (034 386) 234.	Fly fishing only. 3 boats available. Bank fishing.
Loch Insh	Kincraig	Salmon Sea Trout Brown Trout Char Pike	11 Feb. to 30 Sept.	Alvie Estate Office, Kincraig, by Kingussie. Tel: (0540) 651255/651249. Dalraddy Caravan Park, Aviemore. Tel: (0479) 810330.	One boat. Boat fishing only. Fly fishing or spinning.
		Salmon Sea Trout Brown Trout Arctic Char Pike	May to Sept.	Loch Insh Watersports, Boat House, Kincraig.	Boat are available.
Loch Lochindorb	by Forres	Brown Trout	15 Mar. to 6 Oct.	J. Mitchell, Tackle Shop, 97D High Street, Forres. Tel: (0309) 672936.	Average weight of fish caught: 4oz to 1lb. Popular flies: black flies. Spinning and worming allowed. Boat and bank fishing.
Loch McLeod	Nr. Grantown on Spey	Brown/ Rainbow Trout	1 Apr. to 30 Sept.	Strathspey Estate Office, 14 The Square, Grantown-on-Spey. Tel: (0479) 2529.	Bank fishing only. No fishing on Sundays. 2 rods per day. Fly fishing only (10am-6pm).
Millbuies Loch	By Elgin	Brown/ Rainbow Trout	Easter to Mid-Oct.	Moray District Council, Dept. of Leisure & Libraries, High Street, Elgin. Warden at Millbuies. Tel: 034 386 234.	Boat fishing. Fly fishing only. Four boats available.
Loch Mor	Dulnain Bridge	Brown/ Rainbow Trout	Apr. to Sept.	Mortimer's 3 High Street, Grantown-on-Spey. Tel: (0479) 2684.	Fly fishing only.
Loch Na Bo	Lhanbryde	Brown Trout	1 Apr. to 30 Sept.	D. Kinloch, Gardener's Cottage, Loch-na-Bo, Lhanbryde, Elgin. Tel: (0343 84) 2214.	Fly fishing only.
Rothiemurchus Estate (Fish farm, Loch, Loch Pityoulish, Lily Loch	Aviemore	Rainbow/ Brown Trout Pike	Check with manager, Aviemore.	Rothiemurchus Fish Farm, by Aviemore PH22 1QH. Tel: (0479) 810703.	Stocked rainbow trout loch. Open all year except when frozen.

Water	Location	Species	Season	Permit available from	Other information
Loch Saugh	Fettercairn/ Drumtochty Glen	Brown Trout	15 Mar. to 6 Oct.	Brechin Angling Club, W.G. Balfour, 9 Cookston Crescent, Brechin DD9 6BP. Tel. (0356) 622753. Ramsay Arms Hotel, Fettercairn. Tel. (05614) 334. Drumtochty Arms Hotel, Auchenblae AB30 1XR. Tel: (0561) 320210. David Rollston-Smith, Fishing Tackle, Guns & Sport, 180 High Street, Montrose. Tel: (0674) 72692.	
Glen Tanar Loch	Glen Tanar	Rainbow Trout	Apr. to Oct.	Brooks House, Glen Tanar, Aboyne. Tel: (03398) 86451.	2 boats. Boat fishing by day or evening, April to October.
Loch Vaa	Aviemore	Brown/ Rainbow Trout	1 Apr. to 30 Sept.	Mortimer's 3 High Street, Grantown-on-Spey. Tel: (0479) 2684.	Boat fishing only. 2 boats - 2 rods per boat. Fly fishing only. No Sunday fishing. Fishing 10am-6pm only.
Loch Vrotichan	Cairnwell	Brown Trout	18 Mar. to 11 Aug.	Invercauld Estates Office, Braemar AB35 5XQ. Tel: Braemar 41224. Ballater A.A., 59 Golf Road, Ballater. Tel: Ballater 55365. Tourist Information Centre, Braemar. Tourist Information Centre, Ballater.	Fly fishing only.

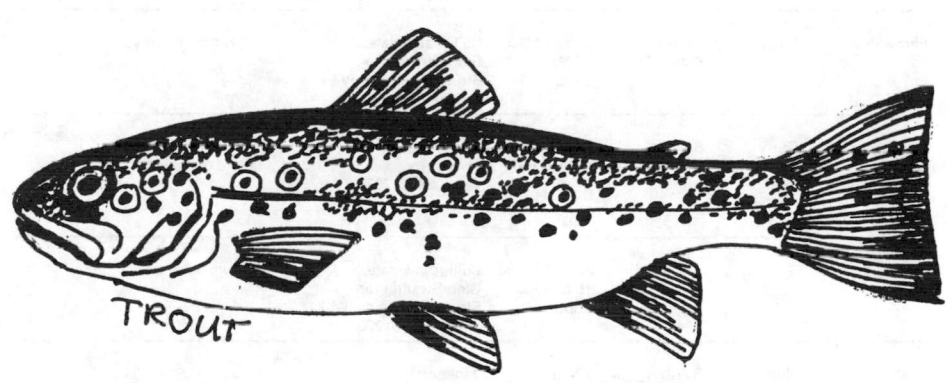

TROUT

GREAT GLEN and SKYE RIVERS AND LOCHS

Constituent Area Tourist Boards

Fort William and Lochaber Tourist Board
Area Tourist Officer,
Fort William and Lochaber Tourist Board,
Cameron Centre, Cameron Square,
Fort William,
Inverness-shire PH33 6AJ.
Tel: Fort William (0397) 703781.

Isle of Skye and South West Ross Tourist Board
Area Tourist Officer,
Isle of Skye and South West Ross Tourist Board,
Tourist Information Centre, Portree,
Isle of Skye IV51 9BZ.
Tel: Portree (0478) 2137.

**Inverness, Loch Ness and Nairn
Tourist Board**
Area Tourist Officer,
Inverness, Loch Ness and Nairn Tourist Board,
Castle Wynd, Inverness IV2 3BG.
Tel: Inverness (0463) 234353.

**RIVER PURIFICATION BOARD
HIGHLAND RIVER PURIFICATION BOARD**
Strathpeffer Road,
Dingwall IV15 9QY.
Tel: Dingwall 62021.

RIVERS

Water	Location	Species	Season	Permit available from	Other information
Brogaig	North Skye	Salmon Sea Trout Brown Trout	1 Mar. to 31 Oct.	Jansport, Wentworth Street, Portree, Skye. Tel: (0478) 2559.	
Coe	Glencoe	Salmon Sea Trout	15 Apr. to 15 Oct.	National Trust for Scotland, Achnambeithach Farm, Glencoe. Tel: (08552) 311.	No Sunday fishing.
Croe		Salmon Sea Trout	1 Mar. to 30 Sept.	National Trust for Scotland, Morvich Farm, Inverinate, By Kyle. Tel: Glenshiel (059981) 219.	Fly fishing only.
Farrar	Struy	Salmon Brown Trout	June-15 Oct. 15 Mar.-30 Sept.	Culligran Estate, Glen Strathfarrar, Struy, Nr. Beauly IV4 7JX. Tel: (046376) 285.	Fly fishing only.
Garry (upper)	Garry Gualach to Poulary Bridge	Salmon Brown Trout	15 Mar.-14 Oct. !5 Mar.-6 Oct.	Garry Gualach, Invergarry. Tel: (08092) 230.	Fly only 1 May to end of season.
Glass	Struy	Salmon Brown Trout	June-15 Oct. 15 Mar.-30 Sept.	Culligran Estate, Glen Strathfarrar, Struy, Nr. Beauly IV4 7JX. Tel: (046376) 285.	Fly fishing only.
Lealt	North Skye	Salmon Sea Trout Brown Trout	1 Mar. to 31 Oct.	Jansport, Wentworth Street, Portree, Skye. Tel: (0478) 2559.	
Lochy	Fort William	Salmon Sea Trout	May to Sept.	Rod & Gun Shop, 18 High Street, Fort William. Tel:(0397) 702656.	

Water	Location	Species	Season	Permit available from	Other information
Moriston	Glen-moriston Estuary beat	Salmon	15 Jan. to 15 Oct.	A. MacKintosh, Head Gamekeeper. Tel: (0320) 51219. Fly & spinning only.	
	Dundreggan Beat	Salmon Brown Trout	1 May-end Sept. Mar.to Sept.	A. MacKintosh, Head Keeper. Tel: (0320) 51219.	Fly and spinning only.
Nairn	Nairn/ Culloden Moor	Salmon Sea Trout	11 Feb. to 30 Sept.	Nairn Angling Association P. Fraser, High Street, Nairn. Clava Lodge Holiday Homes, Culloden Moor, Inverness IV1 2EJ. Tel: (0463) 790228,	
Nevis	Fort William	Salmon Sea Trout		Rod & Gun Shop 18 High Street, Fort William. Tel: (0397) 702656.	
Polloch	Strontian	Salmon Sea Trout Brown Trout	1 May to 31 Oct.	The Centre, Strontian. Post Office, Strontian.	Average weight of fish caught: Salmon – 6lbs, Sea Trout – 1lb, Brown Trout – 1lb. Popular flies: dark flies. Worm & spinning allowed. No prawn fishing.
Snizort	Skye	Salmon Sea Trout Brown Trout	1 Jul. to 15 Oct.	Skeabost House Hotel, Skeabost, Isle of Skye. Tel: (047 032) 202.	Discounts for residents.
Staffin	North Skye	Salmon Sea Trout Brown Trout	1 Mar. to 31 Oct.	Jansport, Wentworth Street, Portree, Skye. Tel: (0478) 2559.	
Strontian	Strontian	Salmon Sea Trout Brown Trout	1 May to 31 Oct.	The Centre, Strontian. Post Office Strontian.	Average weight of fish caught: Salmon – 6 to 10 lbs. Sea Trout – 1lb. Popular flies: Blue Charm, Hair Fly. Worm (if river in spate) & spinning. No prawns.

LOCHS

Water	Location	Species	Season	Permit available from	Other information
Ardtornish Estate Waters	Morvern	Salmon Sea Trout Brown Trout	Apr.-Oct.	Ardtornish Estate Office, Morvern, by Oban, Argyll. Tel: (0967) 421288.	Six boats for hire.
Loch Arkaig	Fort William	Sea Trout Brown Trout Salmon (occasional) Pike	Mar.-Oct.	Locheil Estate Fishings, West Highland Estates Office, 33 High Street, Fort William. Tel: (0397) 702433.	
Loch Beannachran	Glen Strathfarrar	Brown Trout	15 Mar. to 6 Oct.	Glen Affric Hotel, Cannich. Tel: Cannich 214.	Fly fishing only. 1 boat. No bank fishing.

Please mention this Pastime Publications guide

Water	Location	Species	Season	Permit available from	Other information
Loch Benevean (Bheinn a' Mheadhoin)	Glen Affric	Brown Trout	15 Mar. to 6 Oct.	Glen Affric Hotel, Cannich. Tel: Cannich 214.	Fly fishing only. 6 Boats available. No bank fishing.
Loch Dochfour	Inverness	Brown Trout	15 Mar. to 6 Oct.	Dochfour Estate Office, Dochgarroch, by Inverness. Tel: Dochgarroch 218. Dochgarroch Shop & Post Office, Dochgarroch, by Inverness.	No Sunday fishing. Bank fishing only.
Loch Doilet	Strontian	Salmon Sea Trout Brown Trout	1 May to 31 Oct.	George Fisher, Polloch Lodge, Strontian.	Average weight of fish caught: Salmon – 6lbs, Sea Trout 1lb. Popular flies: black flies. Worm and spinning permitted. No prawns. Boats available from: (0967) 2408 or (0967) 2412.
Glenmoriston Hill Lochs (21)	Glenmoriston	Brown Trout	May to Oct.	Mr. A. Mackintosh (Gamekeeper), Levishie, Glenmoriston, Tel: (0320) 51 219 (Eve.)	1 boat available.
Guisachan Hill Lochs	Tomich	Brown Trout	Apr. to Sept.	Tomich Hotel, Tomich, by Beauly. Tel: (04565) 399.	Fly fishing only. Rainbow Trout on 2 lochs.
Loch Inchlaggan & Loch Garry	Invergarry	Brown Trout Arctic Char	May-Sept.	Garry Gualach, Invergarry. Tel: (08092) 230.	Boats available. Loch Inchlaggan fly only.
Loch Insh	Kincraig	Salmon Trout Arctic Char Pike	May to September	Loch Insh Watersports, Boat House, Kincraig.	Boats are available.
Loch Lundavra	Nr. Fort William	Brown Trout	15 Apr. to 30 Sept.	Mrs. A. MacCallum, Lundavra Farm, Fort William. Tel: (0397) 702582.	Average weight of fish caught: 8oz. Popular flies: Black Pennel, Bloody Butcher, Peter Ross. Fly fishing only. 2 boats available. Bank fishing.
Loch Lungard	Glen Cannich	Brown Trout	15 Mar. to 6 Oct.	Glen Affric Hotel, Cannich. Tel: Cannich 214.	Fly fishing only. No bank fishing. Boats available from Loch Mullardoch.
Loch Mealt	North Skye	Brown Trout Arctic Char	15 Mar. to 30 Sept.	Jansport, Wentworth Street, Portree, Skye. Tel: (0478) 2559.	
Loch Monar	Glen Strathfarrar	Brown Trout	15 Mar. to 6 Oct.	Glen Affric Hotel, Cannich. Tel: Cannich 214.	Fly fishing only. Boat for hire. No bank fishing.
Loch Morar (and hill lochs)	Morar	Salmon Sea Trout Brown Trout Arctic Char	15 Mar. to 6 Oct.	The Morar District Salmon Fishery Board, Superintendant, David de-Gernier. Tel: (0687) 2388.	6 boats for hire, and ghillie if required.

Water	Location	Species	Season	Permit available from	Other information
Loch Mullardoch	Cannich	Brown Trout	15 Mar. to 6 Oct.	Glen Affric Hotel, Cannich. Tel: Cannich 214.	Fly fishing only. 4 boats. No bank fishing.
Loch Ness	Glenmoriston	Salmon Trout	15 Jan.	Mr. A. MacKintosh (Gamekeeper), Levishie, Glenmoriston. Tel: (0320) 51219 (Eve.)	1 boat available.
Loch Ruthven	Farr	Brown Trout	15 Mar. to 6 Oct.	J. Graham & Co., 37/39 Castle Street, Inverness. Tel: (0463) 233178.	Fly fishing only.
Loch Sheil	Glenfinnan	Salmon Sea Trout	Apr.-Oct.	The Stage House, Glenfinnan, Inverness-shire. Tel: (0397) 83246.	4 boats available with outboards. Advance bookings only.
South Skye Fishings (various lochs)	South Skye	Sea Trout Brown Trout	Apr.-Oct.	Fearann Eilean Iarmain, Eilean Iarmain, Isle of Skye. Tel: (047 13) 266.	
Storr Lochs (and hill lochs)	North Skye	Brown Trout	1 Apr. to 30 Sept.	Jansport, Wentworth Street, Portree, Skye. Tel: (0478) 2559.	Further info: Sec., Portree Angling Assoc., Hillcroft, Treaslane, By Portree.
Tomich Hill Lochs	Tomich	Brown Trout	15 Mar. to 6 Oct.	Caledonian Hotel, Beauly. Tel: (0463) 782278.	Fly fishing only. boats available.
Whitebridge Lochs (Knockie, Bran & Killin)	White- bridge	Brown Trout	Mar.-Oct.	Whitebridge Hotel, Stratherrick, Gorthleck, Inverness-shire. Tel: Gorthleck 226.	Boats available. Fly fishing only.

Constituent Area Tourist Boards

Caithness Tourist Board
Area Tourist Office,
Caithness Tourist Board,
Whitechapel Road, Wick,
Caithness KW1 4EA.
Tel: Wick (0955) 2596.

Sutherland Tourist Board
Area Tourist Officer,
Sutherland Tourist Board,
The Square, Dornoch,
Sutherland IV25 3SD.
Tel: Dornoch (0862) 810400.

Ross and Cromarty Tourist Board
Area Tourist Officer,
Ross and Cromarty Tourist Board,
Information Centre, North Kessock,
Black Isle, Ross-shire IV5 1XB.
Tel: Kessock (0463 73) 505.

RIVER PURIFICATION BOARD
HIGHLAND RIVER PURIFICATION BOARD
Strathpeffer Road,
Dingwall IV15 9QY.
Tel: Dingwall 62021.

RIVERS

Water	Location	Species	Season	Permit available from	Other information
Alness	Alness	Salmon Sea Trout	5 May to 16 Oct.	Novar Estates, Estate Office, Evanton, Ross-shire. Tel: (0349) 830205.	Fly fishing only. 6 beats on rotation. 4 rods per beat.
Beauly	Muir of Ord	Salmon Sea Trout Brown Trout	May to Sept.	Ord House Hotel, Muir of Ord. Tel: (0463) 870492.	
Blackwater	Strathpeffer	Salmon Sea Trout	Apr. to end Sept.		Further info. from: Craigdarroch Lodge Hotel, Contin, by Strathpeffer. Tel: Strathpeffer 21265.
Upper Blackwater	Contin	Salmon Brown Trout	1 June-30 Sept. 1 Apr.-30 Sept.	John MacMillan Newsagent, The Square, Strathpeffer. Tel: (0997) 421346.	Popular flies: Black Brahan, G.P., Stoats Tail, Red Shrimp & standard trout patterns. Fly fishing. Spinning only in high water. 1 boat available.
Brora (Lower)	Brora	Salmon Sea Trout	1 Feb. to 15 Oct.	Mr. & Mrs. Hammond, Sciberscross Lodge, Strath Brora, Rogart. Tel: (0408) 641246.	Popular flies: Orange, black, red Waddingtons, Willie Gunn.
Conon	Contin	Salmon Sea Trout	26 Jan. to 30 Sept.	Coul House Hotel, Contin, by Strathpeffer. Tel: Strathpeffer 421487.	Lower/middle/upper Brahan, lower Fairburn beats various times. Ghillies, boats. Fly (& spinning until end May).
	Maryburgh	Brown/ Rainbow Trout Pike	15 Mar. to 15 Oct.	Seaforth Highland Estate, Brahan, Dingwall. Tel: (0349) 61192.	Stocked pond. Loch fishing and river in the lower, middle and upper Conon. Fishing available in the stocked pond and loch all year round.
	Muir of Ord	Salmon Sea Trout Brown Trout	May to Sept.	Ord House Hotel, Muir of Ord. Tel: (0463) 870492.	

Water	Location	Species	Season	Permit available from	Other information
Conon cont.	Strathpeffer	Salmon Brown Trout	1 Apr. to 30 Sept.		Further info. from: Craigdarroch Lodge Hotel, Contin, by Strathpeffer. Tel: Strathpeffer 21265.
	Dingwall	Salmon Sea Trout	25 Jan. to 30 Sept.	The Sports & Model Shop, Tulloch Street, Dingwall. Tel: (0349) 62346.	Popular flies: Greenwell's Glory, Peter Ross, Black Pennel. Fly fishing only. Thigh waders only.
Lower Conon	Contin	Salmon Sea Trout	26 Jan. to 30 Sept.	Dingwall & District A.C., c/o Sports & Model Shop, Tulloch Street, Dingwall. Tel: (0349) 62346.	Fly only. Thigh waders only.
Upper Conon	Strathconon	Salmon Brown Trout	1 Apr. to 30 Sept.	John MacMillan Newsagent, The Square, Strathpeffer. Tel: (0997) 421346.	Popular flies: Stoats Tail, Red Shrimp, Munro Killer, Black Brahan & standard trout patterns. Fly fishing with spinning during periods of high water.
Doinard	Durness	Salmon Sea Trout		Cape Wrath Hotel, Durness, Sutherland. Tel: 097 181 274.	Please phone in advance, especially in high season.
Glass	Evanton	Brown Trout	15 Mar. to 6 Oct.	Novar Estates, Estate Office, Evanton, Ross-shire. Tel: (0349) 830205.	Fly fishing only.
Halladale	Forsinard (2 mile upper beat)	Salmon	11 Jan. to 30 Sept.	Forsinard Hotel, Forsinard KW13 6YT. Tel: (06417) 221.	Fly fishing only (spate river).
	Forsinard to Melvich Bay	Salmon	11 Jan. to 30 Sept.	Mrs. J. Atkinson, 8 Sinclair Street, Thurso, Caithness.	Lodge also available.
Helmsdale	Helmsdale	Salmon Sea Trout	11 Jan. to 30 Sept.	Strathullie Crafts & Fishing Tackle, Dunrobin Street, Helmsdale KW8 6AH. Tel: (043 12) 343.	Association beat. Fly fishing only.
Kerry	Gairloch	Salmon Sea Trout	May to Oct.	Creag Mor Hotel, Charleston, Gairloch. Tel: (0445) 2068.	Maximum 4 rods daily. Fly fishing only.
Kirkaig	Lochinver	Salmon	1 May to 15 Oct.	Inver Lodge Hotel, Lochinver IV27 4LU. Tel: (05714) 496.	
Kyle of Sutherland	Bonar Bridge	Salmon Sea Trout	1 June to 30 Sept.	Dunroamin Hotel, Bonar Bridge IV24 3EB. Tel: (08632) 236.	
Okyel	Sutherland	Salmon Sea Trout	End June to 30 Sept.	Inver Lodge Hotel, Lochinver IV27 4LU. Tel: (05714) 496.	2 top beats only (3 miles).
Thurso	Thurso/ Halkirk	Salmon Trout	11 Jan. to 5 Oct.	Thurso Fisheries Ltd., Estate Office, Thurso East, Thurso. Tel: (0847) 63134.	Fly fishing only. Twelve 2 rod beats in rotation.

Please mention this Pastime Publications guide

Water	Location	Species	Season	Permit available from	Other information
Torridon	Torridon	Salmon Sea Trout	1 May. to 31 Oct.	Loch Torridon Hotel, Torridon, by Achnasheen. Tel: (044 587) 242.	Fly fishing only.
Ullapool	Ullapool	Salmon Sea Trout Brown Trout	May to 30 Sept.	Lochbroom Hardware Shop, Shore Street, Ullapool. Tel: (0854) 612356.	
Weaster	by Wick	Salmon Sea Trout Brown Trout	1 Mar. to 31 Oct.	Mrs. G. Dunnet, Auckhorn Lyth, by Wick KW1 4UD. Tel: (095583) 208.	
Wick	Wick	Salmon Sea Trout Brown Trout	11 Feb. to 21 Oct.	Hugo Ross Tackle Shop, 16 Breadalbane Crescent, Wick. Tel/Fax: (0955) 4200.	Fly/worm fishing. Spate river with good holding pools.

LOCHS

Water	Location	Species	Season	Permit available from	Other information
Loch A'chroisg	Achnasheen	Brown Trout Pike Perch	No close season	Ledgowan Lodge Hotel, Achnasheen. Tel: (044 588) 252.	Free to residents.
Loch a'Ghriama	Overscaig	Brown Trout	30 Apr. to 30 Sept.	Overscaig Lochside Hotel, Loch Shin, by Lairg IV27 4NY. Tel: 054 983 203.	Boats available. No Sunday fishing.
Loch an Lascaigh	Torridon	Salmon Sea Trout Brown Trout	1 May to 31 Oct.	Loch Torridon Hotel, Torridon, by Achnasheen, Wester Ross IV22 2EY. Tel: (044 587 242.	
Loch an Ruthair	by Kinbrace	Brown Trout	Apr. to end Sept.	Head Keeper, Achentoul Estate, Kinbrace. Tel: (04313) 227.	Average weight of fish caught: 8 to 12oz. Popular flies: Soldier Palmer, Black pennel. Bait fishing and spinning allowed. 2 boats available.
Loch Achall	by Ullapool	Salmon Sea Trout Brown Trout	1 May to 30 Sept. 15 Mar.-6 Oct.	Lochbroom Hardware Shop, Shore Street, Ullapool. Tel: (0854) 612356.	Popular flies: Soldier Palmer, Butcher, Grouse & Claret, 3 boats available. Bank fishing.
Loch Achonachie	Strathconon	Salmon Brown Trout	1 Apr. to 30 Sept.	John MacMillan Newsagent, The Square, Strathpeffer. Tel: (0997) 421346.	Popular flies: standard loch patterns. Spinning, trolling & fly fishing permitted. 2 boats are available.
Lochs Airigh Leathaid	By Westerdale, Halkirk	Brown Trout	Apr. to 7th Oct.	Ulbster Arms, Hotel, Halkirk.	Fly only. Average Weight: 1lb 2oz.
Loch Ascaig	Helmsdale	Salmon Sea Trout Brown Trout	1 June to 30 Sept. 15 Mar.-6 Oct.	M. Wigan, Borrobol, Kinbrace KW11 6UB. Tel: (04313) 264/252 or 071-289 5126 (Jan. to Mar.)	Popular flies: Loch Ordie, Soldier Palmer, Fly fishing only. 3 boats available.
Loch Badagyle	Nr. Achiltibuie	Sea Trout Brown Trout Arctic Char	1 Apr. to 30 Sept.	Polly Estates Ltd., Inverpolly, Ullapool IV26 2YB. Tel: 085 482 452.	Fly fishing only. No Sunday fishing. Boats with or without motors are available.

Water	Location	Species	Season	Permit available from	Other information
Loch Badanloch (& other hill lochs)	Kinbrace	Brown Trout	15 Mar. to 6 Oct.	Richard McNicol, Badanloch, Kinbrace, Sutherland. Tel: (043 13) 232.	Average weight of fish caught: 8oz. Popular flies: Loch Ordie, Black Pennel, Soldier Palmer. 6 boats. Fly only. Sunday fishing.
Loch Beannach	Lairg	Brown Trout	30 Apr. to 30 Sept.	Boat permits: R. Ross (Fishing Tackle), Main Street, Lairg IV27 4DB. Tel: (0549) 2239.	Average weight of fish caught: 1lb. Popular flies: Kate McLaren, Loch Ordie. Strictly fly fishing only. Boats available from above.
Loch Beannacharain (Scardroy)	Strathconon	Brown Trout	1 Apr. to 30 Sept.	John MacMillan Newsagent, The Square, Strathpeffer. Tel: (0997) 421346.	Average weight of fish caught: 8oz. Fly and spinning permitted. 2 boats available.
Bad an Scalaig	Nr. Gairloch	Brown Trout Pike	Mar. to Oct.	Wildcat Stores, Gairloch.	Spinning allowed for Pike. 2 boats are available.
Loch Bad na H-Achlaise (Green Loch)	Nr. Achiltibuie	Brown/ Sea Trout	1 Apr. to 30 Sept.	Polly Estates Ltd., Inverpolly, Ullapool IV26 2YB. Tel: 085 482 452.	Fly fishing only. No Sunday fishing.
Loch Bad na H Erba	Sciberscross	Wild Brown Trout	1 Apr. to 15 Oct.	Mr. & Mrs. Hammond, Sciberscross Lodge, Strath Brora, Rogart IV28 3YQ. Tel: (0408) 641246.	Average weight of fish caught: 12oz. Popular flies: Black Pennel, Ke-He, Loch Ordie, Dunkeld. Boats are available.
Black Loch	Nr. Achiltibuie	Brown Trout	1 Apr. to 30 Sept.	Polly Estates Ltd., Inverpolly, Ullapool IV26 2YB. Tel: 085 482 452.	Fly fishing only. No Sunday fishing. Boat available.
Loch Borralan	Ledmore	Brown/ Rainbow Trout Arctic Char	15 Mar. to 6 Oct.	The Alt Bar, The Altnacealgach, Ledmore, by Lairg. Tel: 085 486 220.	Any legal method permitted. Boat & bank fishing.
Loch Borralie	Durness	Brown Trout	Apr. to End Sept.	Cape Wrath Hotel, Durness, Sutherland. Tel: 097 181 274.	Limestone loch. Fly fishing only. Boats available. Please phone in advance, especially in high season.
Loch Brora	Brora	Salmon Sea Trout Brown Trout Salmon Sea Trout Brown Trout Char	Apr. to Oct. 1 May to 15 Oct.	Rob Wilson Rods & Guns, Rosslyn Street, Brora. Tel: Brora 621373. Mr. & Mrs. Hammond, Sciberscross Lodge, Strath Brora, Rogart IV28 3YQ. Tel: (0408) 641246.	Boats available. Popular flies: General Practitioner, Stoats Tail, Dunkeld. Boats available with outboard, if required.
Loch Caise	Forsinard	Brown Trout	1 May to 30 Sept.	Forsinard Hotel, Forsinard. Tel: (06417) 221.	
Loch Caladail	Durness	Brown Trout	Apr. to End Sept.	Cape Wrath Hotel, Durness, Sutherland. Tel: 097 181 274.	Limestone loch. Fly fishing only. Boats available. Please phone in advance, especially in high season.

Water	Location	Species	Season	Permit available from	Other information
Loch Calder	Thurso	Brown Trout	15 Mar. to 6 Oct.	Harper's Fishing Tackle, 57 High Street, Thurso. Tel: (0847) 63179. Pentland Sports, Thurso. Loch Watten Hotel, Watten.	Average weight of fish caught: 12oz to 1lb (fish upto 7lbs). Popular flies: Bibio, Black Pennel, Kate McLaren. Spinning & bait fishing permitted, but fly fishing preferred. Boats available.
Caol Loch	Forsinard	Brown Trout	1 May to 30 Sept.	Forsinard Hotel, Forsinard. Tel: (06417) 221.	Boat & bank fishing. Use standard pattern loch flies.
Cape Wrath & hill lochs (30 plus)	Durness	Brown Trout	Apr. to End Sept.	Cape Wrath Hotel, Durness, Sutherland. Tel: 097 181 274.	Please phone in advance, especially in high season.
Cherigal Loch	By Westerdale, Halkirk	Brown Trout	Apr. to 7th Oct.	Ulbster Arms Hotel, Halkirk.	Fly only. Average weight: 12 oz.
Col Loch Beg		Wild Brown Trout	1 Apr. to 15 Oct.	Garvault Hotel, by Kinbrace. Tel: Kinbrace 224.	Average weight of fish caught: 8oz. Popular flies: Loch Ordie, Black Spider, Black Pennel. Fly fishing only.
Col Loch Mhor		Wild Brown Trout	1 Apr. to 15 Oct.	Garvault Hotel, by Kinbrace. Tel: Kinbrace 224.	Average weight of fish caught: 8oz. Popular flies: Loch Ordie, Black Spider, Black Pennel. Fly fishing only.
Loch Cracail	By Bonar Bridge	Brown Trout May to 31 Oct.		Dunroamin Hotel, Bonar Bridge, Sutherland. Tel: (08632) 236.	1 boat available.
Loch Craggie	Tongue	Brown Trout	15 Mar. to 6 Oct.	Ben Loyal Hotel, Tongue. Tel: Tongue 216. Post Office, Tongue. Tel: Tongue 201.	Fly fishing only. Boat available.
		Brown Trout	Mar. to Sept.	Altnaharra Hotel, By Lairg IV27 4UE.	Average weight of fish caught: 8oz to 1lb. Popular flies: Pennel, Goats Toe, Zulu. Boat available.
Loch Croispol	Durness	Brown Trout	Apr. to End Sept.	Cape Wrath Hotel, Durness, Sutherland. Tel: 097 181 274.	Limestone loch. Fly fishing only. Boats available. Please phone in advance, especially in high season.
Loch Culag (and numerous other lochs)	Lochinver	Brown Trout	Mid-May to 6 Oct.	Inver Lodge Hotel, Lochinver, Sutherland. Tel: Lochinver 496.	7 lochs with boats. 2 lochs for residents of hotel only. (Check for details).
The Dam Lochs	Nr. Ullapool	Brown Trout	15 Mar. to 6 Oct.	Ullasport, West Argyle Street, Ullapool. Tel: (0854) 612621.	Fly fishing only.

Water	Location	Species	Season	Permit available from	Other information
Loch Damph	Torridon	Salmon Sea Trout Brown Trout	1 May to 31 Oct.	Loch Torridon Hotel, Torridon, by Achnasheen, Wester Ross IV22 2EY. Tel: 044 587242.	Fly fishing only. No Sunday fishing. 2 boats are available.
Loch Doir na H-Airbhe (Stac Loch)	Nr. Achiltibuie	Brown/ Sea Trout	1 Apr. to 30 Sept.	Polly Estates Ltd., Inverpolly, Ullapool IV26 2YB. Tel: 085 482 452.	Fly fishing only. No Sunday fishing.
Dornoch & District A.C. (7 lochs)	Dornoch	Salmon Sea Trout Brown Trout	15 Mar. to 6 Oct.	Dornoch & District A.A., William A. McDonald, Castle Street, Dornoch. Tel: (0862) 810301.	No Sunday fishing. Fly fishing only. 7 boats available.
Lochan Dubh na H-Amaite	Sciberscross	Wild Brown Trout	1 Apr. to 15 Oct.	Mr. & Mrs. Hammond, Sciberscross Lodge, Strath Brora, Rogart IV28 3YQ. Tel: (0408) 641246.	Average weight of fish caught: 1lb. Popular flies: Black Pennel, Ke-He, Loch Ordie, Dunkeld. Boats are available.
Dubh-nan-Geodh	By Westerdale, Halkirk	Brown Trout	Apr. to 7th Oct.	Ulbster Arms Hotel, Halkirk.	Fly only. Average Weight: 1lb 10oz.
Dunnet Head Loch	Dunnet Head (B855)	Brown Trout	May to Oct.	Dunnet Head Tearoom, Brough Village, Dunnet Head. Tel: (084 785) 774.	Loch well stocked. Fly from bank only. No Sunday fishing. Sea fishing from rocks.
Eileanach Loch	By Westerdale, Halkirk	Brown Trout	Apr. to 7th Oct.	Ulbster Arms Hotel, Halkirk.	Fly only. Average weight: 9oz.
Eun Loch	By Westerdale, Halkirk	Brown Trout	Apr. to 7th Oct.	Ulbster Arms Hotel, Halkirk.	Fly only. Average Weight: 1lb 8oz.
Fionn Loch	Gairloch	Salmon Brown Trout	Mid-May to 6 Oct.	Inver Lodge Hotel, Lochinver, Sutherland. Tel: Lochinver 496. K Guns, Gairloch. Tel: (0445) 2400.	Fly only.
Forsinard Loch (& many others)	Forsinard	Brown Trout	1 May, to 30 Sept.	Forsinard Hotel, Forsinard, Sutherland. Tel: Halladale 221.	Fly fishing only. Bank & boat fishing (5 boats).
	Kyle of Tongue	Salmon Sea Trout Sea Bass	11 Feb. to 31 Oct.	Ben Loyal Hotel, Tongue. Tel: Tongue 216. Post Office, Tongue. Tel: Tongue 201.	No Sunday fishing. Bank fishing only.
Gainaimh Loch	By Westerdale, Halkirk.	Brown Trout	Apr. to 7th Oct.	Ulbster Arms Hotel, Halkirk.	Fly only. Average weight: 7oz.
Loch Ganneigh		Wild Brown Trout	1 Apr. to 15 Oct.	Garvault Hotel, by Kinbrace. Tel: Kinbrace 224.	Average weight of fish caught: 8oz. Popular flies: Loch Ordie, Black Spider, Black Pennel. Fly fishing only.
Loch Glascarnoch	Aultguish	Brown Trout Pike	Mar to Sept. All year	Tel: (09975) 254 to obtain permission.	

Please mention this Pastime Publications guide

Water	Location	Species	Season	Permit available from	Other information
Loch Glass	Head of River Glass	Brown Trout	15 Mar. to 6 Oct.	Novar Estates, Estate Office, Evanton, Ross-shire. Tel: (0349) 830205.	Bank fishing only. Any legal method.
Garbh Loch	Forsinard	Brown Trout	1 May to 30 Sept.	Forsinard Hotel, Forsinard. Tel: (06417) 221.	Bank & boat fishing. Popular flies: Black Pennel, Ke-He, Invicta.
Golspie A.C. Waters (Loch Brora Loch Lundie Loch Horn Loch Buidhe)		Salmon Sea Trout Brown Trout	1 Apr. to 15 Oct.	Golspie A.C., Lindsay & Co., Main Street, Golspie. Tel: (0408) 683212.	Fly fishing only. Bank & boat fishing. No Sunday fishing.
Loch Heilan	Castleton	Brown Trout	May to Sept.	H.T. Pottinger, Greenland Mains, Castleton, Thurso. Tel: (0847) 82210.	Boats are available.
Loch Hempriggs	South of Wick	Brown Trout	14 Mar.to 14 Oct.	Thrumster Filling Station. Hugo Ross Fishing Tackle Shop, Wick.	Average weight of fish caught: 12oz to 1lb.
Hill Loch (32)	Around Assynt	Brown Trout	15 Mar.to 6 Oct.	Tourist Information Centre, Lochinver.	Mainly fly fishing, there are 6 lochs where spinning or bait can be used. Bank fishing only.
Loch Hope	Nr. Tongue	Salmon Sea Trout	18 June to 30 Sept.	Ian MacDonald, The Keepers House, Hope, by Lairg. Tel: 084 756 272.	Fly fishing from boats only. 3 rods per boat.
		Salmon Sea Trout	Mid-Apr.to Sept. June to Sept.	Altnaharra Hotel, by Lairg IV27 4UE.	Average weight of fish caught: Salmon - 8lbs, Sea Trout - 3lbs. Popular flies: Salmon - Invicta, Pennel. Sea Trout - Peter Ross. Other baits: Toby, sprat. 6 boats are available.
Lochs Kernsary Tournaig Goose Ghiuragarstidh	Gairloch	Brown Trout	15 Mar. to 6 Oct.	National Trust for Scotland, Inverewe Visitor Centre, Poolewe, Ross-shire. Tel: (044 586) 229.	
Kyle of Tongue & local lochs	Tongue & Farr	Salmon Sea Trout Brown Trout		Tongue Stores & P. Office, Main Street, Tongue. Tel: 084 755 201.	Sunday fishing for brown trout only. Boats available from: Woodside Cottage.
Loch Lagain	By Bonar Bridge	Brown Trout	May to 31 Oct.	Dunroamin Hotel, Bonar Bridge, Sutherland. Tel: (08632) 236.	1 boat available.
Loch Laro	By Bonar Bridge	Brown Trout	May to 31 Oct.	Dunroamin Hotel, Bonar Bridge, Sutherland. Tel: (08632) 236.	
Leckmelm Hill Lochs	Ullapool	Brown Trout	May to Sept.	Leckmelm Holiday Cottages, Leckmelm, Ullapool. Tel: (0854) 2471.	Bank fishing only. No Sunday fishing.

120

Water	Location	Species	Season	Permit available from	Other Information
Loch Loyal	Tongue	Salmon Sea Trout Brown Trout	15 Mar. to 6 Oct.	Ben Loyal Hotel, Tongue. Tel: Tongue: 216. Post Office, Tongue. Tel: Tongue 201.	Fly fishing only. Bank or boat fishing.
		Brown Trout	Mar. to Sept.	Altnaharra Hotel, By Lairg IV27 4UE.	Average weight of fish caught: 8oz to 1lb. Popular flies: Pennel, Goats Toe, Zulu. 1 boat available.
Loch Lurgainn	Nr. Achiltibuie	Brown/ Sea Trout	1 Apr. to 30 Sept.	Polly Estates Ltd., Inverpolly, Ullapool IV26 2YB. Tel: 085 482 452.	Fly fishing only. No Sunday fishing. Boats with or without motors available.
Loch Maree	Wester Ross	Salmon Sea Trout Brown Trout	May-Oct.	Loch Maree Hotel, Achnasheen IV22 2HL. Tel: (044 584) 288.	Several boats available.
				Kinlochewe Holiday Chalets, Kinlochewe. Tel: (044 584) 234/256.	2 boats available. Fly only - end June onwards.
Meadie Loch	By Westerdale, Halkirk	Brown Trout	Apr. to 7th Oct.	Ulbster Arms Hotel, Halkirk.	Fly only. Average weight: 10oz.
Loch Meadie	Tongue	Brown Trout	Mar. to Sept.	Altnaharra Hotel, By Lairg IV27 4UE.	Average weight of fish caught: 8oz to 1lb. Popular flies: Pennel, Goats Toe, Zulu. 1 boat available.
Loch Meig	Strathconon	Brown Trout	1 Apr. to 30 Sept.	John MacMillan Newsagent, The Square, Strathpeffer. Tel: (0997) 421346.	Average weight of fish caught: 1lb. Strictly fly fishing only. 3 boats are available.
Loch Merkland	Overscaig	Brown Trout	30 Apr. to 30 Sept.	Overscaig Lochside Hotel, Loch Shin, by Lairg IV27 4NY. Tel: 054 983 203.	Boat available. Fly only. No Sunday fishing.
Loch Migdale	By Bonar Bridge	Brown Trout	May to 31 Oct.	Dunroamin Hotel, Bonar Bridge, Sutherland. Tel: (08632) 236.	1 boat available.
More Loch	By Westerdale, Halkirk	Brown Trout	Apr. to 7th Oct.	Ulbster Arms Hotel, Halkirk.	Fly only. Average weight: 9oz.
Loch More	N.W. Sutherland	Salmon Sea Trout Brown Trout	1 May to 15 Oct.	Scourie Hotel, Scourie IV27 4SX. Tel: (0971) 502396.	Fly fishing only. Boats available.
Loch Morie	Head of River Alness	Brown Trout	15 Mar. to 6 Oct.	Novar Estates, Estate Office, Evanton, Ross-shire. Tel: (0349) 830205.	Bank fishing only. Any legal method.
Loch na Dail (Polly Loch)	Nr. Achiltibuie	Brown/ Sea Trout	1 Apr. to 30 Sept.	Polly Estates Ltd,. Inverpolly, Ullapool IV26 2YB. Tel: 085 482 452.	Fly fishing only. No Sunday fishing. Boat available.

Please mention this Pastime Publications guide

Water	Location	Species	Season	Permit available from	Other information
Loch nan Clar		Wild Brown Trout	1 Apr. to 15 Oct.	Garvault Hotel, by Kinbrace. Tel: Kinbrace 224.	Average weight of fish caught: 8oz. Popular flies: Loch Ordie, Black Spider, Black Pennel. Fly fishing only.
Loch Navar		Salmon Brown Trout	March to End Sept.	Altnaharra Hotel, By Lairg IV27 4UE.	Average weight of fish caught: Salmon - 8lbs, Brown Trout - 8oz. Popular flies: Trout - Pennel, Zulu, Peter Ross. Salmon - Invicta, Pennel. Other baits: toby and sprat. 3 boats available.
Loch Palm		Wild Brown Trout	1 Apr. to 15 Oct.	Garvault Hotel, by Kinbrace. Tel: Kinbrace 224.	Average weight of fish caught: 8oz. Popular flies: Loch Ordie, Black Spider, Black Pennel. Fly fishing only.
Loch Rangag	Latheron	Brown Trout	1 Apr. to 30 Sept.	John Anderson, Lochend Cottage, Latheron, Caithness. Tel: (05934) 230.	Average weight of fish caught: 12oz. Fly fishing only. Boats are available.
Rhiconich (50 lochs)	Nr. Kinlochbervie	Salmon Sea Trout Brown Trout	15 Feb. to 15 Oct.	Rhiconich Hotel, Kinlochbervie.	Fly fishing only. 7 boats available.
Loch Rhifail		Wild Brown Trout	1 Apr. to 15 Oct.	Garvault Hotel, by Kinbrace. Tel: Kinbrace 224.	Average weight of fish caught: 8oz. Popular flies: Loch Ordie, Black Spider, Black Pennel. Fly fishing only.
Loch Rhimsdale		Wild Brown Trout	1 Apr. to 15 Oct.	Garvault Hotel, by Kinbrace. Tel: Kinbrace 224.	Average weight of fish caught: 8oz. Popular flies: Loch Ordie, Black Spider. Fly fishing only.
Loch Rhuard	Latheron	Brown Trout	1 Apr. to 30 Sept.	John Anderson, Lochend Cottage, Latheron, Caithness Tel: (05934) 230.	Average weight of fish caught: 12oz. Fly fishing only. Boats are available.
Loch Rossail		Wild Brown Trout	1 Apr. to 15 Oct.	Garvault Hotel, by Kinbrace. Tel: Kinbrace 224.	Average weight of fish caught: 8oz. Popular flies: Loch Ordie, Black Spider, Black Pennel. Fly fishing only.
Loch Ruith a Phuil	by Strathpeffer	Brown Trout Rainbow Trout	15 Mar.-6 Oct. All year	The Tarvie Lochs Trout Fishery, Tarvie, by Strathpeffer IV14 9EJ. Tel: (0997) 421250.	Average weight of fish caught: Rainbow - 1lb 8oz, Brown - 12oz. Popular flies: Black Pennel, Zulu, Invicta, Sedge. Any legal baits or methods permitted. Bank fishing only. Open all year, except Xmas.

Water	Location	Species	Season	Permit available from	Other information
Loch St. Johns	Caithness	Wild Brown Trout	7 Apr. to 31 Sept.	Hugo Ross Fishing Tackle, 16 Breadalbane Crescent, Wick. Tel/Fax: (0955) 4200.	Boats are available from above.
Sarclet Loch	Thrumster	Brown Trout	15 Mar.to 14 Oct.	Thrumster Filling Station.	Average weight of fish caught: 8oz to 1lb and + Popular Flies: Cocky Bundu, Soldier Palmer, Loch Orpy, Black Pennel.
Scourie Lochs	N.W. Sutherland	Salmon Sea Trout Brown Trout	1 May to 15 Oct.	Scourie Hotel, Scourie IV27 4SX. Tel: (0971) 502396.	Fly fishing only. Boats available.
Loch Sgeirach		Wild Brown Trout	1 Apr. to 15 Oct.	Garvault Hotel, by Kinbrace. Tel: Kinbrace 224.	Average weight of fish caught: 8oz. Popular flies: Loch Ordie, Black Spider, Black Pennel. Fly fishing only.
Loch Shin	Overscaig	Brown Trout Ferox Trout	30 Apr. to 30 Sept.	Overscaig Lochside Hotel, Loch Shin, by Lairg IV27 4NY. Tel: 054 983 203.	Boats and outboards available.
	Lairg	Brown Trout Char	15 Apr. to 30 Sept.	Bank permits: R. Ross (Fishing Tackle), Main Street, Lairg IV27 4DB. Tel: (0549) 2239.	Average weight of fish caught: 7 oz. Popular flies: Kate McLaren. Spinning & worm permitted, fly preferred. Boats and engines available from boathouse from 1 June.
Loch Sionascaig (& 9 other lochs)	Ullapool	Brown Trout	1 Apr. to 30 Sept.	Polly Estate Office, Inverpolly, Ullapool IV26 2YB. Tel: 085 482 452.	Boats & outboards available. No Sunday fishing. Fly fishing only, trawling for ferox permitted. Noted for large ferox.
Skyline Loch	Forsinard	Brown Trout	1 May to 30 Sept.	Forsinard Hotel, Forsinard. Tel: (06417) 221.	Popular flies: Black Zulu, Silver Butcher.
Loch Sletill	Forsinard	Brown Trout	1 May to 30 Sept.	Forsinard Hotel, Forsinard, Sutherland. Tel: Halladale 221.	Fly fishing only. Bank & boat fishing.
Loch Stack	N.W. Sutherland	Salmon Sea Trout Brown Trout	1 May to 15 Oct.	Scourie Hotel, Scourie IV27 4SX. Tel: (0971) 502396.	Fly fishing only. Boats are available. Ghillie mandatory on loch.
Loch Staink	Tongue	Brown Trout	Mar. to Sept.	Altnaharra Hotel, By Lairg IV27 4UE.	Average weight of fish caught: 8oz to 1lb. Popular flies: Pennel, Goats Toe, Zulu, 1 Boat available.
Loch Stemster	Latheron	Brown Trout	1 Apr. to 30 Sept.	John Anderson, Lochend Cottage, Latheron, Caithness. Tel: (05934) 230.	Average weight of fish caught: 12oz. Fly fishing only. Boats are available.

Please mention this Pastime Publications guide

Water	Location	Species	Season	Permit available from	Other information
Tarvie Lochs	By Contin	Brown/ Rainbow Trout (stocked)		Sports & Model Shop, Tulloch Street, Dingwall. Tel: (0349) 62346.	Main loch: Fly fishing only. Boat available. 'Troutmaster water.' Small loch only: coarse methods.
Loch Tarvie	by Strathpeffer	Brown/ Rainbow Trout	15 Mar.-6 Oct. All year	The Tarvie Lochs Trout Fishery, Tarvie, by Strathpeffer IV14 9EJ. Tel: (0997) 421250.	Average weight of fish caught: Rainbow - 2lbs 4oz, Brown - 1lb 12oz. Popular flies: Black Pennel, Zulu, Invicta, Sedge. Fly fishing only. Boat fishing only. Open all year, except Xmas.
Tongue Lochs (14)	Tongue	Brown Trout	15 Mar. to 6 Oct.	Ben Loyal Hotel, Tongue. Tel: Tongue 216. Post Office, Tongue. Tel: Tongue 201.	
Loch Uidh Tarraigean (Upper Polly Lochs)	by Achiltibuie	Brown Trout	1 Apr. to 30 Sept.	Polly Estates Ltd., Inverpolly, Ullapool IV26 2YB. Tel: 085 482 452.	Fly fishing only. No Sunday fishing.
Ulbster Estate Lochs (9 hill lochs)	Halkirk	Brown Trout	15 Mar. to 6 Oct.	Ulbster Arms Hotel, Halkirk, Caithness. Tel: (084783) 206.	No Sunday fishing. Fly fishing only. 1 boat on each of 5 lochs.
Loch Watenan	Ulbster	Brown Trout	1 May to 30 Sept.	Mr. J. Swanson, Aspen Bank, Banks Road, Watten. Tel: (095582) 326/208.	Fly fishing only. 1 boat available.
Loch Watten	Watten Village	Brown Trout	1 May to 31 Sept.	Hugo Ross Fishing Tackle, 16 Breadalbane Crescent, Wick. Tel/Fax: (0955) 4200.	Boats for hire from tackle shop. Fish min. size 10". No Sunday fishing. Fly only.
		Brown Trout	1 May to 1 Oct.	J.A. Barnetson, Lynegar Farm, Watten. Tel: (095582) 217.	Average weight of fish caught: 12oz. Popular flies: March Brown, Butcher, Peter Ross. Fly fishing only. 1 boat available.
	(A882) Between Wick & Thurso	Stocked Brown Trout	1 May to 30 Sept.	John F. Swanson, Aspen Bank, Banks Lodge, Watten. Tel: (095582) 326/208.	Average weight of fish caught: 12oz to 1lb. Fly fishing only. 4 boats are available.
Loch Weaster	by Wick	Salmon Sea Trout Brown Trout	1 Mar. to 31 Oct.	Mrs. G. Dunnet, Auckhorn Lyth, by Wick KW1 4UD. Tel: (095583) 208.	Fly fishing only. Boats available: 1 July to 31 Oct.
Yarrows Loch	Thrumster	Brown Trout	15 Mar. to 14 Oct.	Thrumster Filling Station.	Average weight of fish caught: 12oz to 1lb (heavier fish have been caught). Popular Flies: Black Pennel, Cinnamon & Golf, Peter Ross, Soldier Palmer. Boats are available - ask at Thrumster Filling Station.

Constituent Area Tourist Board

Western Isles Tourist Board,
Area Tourist Officer,
Western Isles Tourist Board,
4 South Beach Street,
Stornoway,
Isle of Lewis PA87 2XY.
Tel: Stornoway (0851) 703088.

RIVER PURIFICATION AUTHORITY
WESTERN ISLES ISLAND AREA
(No formal Board constituted)

LOCHS

Water	Location	Species	Season	Permit available from	Other information
LOCHS LEWIS					
Beag-Na-Craoibhe	Stornoway	Brown Trout	15 Mar. to 6 Oct.	Sportsworld, 1 Francis Street, Stornoway. Tel: (0851) 705464.	Bank fishing. 1 boat available.
Loch Blackwater	13m West of Stornoway	Salmon Sea Trout Brown Trout	1 Jul.-14 Oct. 15 Mar. to 30 Sept.	The Manager, Garynahine Estate Office, Isle of Lewis.	Fly fishing only. Boats are available.
Loch Breivat	Nr. Stornoway	Brown Trout Arctic Char	15 Mar. to 30 Sept.	Estate Office, Scaliscro, Timsgarry, Isle of Lewis. Tel: (0851) 75 325.	Popular flies: Brown Muddler, Invicta, Soldier Palmer. Boats are available.
Breugach	Stornoway	Brown Trout	15 Mar. to 6 Oct.	Sportsworld, 1 Francis Street, Stornoway. Tel: (0851) 705464.	Bank fishing. Two boats available.
Loch Bruiche	Nr. Stornoway	Brown Trout Arctic Char	15 Mar. to 30 Sept.	Estate Office, Scaliscro, Timsgarry, Isle of Lewis. Tel: (0851) 75 325.	Popular flies: Brown Muddler, Invicta, Soldier Palmer. Boats are available.
Loch Coirigeroid	Nr. Stornoway	Brown Trout Arctic Char	15 Mar. to 30 Sept.	Estate Office, Scaliscro, Timsgarry, Isle of Lewis. Tel: (0851) 75 325.	Popular flies: Brown Muddler, Invicta, Soldier Palmer. Boats are available.
Loch Fhir Mhaoil	Nr. Stornoway	Salmon Sea Trout Brown Trout	June to 15 Oct.	Estate Office, Scaliscro, Timsgarry, Isle of Lewis. Tel: (0851) 75 325.	Spinning and worm fishing permitted. Boats are available.
Keose (and other lochs in Keose Glebe fishings	10 mls South of Stornoway	Brown Trout	15 Mar. to 30 Sept.	M. Morrison, 'Handa', 18 Keose Glebe, Lochs, Isle of Lewis PA86 9JX. Tel: 085 183 334. Sportsworld, 1 Francis Street, Stornoway. Tel: (0851) 705464. Tourist Office, South Beach, Stornoway.	Two boats, rods, tackle, life jackets. No Sunday fishing.

Water	Location	Species	Season	Permit available from	Other information
Loch Langavat	Nr. Stornoway	Salmon Sea Trout Brown Trout Arctic Char	15 Mar. to 15 Oct.	Estate Office, Scaliscro, Timsgarry, Isle of Lewis. Tel: (0851) 75 325.	Spinning and worming permitted. boats are available.
Loch MacLeod	Nr. Stornoway	Salmon Sea Trout	1 June to 15 Oct.	Estate Office, Scaliscro, Timsgarry, Isle of Lewis. Tel: (0851) 75325.	Popular flies: Garry Dog, Blue Charm, Donegal Blue. Boats are available.
		Salmon Sea Trout Brown Trout	1 Jul.-14 Oct. 15 Mar. to 30 Sept.	The Manager, Garynahine Estate Office, Isle of Lewis.	All legal methods permitted. Boats are available.
Loch nan Culaidhean	Nr. Stornoway	Salmon Sea Trout Brown Trout	1 Jul.-14 Oct. 15 Mar. to 30 Sept.	The Manager, Garynahine Estate Office, Isle of Lewis.	Any legal method permitted. Boats available.
Lochs Sgibacleit, Shromois, Airigh Thormaid	Nr. Stornoway	Salmon Sea Trout Brown Trout	May to 30 Oct.	Estate Office, Scaliscro, Timsgarry, Isle of Lewis. Tel: (0851) 75 325.	Spinning & worm fishing permitted. Boats are available.
Loch Tarbart	Nr. Stornoway	Salmon Sea Trout	1 June to 15 Oct.	Estate Office, Scaliscro, Timsgarry, Isle of Lewis. Tel: (0851) 75325.	Popular flies: Garry Dog, Blue Charm, Donegal Blue. Boats are available.
		Salmon Sea Trout Brown Trout	1 Jul.-14 Oct. 15 Mar. to 30 Sept.	The Manager, Garynahine Estate Office, Isle of Lewis.	All legal methods permitted. Boats are available.
Loch Tungavat	Nr. Stornoway	Brown Trout	15 Mar. to 15 Oct.	Estate Office, Scaliscro, Timsgarry, Isle of Lewis. Tel: 0851 75 325.	Average weight of fish caught: 6 to 8oz Popular flies: Soldier Palmer, Butcher, Invicta. Boats are available.
Vatandip	Stornoway	Brown Trout	15 Mar. to 6 Oct.	Sportsworld, 1 Francis Street, Stornoway. Tel: (0851) 705464.	Bank fishing. 1 boat available.
BENBECULA Loch Eilean Iain	Benbecula	Brown Trout	Mar. to Sept.	Orasay Inn, Lochcarnan, South Uist PA81 5PD. Tel: (08704) 298.	Average weight of fish caught: 1 to 3lbs. Popular flies: Soldier Palmer, Black Pennel, Ke-He, Worm Fly. 1 boat available.
Loch Hermidale	Benbecula	Brown Trout		Orasay Inn, Lochcarnan, South Uist PA81 5PD. Tel: (08704) 298. Colin Campbell Sports, Benbecula. Tel: (0870) 2236. Bornish Stores, Bornish South Uist.	Average weight of fish caught: 12oz to 1lb. Popular flies: Black Spider, Blue Zulu, Peter Ross, Invicta. 1 boat is available.
South Langavat (Heorovay - Olavat) and numerous other lochs	Benbecula	Brown Trout	15 Mar.-30 Sept.	Bornish Stores, Tel: 08785-366. Colin Campbell Sports Ltd., Balivanich. Tel: (0870) 2236.	Fly only. Boats available.

Water	Location	Species	Season	Permit available from	Other information
Loch Olavat (West)	Benbecula	Brown/ Sea Trout		Orasay Inn, Lochcarnan, South Uist PA81 5PD. Tel: (08704) 298.	Popular flies. Black Pennel, Invicta, Peter Ross, Grouse & Claret. 2 boats are available.
SOUTH UIST **Loch Druim an Lasgair**	South Uist	Brown Trout	15 Mar. to 6 Oct.	Orasay Inn, Lochcarnan, South Uist PA81 5PD. Tel: (08704) 298.	Average weight of fish caught: 12oz to 1lb. Popular flies: Soldier Palmer, Butchers, Black Spider.
East Loch Bee	South Uist	Brown Trout	Mar. to Sept.	Orasay Inn, Lochcarnan, South Uist PA81 5PD. Tel: (08704) 298. Colin Campbell Sports, Benbecula. Tel: (0870) 2236. Bornish Stores, Bornish South Uist.	Average weight of fish caught: 12oz to 1lb 8oz. Popular flies: Black Pennel, Ke-He, Bloody Butcher. 2 boats are available.
All hill and Machair Lochs	South Uist	Salmon Sea Trout Brown Trout	Jul. to Oct. Apr-End Sept.	Resident Manager, Lochboisdale Hotel, Lochboisdale, South Uist. Tel: Lochboisdale (08784) 332. Orasay Inn, Lochcarnan, South Uist PA81 5PD. Tel: (08704) 298.	Fourteen boats available on lochs. Fly fishing only.
Loch Naid	South Uist	Brown Trout		Orasay Inn, Lochcarnan, South Uist PA81 5PD. Tel: (08704) 298.	Average weight of fish caught: 12oz to 1lb. Popular flies:: Grouse & Claret, Black Pennel, Black Spider, Butchers.
NORTH UIST **Lochs & Sea Pools in North Uist**		Salmon Sea Trout Brown Trout	25 Feb.-15 Oct. 15 Mar.-31 Oct. 15 Mar.-30 Sept.	Bill Quarm, Lochmaddy Hotel, North Uist. Tel: 087 63 331.	Average weight of fish caught. Salmon 5lbs 5oz, Sea Trout - 2lbs 5oz, Brown Trout - 8oz. Fly fishing only. No Sunday fishing. Boats are available on some lochs.
ISLE OF HARRIS **Laxdale System**	Isle of Harris	Salmon Sea Trout Brown Trout	15 Mar. to 15 Oct.	Tony Scherr, Borve Lodge Estates, Isle of Harris. Tel: 085 985 202.	Fly fishing only. Permits cannot be reserved in advance.

TO ASSIST WITH YOUR BOOKINGS
OR ENQUIRIES YOU WILL FIND IT HELPFUL
TO MENTION THIS
Pastime Publications Guide

Constituent Area Tourist Boards

Orkney Tourist Board,
Information Centre,
6 Broad Street, Kirkwall,
Orkney KW15 1NX.
Tel: Kirkwall (0856) 2856.

Shetland Islands Tourism
Area Tourist Officer,
Shetland Islands Tourism,
Information Centre,
Market Cross, Lerwick,
Sheltand ZE1 0LU.
Tel: Lerwick (0595) 3434.

**PURIFICATION AUTHORITY
ORKNEY ISLANDS AREA
SHETLAND ISLANDS AREA**
(No formal Boards constituted)

LOCHS

Water	Location	Species	Season	Permit available from	Other information
ORKNEY Boardhouse	Mainland	Brown Trout	15 Mar.-6 Oct.	None required	Boats available locally. All legal methods permitted. Anglers are recommended to join Orkney Trout Fishing Association, Kirkwall, who make facilities available to visitors.
Harray	Mainland	Brown Trout	15 Mar.-6 Oct.	Merkister Hotel. Loch Harray, Orkney. Tel: 085 677 366.	See Orkney for further information.
Hundland	Mainland	Brown Trout	15 Mar.-6 Oct.	None required	See Orkney for further information.
Kirbister	Mainland	Brown Trout	15 Mar.-6 Oct.	None required	See Orkney for further information.
Stenness	Mainland	Sea Trout Brown Trout	25 Feb.-31 Oct. 15 Mar.-6 Oct.	None required.	See Orkney for further information.
Swannay	Mainland	Brown Trout	15 Mar.-6 Oct.	None required	See Orkney for further information.
SHETLAND 1000 lochs & voes	Shetland Islands	Sea Trout Grisle Brown Trout	25 Feb. to 31 Oct. 15 Mar.-6 Oct.	Shetland Anglers Association, A. Miller, Hon. Sec., 3 Gladstone Terrace, Lerwick. Shetland Tourist Info. Centre, Commercial Street, Lerwick. Anderson & Co., Market Cross, Lerwick.	Average weight of fish caught: Brown Trout - 1 to 1lb 8oz, Sea Trout & Grilse - 2 to 8lbs. Popular flies: all dark flies - Black Pennel, Grouse & Claret, Ke-He, Invicta, Blue Zulu (sizes 10 & 12). Other baits: spinning where permitted with mepps spoons and toby lures. Association boats available on 5 popular lochs: Spiggie, Benston, Tinewall, Clousta, Punds Water.

Water	Location	Species	Season	Permit available from	Other information
Various	Yell Island	Brown Trout	15 Mar. to 6 Oct.	No permit required, fishing free.	Average weight of fish caught: 8oz to 8lbs+ Popular flies: Bibio, Silver Invicta. Spinning permitted. 1 boat on Littlestar Loch, Burravoe. Boat permit available from Old Haa Museum.
Huxter Loch	Isle of Whalsay	Brown Trout	15 Mar. to 6 Oct.	Brian J. Poleson, Sheardaal, Huxter, Symbister, Whalsay.	Average weight of fish caught: 12 oz. Fly fishing only. 1 boat available.
Ibister Loch	Isle of Whalsay	Brown Trout	15 Mar. to 6 Oct.	Brian J. Poleson, Sheardaal, Huxter, Symbister, Whalsay.	Average weight of fish caught: 10 to 12oz. Fly fishing only. 1 boat available.

MATCHING THE HATCH ON HIGHLAND LOCHS

by Lesley Crawford

It is commonly thought that the wild brown trout is an opportunist feeder, that is, one that will take any old piece of fluff and wool providing that it vaguely resembles something it would normally like to eat. With the trout's varied diet; anything from sticklebacks to snails and from caddis to shrimp with all manner of winged insects and nymphs in between; it is not surprising this theory has evolved over time. However if you are able to fish for wild browns regularly as I do certain traditionally tied patterns begin to emerge as the most successful, ones that can be used time and time again when all else seems to be failing. And more importantly, if you dig a little deeper you will see these traditional patterns are actually designed to 'match the hatch' and follow what the invertebrate life is doing above and below the water surface. In typically canny Highland fashion most of our flies are highly versatile and designed to imitate a number of aquatic life forms rather than just one particular insect.

If you look first at our wild brown trout's staple diet you will see that it consists mainly of stonefly, mayfly, olives, sedges and heather fly together with nymphs, caddis, shrimp and snail. The larger trout also tend to go for sticklebacks in large quantities and as a general rule, tend to have the best and most productive territories. Here they seek out the bottom dwellers like caddis and snail though they will rise with spirit if there is a sustained hatch of bigger

insects like the Mayfly or the Daddy long legs falling on to the water. The smaller fish tend to lie nearer the surface with less fertile lies and without such abundant food sources snatch at most things on the surface providing the weather conditions are favourable.

Whether the angler is after the big or the small trout he must imitate what they are feeding on to some extent to ensure some success. He may do this unconsciously knowing that if puts on a 'Zulu' or a 'Pennel' he will find success because these are flies' recommended to him by experienced locals, less clear is just why these particular patterns will work. A little investigation of the loch environment will help prior to fishing. Simply turning over stones on the waters edge will give invaluable clues as to a lochs invertebrate life and what is found there will lead you quickly into what should be tied on first. For example if a loch has an abundance of freshwater shrimp in the rocky shallows the angler may well tie on the Soldier Palmer for, with its ragged brown hackles and red tag it does vaguely resemble a coloured shrimp with trailing legs. However if there are visible hatches of winged insects, either of the olive or sedge variety, then he would be wise to select the Wickham's Fancy or the Invicta which will match that hatch with an interesting cross over with the Soldier Palmer, if the winged insects have a reddish brown tinge. However there are some invertebrates in the trout's diet which look decidedly odd. For example how does one imitate a gritty stone cased caddis or a stonefly nymph given their bulky and ungainly bodies? The answer in traditional loch style tyings lies more in colour and general representation rather than using an (almost impossible to tie) exact replica. The trout feeding on stoneflies will often take the predominantly brown and black Kate McLaren or a Black Pennel and I have caught trout stuffed with caddis on anything from a Brown Ke He to a Zulu. Snails too are difficult to imitate being small brownish pebble shapes but the Kate McLaren also does well for these molluscs and the big trout snapping up sticklebacks in the shallows will readily take your slimline and sleek Kingfisher Butcher or Silver Invicta if it passes them by.

That most prized of insects the Mayfly also known as the Green Drake is far more prevalent on our lochs than you would think and it hatches in goodly number from around mid June to the beginning of August. All that is required for abundant Mayfly is a slightly silted bottom for the nymph to make its burrow with slightly alkaline and therefore fertile water for its habitat. The North has these waters in abundance and Mayfly can be seen drifting across the most unlikely looking pools to be eagerly engulfed by the waiting trout. There are of course a number of exact imitations of Mayfly to choose from but my favourites are the Irish tied 'Green Drake' and the big fluffy 'French Partridge' fly is also an absolute winner when the Mayfly are on the lochs. The use of these imitations however does not always need to be confined to a Mayfly hatch, a bit of floatant makes them sit up like large

A 2lb. 12oz. wild brown taken on a Wickham fancy.

dry flies on the water surface and they can stir up even the most lethargic of trout during a flat calm or a muggy late evening when there are moths or big sedges about.

Even from this short potted history of some of the traditional loch patterns I hope you can see that their original tyings were cleverly thought out and that even today few flies can rival them for effectiveness and versatility against the wily wild brown trout.

HIGHLAND HIGHLIGHTS

by Lesley Crawford

I am lucky enough to live on the northern border of the counties of Caithness and Sutherland and tend to be almost engulfed by matchless wild brown trout fishing. This makes selecting any highlights an almost impossible task as just as I plump for one loch another springs to mind and then having almost decided I think yes but what about.... and so it goes on. I could of course convey to you in brochure fashion the delights of the principal waters but you will forgive me if I make my selection for personal, even perverse reasons. After all it all depends what you want out of your fishing. Relaxation, escapism, excitement and a challenge to your skills should all play a part as much as the taking of trout. In my childhood I thought of my fishing purely in terms of catching or, more usually, not catching a fish. Nowadays I consider the whole experience of being alone with nature and at peace with an element I love the most important parts of a day. If I catch trout well and good but it is no longer an over-riding concern.

Let's look at those quintessential qualities again. For relaxation I would almost always plump for an evening's fishing on my 'home' loch of LOCH CALDER in Caithness. This big spring fed loch was once thought to be two separate waters which amalgamated when it was dammed and the water levels raised some years ago. Legend has it that there was actually a strip of land running between the SW shore and the big house in trees on the East bank and that locals walked across that on their way to Thurso. Indeed this may have some truth in it for even today shallows in that area can be clearly seen from the boat. When I visit on a summer's evening I am always thrilled with the lengthening horizon and the water glittering gold when the sun dips down behind the big trees on the North Western shore. There is a pervading sense of tranquillity about this loch and, dark and sombre in the shade yet sparkling in the sunlight, it will constantly delight the eye. Divers wail across it, hundreds of geese over winter there and otters make the shoreline their home. I may wade with stealth after one or two of the big trout in the one and a half pound class, caught from the shore where they chase stickleback and snail, but I will content myself with a few bright half pounders for my family while soaking up the restoring silence of its shores.

For real escapism I can think of nowhere better than the remote lochs tucked into the central Sutherland moors. Known collectively as the 'badenlochs' my particular favourites are the ones involving the longest walk. Lochs COIRE NAM MANG and DRUIM A CHLABHAIN are stunningly set behind the Ben Griams and angling there is like fishing where no man seems to have gone before. Though to reach them one must plod for about an hour up a pleasant track that should add to the escape from work/stress or whatever pains you and not detract from it. The trout are of exceptional quality too, averaging around 12oz to 1lb mark with many in the 2lb range also caught and the lochs offer everything that is good about Highland loch fishing. Good boats, good wading and good fishing in a sympathetically managed wilderness environment. To escape to the Badenlochs is an escape to a mini paradise for the trout angler.

For excitement I will always head for the SCOURIE and RHICONICH area for, with so many lochs there, rounding each corner of the winding road brings new delights and the heart beats ever faster in expectation of the new, the old and the unexpected. It would be impossible for me to even begin to name many of the waters in this remote mountainous region where even a half mile walk can cover four or five different lochs and lochans. This is a place where your spirits should soar like the spiralling eagle you may occasionally see on the wing. The trekking can be arduous but that should invigorate you and with the prospect of hard fighting wild trout in view the heart should always beat a little faster here. The occasional hefty specimen will also grab your fly when least expected, bending your rod like a bow and stripping line from the reel in quite extraordinary fashion. That is what Scourie is all about, an exercise in thrilling trout fishing with its excitement lying in the discovery of just one more loch to try before it gets dark and come June the sun never truly sets, now there's a thought!

Something to challenge my angling ability is almost always the most essential ingredient for a good day and the more perverse the better! There are lochs in North Sutherland with a limestone underlay extending from DURNESS across to FORSINARD and from Scourie down the west coast and throughout CAITHNESS there are also numerous 'limestone' lochs with a marl mud base. These lochs are a constant challenge and they are the ones that I will always select when stretching my ability to the limit. Though these slightly alkaline waters can be confoundedly difficult at times, to me that is part of their enjoyment. Indeed if you consider Highland loch fishing as a whole from peaty dubh loch to gneiss rock and from sandstone to limestone, virtually all the lochs can be demanding according to the prevailing weather conditions and a loch full of free rising trout one day can be dour as death the next simply because of a change in the wind direction, a rise or fall in temperature or an alteration in light intensity. The ultimate challenge lies in understanding and interpreting fish behaviour and even when you think you are half way there something new will always come along and throw those carefully thought out theories on to their heads, but I for one would not have it any other way - I'll see you there!

SCOTTISH FEDERATION FOR COARSE ANGLING

The Federation was formed in 1975 to promote and encourage the sport of Coarse Angling in Scotland. It is recognised by the Scottish Sports Council as being the governing body for Coarse Angling throughout Scotland.

Objects and Functions

To obtain waters for coarse angling.

To assist with fisheries management.

To assist with stocking of waters.

To promote and develop coarse angling in Scotland.

To promote and organise competitions and league matches.

To provide team representation at the World Championships (CIPS-FIPS-ED).

To organise international events for Scottish anglers.

Members

At present, 13 clubs are affiliated to the Federation. Individual membership of the Federation is available although it is preferred that individuals join clubs affiliated to the Federation. The annual subscription for Club Membership of the SFCA is £30 with a joining fee of £15. Individual membership is offered at £3.

Coaching and Courses

Some SFCA member clubs hold 'in class' coaching sessions for novice anglers, while others operate 'on the bank' instruction thus providing knowledge under varying conditions.

Committee Structure

The affairs of the Federation are at present conducted by a Management Committee comprising the Chairman, Hon. Secretary, Hon. Treasurer and Club representatives. A development and a Match Angling Committee also exist to deal with specific projects.

Office Bearers

Chairman
Ralston McPherson,
17 Barrhill Court,
Rosebank,
Kirkintilloch G66 3PL.

Secretary
Iain Bain,
33 Gibson Street,
Edinburgh EH11 11AS.

Treasurer
Robert Crossan,
2 Quarryknowe Place,
Bellshill ML4 2AW.

National Team Manager
Alastair Keir,
'Tigh-na-Fleur',
Mill O'Gryffe Road,
Bridge of Weir.

Match Committee Secretary
George Glen,
29 Riverside Grove,
Edinburgh EH12 5QS.

Development Committee Chairman
Stephen McCavney,
165 Airbles Street,
Motherwell ML1 1UH.

Development Committee Secretary
Frank Gibbons,
32 Clark Street,
Motherwell ML1.

Barochan Angling Club

A.H. Keir,
'Tigh Na Fleur,
Mill O'Gryffe Road,
Bridge of Weir.

Edinburgh Coarse Anglers

Ron Woods,
23 Terregles, Penicuik.

Glasgow Match Angling Club

Frank Revell,
93 Woodhead Crescent,
Tannochside,
Uddingston G71.

Glasgow & West of Scotland Regional Association of the Pike Anglers Club of G.B.

Ralston McPherson,
17 Barrhill Court,
Rosebank,
Kirkintilloch G66 3PL.

Kirkintilloch Match Angling Club

Jim Brown,
13 Boghead Road,
Kirkintilloch.

Lanarkshire Colts Angling Club

John Rae,
44 Ryde Road,
Wishaw ML2 7DX.

Linlithgow Coarse Angling Club

David Hood,
161 Bailielands,
Linlithgow.

Monklands Coarse Angling Club

William Sinclair,
17 Ailsa Court,
Monklands, Coatbridge.

Milton Coarse Angling Club

John Keir,
150 Ronaldsay Street,
Milton, Glasgow.

Royal Navy Coarse Angling Club

Royal Air Force (Kincaple A.C.)

Strathclyde Coarse Angling Club

J. Byers,
16 Jade Terrace, Bellshill.

Competition
Summer and Winter Club
Leagues are held each year.
Overall results provide the
Scottish Team and
Individual champions.
Scottish National Junior
Open Championship.

All Scotland championship -
Scottish residents only.

Scottish Federation Open.

Scottish Federation Cup -
Federation members only.

Home International Series.
International friendlies
against other countries.

Participation in the World
Championships.

Scottish Pole Angling
Championship.
Member clubs also arrange
club match programmes
throughout spring, summer
and autumn.

Specimen Group
A newly formed and active
element of the Federation.
Objectives include:
Providing an efficiently
managed fishery befitting
the Federation membership.
Continually updating the
'Available Waters Register'
for the benefits of all
Scottish coarse anglers and
visitors.

THE S.F.C.A. COARSE ANGLER'S COUNTRY CODE

1. Never throw away hooks, line or shot.
   Take them home and get rid of them properly.

2. Plastic bags can kill.
   Take away all rubbish from your spot,
   even if it was there before.

3. Know the fishery rules and return all coarse fish,
   including pike and eels, unharmed.

4. Help protect wildlife, plants and trees.
   Fish well away from birds' nesting places.

5. Place your keepnet to hold your fish properly.
   Stake it out if you can.

6. Use barbless hooks when you can.
   Take care when casting.

7. Park cars away from entrances.
   Keep to paths and close all gates.

8. Carbon rods conduct electricity.
   Keep well away from overhead power lines.

9. Don't light fires.
   Report any sign of pollution.

10. Keep dogs under control.
    Don't disturb the peace of the countryside.

DEFEND YOUR SPORT
JOIN THE SCOTTISH FEDERATION FOR COARSE ANGLING

SCOTTISH FRESHWATER FISH RECORDS

Bream   8lbs, 1oz (3.629kg) Castle Loch, Lochmaben D. Beattie 1990

Carp   26lbs, 2oz (11.849kg) Duddingston S. Killen 1990

Dace   1lb, 3oz, 8dr (0.553kg) River Tweed, Coldstream G. Keech 1979

Eel   5lbs, 8oz (2.495kg) Loch Ochiltree T. May 1987

Goldfish   1lb, 9oz (0.709kg) Forth & Clyde Canal B. Stevenson 1978

Grayling   2lbs, 14oz, 2dr (1.308kg) Lyne Water R. Brown 1987

Perch   4lbs, 14oz (2.210kg) Loch Ard J. Walker 1989

Pike   47lbs, 11oz (21.631kg) Loch Lomond T. Morgan 1947

Roach   2lbs, 11oz (1.219kg) Strathclyde stillwater P. Russell 1987

Tench   6lbs, 00oz, 4dr (2.729kg) Lanark Loch A. Gardner 1991

No record exists for the following species, however qualifying weights are as follows:

Barbel	1lb	**Rudd**	2 lbs
Bleak	2oz	**Ruffe**	4oz
Chub	4lbs	**S/Bream**	8oz
Gudgeon	4oz	**Zander**	1lb
Orfe	2 lbs		

How to claim a record:

1. No claims will be considered for dead fish. All fish must be returned to the water alive.

2. The claim should be made on a form available from the Development Committee who must be satisfied by the evidence that the fish was correctly identified and weighed, and was captured by fair angling.

3. New claims will be considered subject to the following minimum requirements:

   a) Photographs of the fish must be available.

   b) The scales must be certified as being accurate.

   c) Witnesses will assist the claim and if possible these should be experienced anglers.

   In the case of a fish over the British record weight please telephone either Peterborough (0733) 54084 (day) or 25248 (night) for advice.

COARSE FISHING
DUMFRIES & GALLOWAY

RIVERS & LOCHS

Water	Location	Species	Season	Permit available from	Other information
Castle Loch	Lochmaben	Bream Roach Pike		Castle Filling Station, Lochmaben.	Scotland's premier Bream water - fish to 9lbs. Excellent night fishing.
Craichlaw Loch	Newton Stewart	Carp Tench Roach Bream Rudd	Open all Year	Palakona Guest House, Queen Street, Newton Stewart. Tel: (0671) 402323.	Night fishing by arrangement. Non toxic weights.
River Cree (and Pencill Burn)	Drum-lamford Estate	Pike Perch	No close season	Palakona Guest House, Queen Street, Newton Stewart DG8 6JL. Tel: (0671) 402323.	No live bait.
Culscadden Farm Pond	Garlieston	Roach Rudd Perch Carp Tench Bream	Open all year	Palakona Guest House, Queen Street, Newton Stewart. Tel: (0671) 402323.	Baits: Maggot, Corn, Bread.
Dabton Loch	Thornhill	Perch	No close season	Castle Filling Station, Lochmaben. The Buccleuch Estates Ltd., Drumlanrig Mains, Thornhill DG3 4AG. Tel: (08486) 283.	Average weight of fish: 8oz. Baits: Worm, Maggot. Bank fishing. Sunday fishing. Overnight fishing by arrangement.
Glendarroch Loch	Newton Stewart	Roach Rudd Perch Carp Tench Bream		Palakona Guest House, Queen Street, Newton Stewart. Tel: (0671) 402323.	Baits: Maggot, Bread, Corn.
Loch Heron	Nr. Newton Stewart	Perch Roach Pike	Open all Year	Palakona Guest House, Queen Street, Newton Stewart. Tel: (0671) 402323. Three Lochs Caravan Park, Newton Stewart.	
Loch Ken	(West Bank)	Roach Perch Pike	Open all Year	Shops & hotels in New Galloway	Long range tactics pay off early in year.
	(Glenlaggan)	Roach Perch Pike		On bank	Best known match pegs. Fish beyond shelf at 60-70 yds.
Loch Maberry	Drum-lamford Estate	Coarse	Open all year	The Keeper, The Kennels, Drumlamford Estate, Barrhill. Tel: (046 582) 256.	Spinning & bait allowed. Boats available.

Water	Location	Species	Season	Permit available from	Other information
Morton Pond	Thornhill	Tench	No close season	The Buccleuch Estates Ltd., Drumlanrig Mains, Thornhill DG3 4AG. Tel: (08486) 283.	Average weight of fish: 2lbs. Baits: Bread, Sweetcorn. Bank fishing. Sunday fishing. Overnight fishing by arrangement.
Loch Murray	Creetown	Roach Rudd Perch Tench Carp	Open all Year	Castlecary Caravan Park, Creetown.	
Loch Ronald	Nr. Newton Stewart	Pike Perch Roach	No close season	Palakona Guest House, Queen Street, Newton Stewart DG8 6JL. Tel: (0670) 402323.	Any legal method permitted.
Loch Rutton	Lochfoot	Bream Roach Perch Pike	Open all Year		Excellent tip venue.
Loch Stroan	Castle Douglas	Pike Perch	Mar. to Oct.	Forest Enterprise, 21 King Street, Castle Douglas. Tel: (0556) 3626. Ticket machines both ends Raiders Road Forest Drive.	Bank fishing only. Any legal method. Sunday fishing.
Woodhall Loch	Mossdale, Nr. New Galloway	Pike Perch Roach Brown Trout	Open all year	Mossdale Post Office, Mossdale, Castle Douglas DG7 2NF. Tel: (06445) 281.	Any legal method permitted.

STRATHCLYDE

RIVERS & LOCHS

Water	Location	Species	Season	Permit available from	Other information
Auchinstarry Quarry	Kilsyth	Pike Perch Roach Tench Rudd	Open all year		Free fishing
Castle Semple Loch	Lochwinnoch	Roach Perch Pike	No close season	Rangers Office on Lochside Marina.	Shallow loch fishing at distance can pay of. Day permits for bank fishing.
River Clyde	Glasgow Green	Dace Roach occas. Bream Gudgeon	Open all year		Very deep winter venue
	Swanston Street, Glasgow.	Dace Roach	Open all year		Excellent pole and tip venue.
	Dalmarnock Bridge, Glasgow	Dace Roach Eels	Open all year		

Water	Location	Species	Season	Permit available from	Other information
River Clyde cont.	Belvedere, Glasgow	Dace Roach Eels	Open all year		Waggler and stick float pegs.
Forth & Clyde Canal	Bowling	Roach Perch Pike Tench Carp Eels	Open all year	British Waterways, Applecross Street, Glasgow.	Carp to 20lb.
	Dalmuir	Roach Perch Pike Tench Carp Eels	Open all Year	British Waterways, Applecross Street, Glasgow.	Specimen Roach and Eels.
	Westerton	Roach Perch Pike		British Waterways, Applecross Street, Glasgow.	Many big Perch and Roach.
	Firhill Basin, Maryhill	Roach Pike Perch Tench		British Waterways, Applecross Street, Glasgow.	Good summer Tench venue.
	Lambhill	Roach Perch Pike		British Waterways, Applecross Street, Glasgow.	Rarely fished, holds specimen fish.
	Bishopbriggs	Roach Bream Tench Perch Pike		British Waterways, Applecross Street, Glasgow.	Attractive tree lined stretch.
	Torrance to Glasgow Bridge	Roach Bream Carp Tench Perch Pike		J.B. Angling, 37 Eastside, Kirkintilloch.	Heavily stocked club stretch.
	Glasgow Bridge to Kirkintilloch.	Roach Bream Carp Tench Perch Pike		J.B. Angling, 37 Eastside, Kirkintilloch.	Excellent winter venue.
	Hillhead Basin, Kirkintilloch.	Tench Roach Bream Pike		British Waterways, Applecross Street, Glasgow.	Superb winter Tench venue.
	Auchinstarry, Kilsyth	Tench Roach Perch Pike		British Waterways, Applecross Street, Glasgow.	Early morning summer venue nets to 70lbs recorded.
	Dullatur	Roach Perch Tench Bream Pike Eels		British Waterways, Applecross Street, Glasgow.	Quality Perch and Roach in summer.

Water	Location	Species	Season	Permit available from	Other information
Forth & Clyde Canal cont.	Kelvinhead	Roach Perch Tench Bream Pike		British Waterways, Applecross Street, Glasgow.	Tench to 5lb +. Roach to 2lb in late summer.
	Wyndford	Tench Roach		British Waterways, Applecross Street, Glasgow.	Shallow stretch. Good Tench bags possible.
	Castlecary	Roach Perch Tench Pike		British Waterways, Applecross Street, Glasgow.	Attractive tree lined sections.
Hogganfield Loch	Millerston	Carp Roach Pike Perch Bream		Free fishing	Carp to double figures
Lanark Loch	Lanark	Carp Tench Perch	Open all year	On bank	
Linfern Loch	Straiton	Pike	No close season	Mr. R. Heaney, Tallaminnoch, Straiton. Tel: (065 57) 617.	Sunday fishing. 1 May to mid-June no permits are available.
Monklands Canal	Coatbridge	Carp Roach Bream Dace Tench Gudgeon		On bank Monklands C.A.C.	Excellent summer venue
Strathclyde Country Park (Park Loch)	Motherwell	Roach Perch Bream Eels Carp	Open all year	Booking Office, Watersports Centre.	Summer method float Winter swimfeeder.
(River Avon)	Motherwell	Dace Roach Gudgeon Grayling		Booking Office Watersports Centre.	Good Winter sport.
(River Clyde)	Motherwell	Dace Roach		Booking Office, Watersports Centre.	Method swimfeeder.

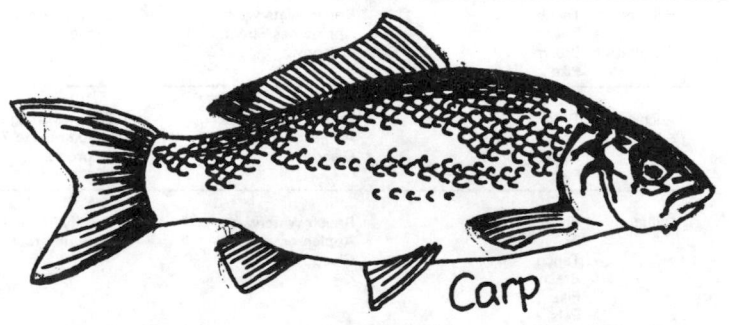

Carp

FORTH & LOMOND

RIVERS & LOCHS

Water	Location	Species	Season	Permit available from	Other information
Duddingston Loch	Edinburgh	Carp Perch	1 May to 30 Sept.	Historic Scotland, 20 Brandon Street, Edinburgh. Tel: 031-244 3085.	Bird Sanctuary. Bank fishing. Restricted area. No lead weights.
River Endrick	Drymen	Dace Chub Roach Eels	Mar.-Oct.	White House, Drymen Bridge.	Fishes from Spring to Autumn.
	Croftamie	Dace Chub Roach	Mar.-Oct.	Bisland Farm, Croftamie.	Good Dace shoals. Odd Chub.
Loch Lomond	Balloch to Ardlui	Pike Perch Roach		Local shops. Tackle dealers.	
Union Canal		Roach Pike Perch Bream	Open all year	Lothian Regional Council, George IV Bridge, Edinburgh. Tel: 031-229 9292 Ext. 3286 Tourist Office, Linlithgow. Tel: (0506) 844600.	Shallow canal fish fine.

Perch

SCOTTISH FEDERATION OF SEA ANGLERS OFFICIALS

President
David Neil,
30 Woodfield Road, Ayr KA8 8LZ.
Tel: (0292) 266549.

Vice-Presidents
George Kinnear,
9 Killoch Drive, Barrhead, Renfrewshire
G78 HX. Tel: 041-881 4127.

Francis Jefferson
No. 1 Sheshader Point, Isle of Lewis
PA86 0EW. Tel: (0851) 870214.

Hon. Treasurer
Robert Keltie,
76 Stewart Avenue, Bo'ness, West Lothian
EH51 9NW. Tel: (0506) 826274

**Hon. Fish Recorder/
Conservation Officer**
Gordon Morris,
8 Burt Avenue, Kinghorn, Fife KY3 9XB.
Tel: (0592) 890055

Coaching Co-ordinator
Henry Hamilton-Willows,
15 Carrick Drive, North Mount Vernon,
Glasgow G32 0RW. Tel: 041-778 4454.

**Public Relations
Officer/Sponsorship**
Brian Burn,
Flat 2, 16 Bellevue Road, Ayr KA7 2SA.
Tel: (0292) 264735.

Secretary/Administrator
Mrs. Helen Murray,
Caledonia House, South Gyle, Edinburgh
EH12 8DQ. Tel: 031-317 7192

REGIONAL SECRETARIES

Clyde & Western
Mr. John Taylor,
1/1, 6 Tower Terrace, Paisley, Renfrewshire
PA1 2JT. Tel: 041-887 0314.

Central
Mrs. Margaret McCallum,
58 Pottery Street, Kirkcaldy KY1 3EU.
Tel: (0592) 51710

West
Mr. William Clark,
4 Fullarton Street, Kilmarnock, Ayrshire.

North East
Mr. Norman Pickard,
3 Grant Street, Whitehills, Banff.
Tel: (0309) 690926.

Eastern
Mr. Adrian Black,
43 Joppa Road, Edinburgh EH15 2HB.
Tel: 031-657 3260.

Highlands & Islands
Mr. W. Mackintosh,
'Schiehallion', 16 Glengarry Road, Inverness
IV3 6NJ. Tel: (0463) 235850.

Western Isles
Mr. F. Jefferson,
No. 1 Sheshader, Point, Isle of Lewis
PA86 0EW. Tel: (0851) 870214.

SCOTTISH BOAT AND SHORE (rod and line caught)
MARINE FISH RECORDS

B - Boat Records   S - Shore Records   Spec. - Specimen Qualifying Weight

Species		lb.	oz.	dm.	kg.	Place of Capture	Angler	Year	Spec. lb.
ANGLERFISH	B	45	0	0	20.412	Sound of Mull	D. Hopper	1978	20
Lophius piscatorius	S	38	0	0	17.237	Blairmore Pier Loch Long	L. C. Hanley	1970	15
ARGENTINE	B		5	3	0.147	Arrochar	I. Millar	1978	4oz.
Argentina sphyraena	S	OPEN AT ANY WEIGHT							
BARRACUDINA	B	OPEN AT ANY WEIGHT							any
(Paralepis coreganoides									
borealis)	S	0	1	14	0.054	Newton Shore	D. Gillop	1987	1½oz.
BASS	B	8	14	3	4.025	Balcary Bay	D. Shaw	1975	6
Dicentrarchus labrax	S	13	4	0	6.010	Almorness Point	G. Stewart	1975	6
BLACKFISH	B	3	10	8	1.658	Heads of Ayr	J. Semple	1972	2½
Centrolophus niger	S	OPEN AT ANY WEIGHT							any
BLENNY, SHANNY	B	OPEN AT ANY WEIGHT							any
Blennius pholis	S	0	1	10	0.046	Carolina Port Dundee Docks	M. S. Ettle	1983	1oz.
BLENNY, TOMPOT	B	OPEN AT ANY WEIGHT							any
Blennius gattorugine	S		2	12	0.078	Portpatrick	G. Dods	1977	2oz.
BLENNY, VIVIPAROUS	B		10	0	0.283	Craigendoran	T. Lambert	1977	7oz.
Zoarces viviparus	S		11	3	0.317	Craigendoran	D. Ramsay	1975	7oz.
BLENNY, YARREL'S	B	OPEN AT ANY WEIGHT							any
Chirolophis ascanii	S		2	1	0.059	Gourock	D. McEntee	1979	1½oz.
BLUEMOUTH	B	3	2	8	1.431	Loch Shell	Mrs A. Lyngholm	1976	2½
Helicolenus	S	OPEN AT ANY WEIGHT							any
dactylopterus									
BREAM, BLACK	B	2	9	0	1.162	Kebock Head Lewis	T. Lumb	1974	1
Spondyllosoma	S	1	13	8	0.836	Gareloch	A. L. Harris	1973	1
cantharus									
BREAM, GILTHEAD	B	OPEN AT ANY WEIGHT							any
Sparus aurata	S	1	1	5	0.490	Dunnet Head	W. Thornton	1988	1
BREAM, RAYS	B	6	3	13	2.829	West of Barra Head	J. Holland	1978	4
Brama brama	S	6	6	8	2.905	Portobello	G. Taylor	1973	4
BREAM RED	B	4	10	0	2.097	Ardnamurchan	R. Steel	1969	1
Pagellus bogaraveo	S	OPEN AT ANY WEIGHT							any
BRILL	B	1	4	0	0.567	Portpatrick	J. Dickson	1984	1
Scophthalmus	S	1	2	0	0.510	Killintrinnan Lighthouse	P. Baisbrown	1971	1
rhombus									
BULL HUSS	B	20	3	8	9.171	Mull of Galloway	J. K. Crawford	1971	15
scyliorhinus stellaris	S	15	8	0	7.031	West Tarbet Mull of Galloway	A. K. Paterson	1976	10
BUTTERFISH	B	OPEN AT ANY WEIGHT							any
Pholis gunnellus	S		1	2	0.032	Gourock	D. McEntee	1978	1oz.
CATFISH, COMMON	B	13	12	11	6.256	Burnmouth	D. Brown	1985	7
Anachichas lupus	S	12	12	8	5.797	Stonehaven	G. M. Taylor	1978	4
COALFISH	B	28	4	0	12.814	Eyemouth	L. Gibson	1982	12
Pollachius virens	S	11	7	8	5.202	Loch Long	S. Mather	1976	7
COD	B	46	0	8	20.879	Gantocks	B. Baird	1970	25
Gadus morhua	S	40	11	8	18.470	Balcary Point	K. Robinson	1988	15
DAB	B	2	12	4	1.254	Gairloch	R. Islip	1975	1½
Limanda limanda	S	2	5	0	1.049	Cairnryan	A. Scott	1969	1½

B - Boat Records   S - Shore Records   Spec. - Specimen Qualifying Weight

Species		lb.	oz.	dm.	kg.	Place of Capture	Angler	Year	Spec. lb.
DAB LONG ROUGH	B		6	6	0.180	Helensburgh	J. Napier	1984	4oz.
Hippoglossoides	S		5	8	0.155	Coulport	I. McGrath	1975	4oz.
platessoides									
DOGFISH	B	2	13	8	1.288	Loch Fyne	J. H. Anderson	1977	1½
BLACK-MOUTHED									
Galeus melastromus	S	OPEN AT ANY WEIGHT							any
DOGFISH	B	3	15	12	1.807	Portpatrick	R. I. Carruthers	1987	3
LESSER-SPOTTED									
Scyliorhinus caniculus	S	4	15	3	2.246	Abbey Burnfoot	S. Ramsay	1988	3
DRAGONET COMMON	B		5	0	0.142	Gareloch	T. J. Ashwell	1985	4oz.
Callionymus lyra	S		5	0	0.143	Loch Long	J. Crawford	1985	4½
EEL, COMMON	B	1	13	7	0.834	Gareloch	P. Fleming	1976	1½
Anguilla anguilla	S	3	0	0	1.360	Ayr Harbour	R. W. Morrice	1972	2
EEL, CONGER	B	48	1		21.820	Largs	R. Bond	1985	30
Conger conger	S	63	8	0	28.803	Balcary	B. Ford	1991	25
FLOUNDER	B	2	13	11	1.295	Portnockie	K. F. Mackay	1985	2½
Platichthys flesus	S	4	11	8	2.140	Musselburgh	R. Armstrong	1970	2½
GARFISH	B	1	11	8	0.799	Brodick	R. Stockwin	1970	1
Belone belone	S	1	11	0	0.764	Bute	Miss McAlorum	1971	1
GOBY BLACK	B		1	4	0.035	Cairnryan	J. Price	1976	1oz.
Gobius niger	S		2	4	0.063	Inveraray	F. O'Brien	1980	1oz.
GURNARD, GREY	B	2	7	0	1.105	Caliach Point	D. Swinbanks	1976	1¾
Eutrigla gurnardus	S	1	5	0	0.595	Peterhead	A. Turnbull	1973	1
		1	5	0	0.595	Port William	J. W. Martin	1977	1
GURNARD, RED	B	2	8	8	1.148	Tobermory	D. V. Relton	1985	1½
Aspitrigla cuculus	S	1	2	5	0.519	Gareloch	G. Smith	1981	12oz.
GURNARD STREAKED	B		10	10	0.301	Isle of Mull	J. Duncan	1985	any
Trigloporus lastoviza	S	1	6	8	0.637	Loch Goil	H. L. Smith	1971	1
GURNARD, TUB	B	5	5	0	2.409	Luce Bay	J. S. Dickinson	1975	3½
Trigla lucerna	S	1	1	0	0.481	Carrick Bay	A. E. Maxwell	1978	12oz.
HADDOCK	B	9	14	12	4.501	Summer Isles	M. Lawton	1980	6
Melanogrammus	S	6	12	0	3.061	Loch Goil	G. B. Stevenson	1976	3
aeglefinus									
HAKE	B	18	5	8	8.321	Shetland	B. Sinclair	1971	10
Merluccius merluccus	S		11	7	0.324	Gourock	S. Moyes	1979	8oz.
HALIBUT	B	234	0	0	106.136	Scrabster	C. Booth	1979	50
Hippoglossus	S	OPEN AT ANY WEIGHT							any
hippoglossus									
HERRING	B	1	2	0	0.510	Loch Long	R. C. Scott	1974	14oz.
Culpea harengus	S		11	11	0.331	Port Logan	R. Smith	1984	10oz.
LING	B	57	8	0	26.082	Stonehaven	I. Duncan	1982	20
Molva molva	S	12	4	0	5.557	Scrabster	A. Allan	1984	6
LUMPSUCKER	B	4	11	4	2.133	Innellan	G. T. Roebuck	1976	3
Cyclopterus lumpus	S	5	12	10	2.626	Cruden Bay	M. Rennie	1987	3
MACKEREL	B	3	12	0	1.701	Ullapool	E. Scobie	1965	2
Scomber scombrus	S	2	5	9	1.063	Wick	W. Richardson	1969	2
MEGRIM	B	3	12	8	1.715	Gareloch	P. Christie	1973	2
Lepidorhombus	S		11	6	0.325	Loch Ryan	C. N. Dickson	1989	any
whiffiagonis									
MULLETT, GOLDEN	B	OPEN AT ANY WEIGHT							any
GREY									
Lisa aurata	S		11	0	0.312	Fairlie	I. McFadyen	1972	8oz.

Species		lb.	oz.	dm.	kg.	Place of Capture	Angler	Year	Spec. lb.
MULLET, THICK LIPPED GREY	B	3	6	0	1.531	Luce Bay	R. Williamson	1976	3
Crenimugil labrosus	S	6	14	14	3.143	Ayr Harbour	T. Parker	1992	4½
NORWAY HADDOCK	B	1	10	5	0.750	Eyemouth	P. Skala	1988	14oz.
Sebastes viviparus	S	OPEN AT ANY WEIGHT							any
PIPEFISH GREATER	B	OPEN AT ANY WEIGHT							any
Sygnathus acus	S		0	13	0.023	Coulport	H. Holding	1975	any
PLAICE	B	10	3	8	4.635	Longa Sound	H. Gardiner	1974	5
Pleuronectes platessa	S	5	8	0	2.494	Arrochar	A. Holt Jnr.	1971	3½
POLLACK	B	18	0	0	8.165	Scrabster	N. Carter	1971	10
Pollachius pollachius	S	13	14	0	6.293	Furnace	J. Arthur	1974	8
POOR COD	B	1	4	0	0.567	Arbroath	F. Chalmers	1969	1
Trisopterus minutus	S	1	0	0	0.453	Loch Fyne	F. Johnstone	1970	12oz.
POUTING	B	3	8	0	1.587	Gourock	J. Lewis	1977	2
Trisopterus luscus	S	3	3	7	1.458	Kirkcudbright	R. Cartwright	1984	1½
RAY BLONDE	B	26	11	0	12.105	Caliach Point	B. Swinbanks	1977	15
Raja brachyura	S	OPEN AT ANY WEIGHT							any
RAY CUCKOO	B	5	4	4	2.388	Gairloch	A. Bridges	1979	4
Raja naevus	S	4	11	0	2.126	Gourock	R. A. H. McCaw	1973	3¾
RAY SPOTTED	B	8	3	14	3.739	Isle of Whithorn	G. Brownlie	1989	4
Raja montagui	S	5	12	0	2.608	Cairnryan	G. C. Styles	1975	4
RAY THORNBACK	B	29	8	10	13.399	Luce Bay	A. McLean	1982	15
Raja clavata	S	21	12		9.866	Kirkcudbright	S. Ramsay	1985	4
ROCKLING, FIVE BEARDED	B	OPEN AT ANY WEIGHT							any
Ciliata mustela	S		7	0	0.198	Balcarry Point	K. Greason	1988	4½oz.
ROCKLING, FOUR BEARDED	B		1	7	0.040	Gourock	S. Hodgson	1981	1¼oz.
Rhinomenus cimbrius	S	OPEN AT ANY WEIGHT							any
ROCKLING SHORE	B	OPEN AT ANY WEIGHT							any
Gairdropsarus mediterraneus	S		14	8	0.411	Loch Long	A. Glen	1982	7oz.
ROCKLING, THREE BEARDED	B	1	14	4	0.857	Stonehaven	W. Murphy	1972	1¼
Gairdropsaus vulgaris	S	3	1	12	1.410	Holburn Head	W. Crothers	1992	1½
SANDEEL, GREATER	B		8	0	0.227	Callach Point	T. J. Ashwell	1984	6oz.
Hyperoplus lanceolatus	S	0	4	4	0.120	Isle of Lewis	R. McMillan	1987	3oz.
SCAD (HORSE MACKEREL)	B	1	7	0	0.652	Loch Sheil	D. MacNeil	1976	1
Trachurus trachurus	S	3	0	14	1.384	Cockenzie	R. Dillon	1981	1
SEA SCORPION, LONGSPINED	B		3	6	0.096	Rhu Narrows	C. Heath	1985	2½oz.
Taurulus bubalis	S		5	9	0.157	Aberdeen	T. J. Ashwell	1982	2½oz.
SEA SCORPION SHORTSPINED	B	2	3	0	0.992	Kepple Pier	R. Stevenson	1973	1¾
Myoxocephalus scorpius	S	2	3	0	0.992	Cloch, Gourock	W. Crawford	1979	1½
SHAD, TWAITE	B	OPEN AT ANY WEIGHT							any
Alosa fallax	S	2	12	0	1.247	Garlieston	J. W. Martin	1978	1½
SHARK, BLUE	B	85	8	0	38.781	Stornoway	J. Morrison	1972	50
Prionace glauca	S								any

B - Boat Records   S - Shore Records   Spec. - Specimen Qualifying Weight

Species		lb.	oz.	dm.	kg.	Place of Capture	Angler	Year	Spec. lb.
SHARK PORBEAGLE	B	414	0	0	188.00	Dunnet Head	R. Richardson	1992	300
Lamna nasus	B	404	0	0	183.244	Sumburgh Head	P. White	1978	300
	S	OPEN AT ANY WEIGHT							any
SKATE, COMMON	B	227	0	0	102.967	Tobermory	R. Banks	1986	100
Raja batis	S	154	0	0	69.854	Achiltibuie	M. J. Traynor	1971	50
SMELT	B	OPEN AT ANY WEIGHT							any
Osmerus Eperlanus	S		5	4	0.149	Riverside, Dundee	M. Ettle	1988	4½oz.
SMOOTHHOUND STARRY	B	OPEN AT ANY WEIGHT							any
Mustelus asterias	S	7	12	14	3.540	Kirkcudbright	M. Roberts	1987	5
SOLE, DOVER	B	1	12	0	0.793	Killintrinnon	W. Hannah	1974	1
Solea Solea	S	2	0	8	0.922	Balcary	W. Lees	1989	8oz.
SOLE LEMON	B	2	2	0	0.963	Lochgoilhead	J. Gordon	1976	1
Microstomus kitt	S	1	6	2	0.627	Peterhead	B. N. Davidson	1982	12oz.
SPURDOG	B	18	14	0	8.560	Tobermory	J. Bean	1988	14
Squalus acanthias	S	12	8	12	5.691	Millport	R. Paterson	1983	8
TADPOLE FISH	B		14	14	0.421	Firth of Clyde	R. Donnelly	1981	8oz.
Raniceps raninus	S	1	3	0	0.538	Dunbar	W. Dickson	1977	10oz.
TOPE	B	74	11	0	33.877	Loch Ryan	P. Marsland	1989	45
Galeorhinus galeus	S	54	4	0	24.606	Loch Ryan	D. Hastings	1975	30
TOPKNOT	B	OPEN AT ANY WEIGHT							any
Zeugopterus punctatus	S		8	8	0.241	Peterhead	G. M. Taylor	1975	6oz.
TORSK	B	15	7	2	7.006	Pentland Firth	D. J. Mackay	1982	8
Brosme brosme	S	OPEN AT ANY WEIGHT							
TRIGGER FISH	B	OPEN AT ANY WEIGHT							any
Balistes Carolinesis	S	1	12	5	0.804	Newton Shore	J. Murphy	1989	1
TURBOT	B	25	4	0	11.453	Mull	I. Jenkins	1982	15
Scophthalmus maximus	S	2	13	12	1.300	Cairnryan	G. Calderwood	1989	1
WEAVER, GREATER	B	OPEN AT ANY WEIGHT							any
Trachinus draco	S	1	1	14	0.508	Mull of Galloway	W. Allison	1984	1
WHITING	B	6	8	0	2.948	Girvan	A. M. Devay	1969	3
Merlangius merlangus	S	3	0	0	1.360	Gourock	D. McTehee	1970	2
WHITING, BLUE (POUTASSOU)	B	1	12	0	0.793	Loch Fyne	J. H. Anderson	1977	8oz.
Micromesistius poutassou	S	OPEN AT ANY WEIGHT							any
WRASSE BALLAN	B	4	12	4	2.161	Calgary Bay, Mull	K. F. J. Hall	1983	3½
Labrus bergylta	S	5	0	0	2.268	Girvan	T. McGeehan	1971	3½
WRASSE, CORKWING	B	OPEN AT ANY WEIGHT							any
Crenilabrus melops	S		6	3	0.175	Wigton	I. Wilson	1989	4oz.
WRASSE, CUCKOO	B	3	0	0	1.361	Scrabster	Mrs H. Campbell	1969	1¼
Labrus mixtus	S	1	2	0	0.510	Neist Point, Skye	Q. A. Oliver	1972	12oz.
WRASSE	B	0	0	12	0.021	Lochaline	D. D. Morrison	1983	1oz.
GOLDSINNY	B		2	8	0.071	Lunderston Bay	J. Baillie	1990	1½oz.
Ctenolabrus rupestris	S		1	13	0.051	Loch Goil	T. Lambert	1977	1½oz.
			1	13	0.051	Mull of Galloway	G. V. R. Griffiths	1985	1½oz.
WRASSE SMALL MOUTHED ROCK COOK	B	OPEN AT ANY WEIGHT							any
Centrolabrus exoletus	S		2	0	0.056	Achiltibuie pier	D. F. McKendrick	1985	1½oz.
WRASSE, SCALE RAYED	B	0	10	15	0.310	Tobermory	J. T. Bishop	1986	8oz.
Acantholabrus palloni	S	OPEN AT ANY WEIGHT							any

The above records are based on information received up to 20 June 1993, by the S.F.S.A. Honorary Fish Recorder, G.T. Morris, 8 Burt Avenue, Kinghorn, Fife.
* It is now illegal to land an Allis Shad (Alosa alosa) and a Twaite Shad (Alosa fallax) even for record purposes.

SCOTTISH FEDERATION OF SEA ANGLERS
SCOTTISH BOAT & SHORE (rod caught) RECORD
AND SPECIMEN MARINE FISH
RULES OF PROCEDURE

1.   (a)   The Claimant should contact the Fish Recorder. Advice will then be given concerning preservation, identification and claims procedure.

     (b)   Notification of claim or intention to claim a record or specimen must be made within 10 days of capture of the fish; a further period of 21 days being allowed for the return of the completed claim form and relevant documents.

2.   Claims must be made in writing to the Fish Recorder, stating:
     (a)   The species of fish and the weight.
     (b)   The date and place of capture and the tackle used, and whether boat or shore caught.
     (c)   The names and addresses of reliable witnesses both as to capture by the claimant and the weight, who will be required to sign the forms supporting the claim. If no witnesses to the capture are available, the claimant must verify his claim by affidavit.

3.   No claim will be accepted unless the Committee is satisfied as to the species, method of capture and weight. The Committee reserves the right to reject any claim if not satisfied on any matter which it may think in the particular circumstances to be material.

4.   IDENTIFICATION OF SPECIES

     (i)   **for Record Claims**
        (a)   To ensure the correct identification, it is essential that claimants should retain the fish and immediately contact The Fish Recorder who will advise as to production of the fish for inspection on behalf of the Committee.
        (b)   No claims will be considered unless the fish in its natural state, dead or alive, is available for inspection.
        (c)   All carriage costs incurred in production of the fish for inspection by the Committee must be borne by the claimant.

     (ii)   **for Specimen Claims**
        Claims should be accompanied by a clear detailed photograph or transparency of the fish in close-up which shows the fish in lateral view with the fins spread. In the case of sharks, a sample of the teeth and a photograph of these in position should be submitted.

5.   METHOD OF CAPTURE

     (a)   Fish caught at sea will be eligible for consideration for record or specimen status if they have been caught from a shore within the political boundary of Scotland, or from a boat, if that boat has set out from and returned to a port within Scotland, without having first called at any port outside Scotland. Fish caught in the territorial waters of other countries will not be eligible.

     (b)   Claims can only be accepted in respect of fish which are caught by fair angling with rod and line. Fair angling is defined by the fish taking the baited hook or lure into its mouth

     (c)   BOAT caught includes those fish caught from any man made structure which may be moored but not permanently anchored to the sea bed. SHORE caught means those fish caught from a natural shore or any man made structure permanently secured to the sea bed.

     (d)   Fish must be caught on rod and line with any legal hook or lure and hooked and played by one person only. No one other than the angler playing the fish may touch any part of the tackle e.g. to adjust the reel clutch, but he may be given assistance in putting on a harness. Assistance to land fish (i.e. gaffing, netting) is permitted provided the helper does not touch any part of the tackle other than the leader.

6. **WEIGHT**

   (a)   The fish must be weighed on land using scales or steelyards which can be tested on behalf of the Committee. Where possible, commercial or trade scales which are checked regularly by the Weights and Measures Department should be used. The sensitivity of the scales should be appropriate to the size of the fish i.e. small fish should be weighed on finely graduated scales and the weight claimed for the fish should be to a division of weight (ounces, dram, gramme) not less than the smallest division of the scales.

   (b)   A Weights and Measures Certificate must be produced certifying the accuracy of the scales used and indicating testing at the claimed weight.

   (c)   The weight must be verified by two independant witnesses who for example should not be relations of the claimant or a member of his club or party.

   Note: Specimen tope and common skate may be weighed on board a boat when this is possible so that they may be returned to the water alive to conserve stocks.

7. Claims can be made for species not included in the Committee's Record Fish List.

8. A fish for which a record is claimed must be normal and not obviously suffering from any disease by which the weight could be enhanced.

9. The activities of the Committee are voluntary and claims are considered and adjudication upon, only on the basis that the Committee shall be under no obligation whatsoever to claimants, that its decisions shall be final and it shall not be obliged to give reasons for its decisions.

The body of the fish should, whenever possible, be kept in a deep freeze until required for identification. If this is not possible, then it should be kept in a solution of one tablespoon of formalin (40% solution of formaldehyde) to a pint of water.

When sending fish for inspection please:

   (a)   notify the Recorder or the person appointed by him that the fish is being sent for identification

   (b)   attach a label to each fish forwarded for identification or inspection giving the captor's name and address, date and place of capture, and weight of fish

   (c)   send deep frozen specimens by express post or rail, first wrapping them In cotton polythene before parcelling them.

   (d)   wrap specimens preserved in formalin in a cloth wrung out in the solution before parcelling them.

S.F.S.A. RULES FOR FISHING EVENTS (3/93)

A. ORGANISATION OF EVENTS

1. The organisers shall publish the fee for participating in an event and shall detail the same as being the sum of:

   (a) An entry fee   (b) boat fee
   (c) daily S.F.S.A. Festival Levy.

2. The organisers will issue official entry cards prior to the start of the event and these shall bear the name and registration number of the entrant and in the case of boat events, the name or number of the boat to which the entrant is allocated.

3. The allocation of boat places is to be made in public.

4. The organisers will publish, prior to the event, the times for Registration, departure, fishing, return and weigh-in. (Departure and fishing times must be such that all anglers have the same opportunity of getting to the fishing grounds before the start of fishing.)

5. The organisers will publish, prior to the event, definable limits within which the event will be fished. In shore events, boundaries apply to stance not to direction of cast.

6. Stewards, whose task is to enforce the rules, will be appointed by the organisers and will be identified by official badges.

7. (a) **Shore Events:**   All Sections of a shore event will be stewarded.
   (b) **Boat Events:**   All boats will carry an official steward.

8. The organisers shall have the right to:
   (a) refuse to accept the entry of any applicant.
   (b) inspect all tackle and items of equipment belonging to any entrants.

9. The organisers will have all weighing machines checked for accuracy and suitability prior to the weigh-in.

10. **Disputes:** Any dispute or complaint arising will be investigated by an adjudicating committee made up of a minimum of three (3) members of the organising committee and an equal number of neutral entrants, together with a neutral, non-voting, chairman who shall have casting vote only. The chairman will be the official representative of the S.F.S.A. if he is not involved as an organiser of the event.

11. In boat events the number of anglers carried in a boat of any particular size will comply with the Department of Trade Recommendations.

12. In shore events, the minimum distance between anglers will be 5 metres (5.5 yards).

13. A JUNIOR is a person who is under sixteen (16) years of age on 1st January.

14. **Tope and Skate Festivals:** The organisers shall provide each boat (or shore section) with a set of tested scales in all events designated as TOPE or SKATE festivals to enable all fish of these species to be weighed immediately after their capture then returned to the water. The boat steward or boat skipper together with one angler, or in a shore event a steward and one angler, shall act as weighmasters.

B.   FISHING RULES

1.   Entrants must be in possession of an entry/weigh-in card which must be produced on demand by a steward or official.

2.   Fishing is only to take place in the times and within the limits laid down by the organisers.

3.   Fishing will be with rod, reel and line only.

4.   Participants may fish with only one rod fully fitted up. Spare rods and reels with terminal tackle not fitted may be carried.

5.   Rods shall have a minimum length of 1.52m. (5ft.). The maximum length for boat fishing will be 3.04m. (10ft.) (from March 1992). A limit on maximum length for shore fishing is not imposed.

6.   Hydraulic, electric and double handed reels are not permitted.

7.   The running line is not to be more than 50lbs. BS for multi-strand types (Dacron etc.) and more than 0.75 mm. diameter for monofilament types. (Rule 7 does not apply for events designated as special events for tope, conger, skate, shark or halibut).

8.   A maximum of three (3) single hooks may be used. Treble hooks count as three (3) hooks and a double hook as two (2) hooks.

9.   Artificial lures may be of any type and size but may only be fitted with hooks whose gape does not exceed 25mm.

10.   Only fish fairly hooked from inside the mouth and landed with the hook in the mouth may be presented for weigh-in.

11.   Fish hooked fairly in the mouth by more than one angler will not be eligible for weighing-in.

12.   Anglers may only receive the help of other persons to gaff or lift a fish.

13.   The rod is not to be rested on boat-gunwhales, capstans or rod seat, etc., while playing a fish. Hand lining is only permitted when the terminal trace can be used for that purpose.

14.   Competitors with physical handicaps may receive help in casting provided they obtain permission in writing from the organisers prior to the event.

15.   Contravention of any of these fishing rules may result in disqualification.

C. MINIMUM QUALIFYING SIZES OF FISH PRESENTED FOR WEIGH-IN FROM 1 JANUARY 1993

1. Bass (Dicentrarchus labrax) — 36 cm. (14.2 in.)
   Brill (Scophthalmus rhombus) — 30 cm. (11.8 in.)
   Coalfish (Pollachius virens) — 35 cm. (13.8 in.)
   Cod (Gadus morhua) — 35 cm. (13.8 in.)
   n.b. In U.K. Fishery area V11a from 1st October to 31 December the minimum size for Cod will be — 45 cm. (17.7 in.)
   Dab (Limanda limanda) — 23 cm. (9.06 in.)
   Dogfish – all species (Scyliorhinus, Squalius sp) — 35 cm. (13.8 in.)
   Eel Common (Anguilla anguilla) — 35 cm. (13.8 in.)**
   Eel Conger (Conger conger) — 58 cm. (22.8 in.)
   Flounder (Platichthys flesus) — 25 cm. (9.8 in.)
   Haddock (Melanogrammus aeglefinus) — 30 cm. (11.8 in.)
   Hake (Merluccius merluccius) — 30 cm. (11.8 in.)
   Halibut (Hippoglossus hippoglossus) — 35 cm. (13.8 in.)
   Ling (Molva molva) — 58 cm. (22.8 in.)**
   Mackerel (Scomber scombrus) — 30 cm. (11.8 in.) (North Sea only)
   Megrim (Lepidorhombus wiffiagonis) — 25 cm. (9.8 in.)
   Pollack (Pollachius pollachius) — 35 cm. (13.8 in.)
   Plaice (Pleuronectes platessa) — 27 cm. (10.6 in.)
   Rays (Raja sp) — 35 cm. (13.8 in.)
   Seabream, Red (Pagellus bogaraveo) — 25 cm. (9.8 in.)
   Seabream, Black (Spondyliosoma cantharus) — 23 cm. (9.05 in.)
   Skates (Raja batis, alba, oxyrinchus sp) — 11.35 kg. (25 lbs.)
   Sole Lemon (Microstomus kitt) — 25 cm. (9.8 in.)
   Sole (Solea solea) — 24 cm. (9.4 in.)
   Tope (Galeorhinus galeus) — 9.10 kg. (20 lbs.)
   Turbot (Scophthalmus maximus) — 30 cm. (11.8 in.)
   Wrasse Ballan — 25 cm. (9.8 in.)
   Whiting (Merlangius merlangus) — 27 cm. (10.6 in.)
   Witches (Glyptocephalus gynoglossus) — 28 cm. (11.0 in.)
   All other species — 20 cm. (7.9 in.)

   **These sizes may be altered when the European Community determine the new limit for the species.

2. A maximum of three mackerel and three herring may be presented for weigh-in.

3. TOPE AND SKATE: Common (R. batis); long-nosed (R. oxyrhinchus) or white (R. alba) are not to be brought ashore during events designated as TOPE or SKATE competitions. They are to be weighed immediately after capture and returned to the sea. (This rule does not apply to potential national record fish which must be brought ashore for weighing.) In designated TOPE competitions no minimum size for weighing will be applied as long as fish are weighed on board and returned alive.

4. Any obviously undersized fish presented for weigh-in will result in the entrant being disqualified.

   Note: Twaite Shad (Alosa Fallax) and Allis Shad (Alosa Alosa) cannot be legally landed.

SEA ANGLING

BORDERS

Sea Angling

The Scottish Borders provide some of the best sea angling in the UK. Based on Eyemouth, which has the largest fishing fleet in the South of Scotland, and the smaller fishing villages of Burnmouth and St. Abbs, the clear unpolluted waters are well stocked with a wide variety of sea fish. So clear is the water that one of the first Marine Reservations has been established off Eyemouth.
The rugged coastline with its unique fauna make a spectacular background to your day's fishing. It should be noted that sea angling is not permitted off St. Abbs Head National Reserve (Petticowick – Long Carr).

Eyemouth is only nine miles north of Berwick-upon-Tweed, just off the A.1. Its colourful boats, fish auction and sandy beach make it a popular resort during the summer. Well known for its excellent rock fishing, the town is also a useful point of access to shoreline to the north and south. Boat fishing has developed over the years due to the efforts of Eyemouth Sea Angling Club who now run a number of shore and boat competitions throughout the season.

The club operates the coast from Burnmouth harbour in the south to the harbour at St. Abbs in the north.
Types of fish: Shore – cod, mackerel, coalfish, flounder, plaice, sole, haddock, whiting, catfish, ling and wrasse.
Boat – the same species can be caught as on shore but larger specimens.
Boats: A large number of fishing boats are usually available from Eyemouth, St. Abbs and Burnmouth for parties of anglers attracted at weekends.

DUMFRIES AND GALLOWAY

Sea Angling

Solway Firth to Isle of Whithorn
The area is renowned for its strong tides which can create difficulties

for boat angling in the wrong conditions. Local advice should be sought before sailing and as a further safety measure the Coastguard should be advised of any intended trips. If a boat trip is cancelled or an angler prefers shore fishing, the coastline abounds with excellent shore marks which produce a great diversity of species. Summer months are undoubtedly the most productive but the winter cod fishing can also be very good with many large fish being taken.

Kippford
Better known as a yachting centre, Kippford still offers good angling opportunities. Shore marks around Kippford yield bags of flatfish and dogfish in the summer with the occasional bass. The area excels in the winter with catches of big cod. The Scottish shore caught record cod came from here. Boat fishing during the summer tends to give more variety with mackerel, thornback and dogfish, both spur and spotted featuring in the catches.
Bait: Lug and ragworm can be dug locally and cockles and mussels picked from the shore.
Season: May to September for comfort and variety. November to February for big cod but wrap up well!

Kirkcudbright
About 5 miles from the open sea on the Dee estuary, Kirkcudbright is at the centre of an excellent shore fishing area. Rocky points in Kirkcudbright bay along the Dundrennan shore to the east and Borgue to the west, give good varied fishing especially during the summer. Dogfish feature heavily in local club matches with the occasional conger, bull huss and thornback. Settled conditions and clear water give good bags of pollack and garfish and mullet are attracted to ground bait. The estuary produces bags of plaice, dabs and flounders with flounders, eels and coalfish giving good sport at the harbour. The bay also fishes well for cod and whiting in the winter. Boat fishing can be good with launching sites at the harbour, Ross Bay and Brighouse but these are restricted by the tides. One charter boat operates from Kirkcudbright. Boat catches are as varied as the shore, but there is always the chance of a tope.

Bait: Lug and ragworm are available locally along with cockles and mussels. Mackerel and herring can be bought in the town.
Tackle: A limited amount available from: Watson Mckinnel in Kirkcudbright.
A better selection from: "Patties", 109 Queensberry Street, Dumfries "Reel em In", Friars Vennel, Dumfries.
Charter Boat: "Howzat" - Howard Williams, Tel: (0557) 30367.
Further Information: Information Centre, Kirkcudbright. Tel: (0557) 30494.

Garlieston & The Isle of Whithorn
Situated on the east side of the Machars Peninsula, the area is sheltered from the prevailing westerly winds giving good shore and boat fishing. Rock marks give good bags of dogfish, pollack and wrasse with conger and mullet also being taken. Burrow Head gives good fishing when the weather is fine. The summer months are the best for both shore and boat fishing. Boats can be launched from both habours on a suitable tide and charter boats operate from the Isle of Whithorn. The biggest attraction for boat anglers is tope which can sometimes be caught in numbers. Some big fish are caught every year and most are released. Spurdog and thornback sometimes take bait meant for tope.
Tackle: Some available locally from: A. Mcghie, Radio Shop, George Street, Whithorn.
J.M. William, Grocer & Harbour Master, The Harbour, Isle of Whithorn. Tel: (09885) 246.
Bait: Lug, rag and shellfish available locally.
Boats: Craig Mills, Main Street, Isle of Whithorn DG8 8LN. Tel: (09885) 393 - (Manu Kea).
Rab McCreadie - (Crusader).
Local Clubs: Kirkcudbright & District SAC, Stuart Ross, "Fanore", 53 St. Cuthbert Street, Kirkcudbright. Tel: (0557) 30845.
Peever Sea Anglers, Jack McKinnel, 20 Merse Strand, Kirkcudbright. Tel: (0557) 31505.

Luce Bay
There are some good shore marks, namely Sandhead Sands for Flatfish, Dogfish and Bass in season, Terrally Bay for these species plus Codling, Whiting, Spurdogfish.
Around East and West Tarbet bays at the Mull of Galloway good

rock fishing may be had for Lesser Spotted Dogfish, Bull Huss, Spurdogfish, Conger Eels, Wrasse, Whiting, Pollack, Coalfish, Flatfish and Mackerel in season, normally from late April to December.
Boats: W. Carter, Castle Daly Angling Centre, Auchenmalg, Glenluce. Tel: 058 15 250. (Self drive boats for hire & hotel accommodation).
Bait: Lug can be dug in most sandy bays around Luce Bay, especially at Sandhead. Some shellfish available, mussels and cockles with razorfish on spring tides.
Launching Sites: Difficult to launch without four wheel drive vehicle.
Sites: Yacht Club at Drummore - high water only. Cailiness Road picnic site. Back of harbour Drummore. East Tarbet Bay - usually necessary to rope the trailer over shingle.
Safety: Dinghy anglers should be aware of the strong tides in the area, especially around the Mull of Galloway area.

Port William
Port William is situated on the east side of Luce Bay and has a good though tidal harbour. It is the starting point for many anglers wishing to fish the lower part of Luce Bay. The once famous shore mark of Monreith Bay, still a good bass beach, lies just to the south of Port William.
Types of fish: Tope, spurdog, rays, cod, pollack, flatfish from boats. Bass, wrasse, codling and pollack from the shore.
Tackle: Available in village
Bait: Lugworm, shellfish an molluscs along beach. Mackerel in bay.
Season for fishing: May- October.

Drummore
Drummore, the main port for anglers wishing to fish the western side of Luce Bay lies 5 miles north of the Mull of Galloway. Hotels and guest houses cater for anglers. There are many good shore marks on sandy beaches north of Drummore, while the Mull of Galloway provides excellent shore fishing over rocky ground. The Mull, the most southerly part of Scotland, is an area of very strong tides and is not recommended as a fishing area to anglers with small boats incapable of at least 10 knots, especially during ebb tides.
Types of fish: Pollack, wrasse from rocky shores, flatfish, bass, mullet and rays from sandy beaches. Pollack, coalfish, cod, whiting,

wrasse, lesser, spotted dogfish, bullhuss, spurdog, tope, rays, conger from boats.
Boats: "On yer Marks" Ian or Sue Burrett, Cardrain Cottage, Drummore, Tel: (0776) 84 346.
Charter Boats: Ian Hutton - Tel. (0776) 86981.
Stuart Aylott - Tel: (0776) 84226.
Bait: All types available on shore at low tide. Mackerel from Mull of Galloway shore marks.

Port Logan
Port Logan is the small community which is situated about 7.5 miles north of the Mull of Galloway on the west side of the Galloway Peninsula. An area with many good shore marks both to the north and south of the village. It is one of the few relatively easy launching sites on this coastline south of Portpatrick. A good alternative for the angler with his own boat when easterly winds prevent fishing in Luce Bay. Like the Mull of Galloway an area of strong tides, especially off Crammoc Head, to the south of Port Logan Bay.
Types of fish: As for the southern part of Luce Bay with occasional haddock. Herring in June and July.
Ideal to launch dinghies at Port Logan from concrete slipway onto hard sand where two wheel drive vehicles can run onto beach. Slack water occures 1.5 hours before high and low water.
Boats: Ian Burrett, Cardrain Cottage, Drummore. Tel: (0776) 84346.

Portpatrick
The small fishing port and holiday resort of Portpatrick lies on the west coast of Wigtownshire, 8 miles from Stranraer. There is good shore fishing from the many rocky points north and south of the resort, the best known being the Yellow Isle, 0.5 mile north of the harbour. Sandeel Bay, a little further north, and Killintringan Lighthouse are also worth fishing.
Types of fish: Pollack, coalfish, plaice, flounder, codling, mackerel, dogfish, conger, wrasse, and tope occasionally.
Boats: Peter & Martin Green, 2 Eastcliff, Portpatrick. Tel: (0776) 81 534.
Brian Tyreman, Pinminnoch Cottage, Portpatrick DG9 9AB. Tel: (0776) 81468 - "Cornubia".
Bait: None sold locally. Lugworm and some ragworm can be dug east of the railway pier, Stranraer.
Season for fishing: May-December.

Further information from:
Mr R. Smith, 24 Millbank Road, Stranraer. Tel: Stranraer (0776) 3691.

Stranraer & Loch Ryan
Stranraer, at the head of Loch Ryan, offers the angler, as a rail and bus terminal, a good stepping off point for many sea angling marks and areas in this part of Scotland, with Sandhead on Luce Bay (8 miles) to the south, Portpatrick (8 miles) to the west and Lady Bay (8 miles) on the west side of Loch Ryan with Cairnryan (6 miles) and Finnart Bay (10 miles) on the opposite side of the loch. Best Shore marks being Cairnryan Village, South of Townsend Thoresen ferry terminal. Old House Point and Concrete Barges north of Cairnryan Village, Finnart Bay on East Mouth of Loch, Wig Bay, Jamiesons Point and Lady Bay on west side of Loch Ryan. Boats may be launched at Wig Bay Slipway, Lady Bay and at Stranraer Market Street.
Access Safety: Most landowners will grant permission to cross lands to fish if this is requested and will advise best routes to avoid crossing crops. Most rock marks are safe but caution is needed in wet conditions as they may become slippy. In Lochryan anglers fishing from rocks or beaches should be aware of the wash from ferries and seacat as these can be dangerous if caught in the drive up the beaches or rocks.
Please note: No fishing is allowed on the jetty at Cairnryan at any time and the owners are going to take legal action against anglers who break through the boundary fence to obtain access. The jetty is unsafe and no insurance is in force.
Types of fish: taken from shore - pollack, codling, coalfish, plaice, dabs, wrasse, whiting, conger eel, lesserspotted dogfish, flounder, with spurdog, thornback ray and bull huss at times. Occasional tope.
Taken from boat: Pollack, codling, coalfish, plaice, dabs, wrasse, whiting, conger eel, lesserspotted dogfish, flounder with spurdog thornback ray and bull huss at times. Turbot, monkfish and spotted and cuckoo ray in the deeper water.
Boat: Mike Watson, Main Street, Stranraer. Tel: (0776) 85 3225.
Tackle: The Sports Shop, George Street, Stranraer, Tel: (0776) 2705, (frozen bait stocked).

Bait: Lugworm can be dug in most sandy bays, with the cockle shore at Stranraer the most popular. Loch Ryan Sea Angling Association has a lease on the cockle shore at Stranraer to restrict bait digging and the conditions are that anglers are only allowed to dig sufficient bait for one day's fishing. Ragworm can be dug in places. Cultured ragworm on sale at sports shop in Stranraer along with a good assortment of frozen baits. Mussel can be obtained on most beaches. Mackerel caught from shore and boat in season.

Season: Sea fishing is carried out all year but from May to October the best for daylight with a lot of night fishing giving better results.

Local Clubs: Lochryan Sea Angling Association, Paul Paterson, 46 Antrim Avenue, Stranraer. Tel: (0776) 3529. Sealink S.A.C., Niven Dickson, Seabank Road, Stranraer. Tel: (0776) 4895.

Further information from above or: Mr. R. Smith, 24 Millbank Road, Stranraer. Tel: (0776) 3691.

STRATHCLYDE SOUTH

Sea Angling

Loch Ryan to Ardrossan
The angling potential of much of the coast between Loch Ryan and Girvan remains unknown, the many rocky shores, small headlands and sandy beaches probably only attracting the anglers in an exploratory mood, or those seeking solitude in pursuit of their hobby.

Girvan
Girvan has a sheltered port and is a family holiday resort. From the end of the pier good fishing can be had for fair-sized plaice, flounders and spotted dog. Night fishing is good for rock cod. Just one mile to the south of the town lies the noted 'Horse Rock', only about 50 yards from the main Stranraer road. Access to the rock may be gained from about half-tide. Except during very high tides and during storms it is a good shore mark providing access to water of about 20 feet on the sea-side even at low tide.

Types of fish: Plaice, codling, rays, flounder, pollack and ling, whiting, and gurnard (mostly from boat). (Mullet in harbour during the summer months).

Boats: M. McCrindle, 7 Harbour Street, Girvan KA26 9AJ. Tel: (0465) 3219.
Tony Wass, 22 Templand Road, Dalry KA24 5EU. Tel: (0294) 833724.

Baits: Lugworm and ragworm can be dug at beach nearby or fresh mackerel from boat.

Tackle: Available from Girvan Chandlers, 4 Knockcushon Street, Girvan KA26 9AG.

Season for fishing: March to October.

Further information from: Brian Burn (S.F.S.A.), Tel: (0292) 264735.

Ayr
Ayr is a popular holiday town on the estuaries of the Rivers Ayr and Doon, 32 miles south-west of Glasgow. Good shore fishing can be had on the Newton Shore, north of the harbour for flounders and the odd doggie during summer months with a few coallies, codling and whiting throughout the winter, especially when there is a good storm. Some flounders and eels are taken from the harbour and at times excellent mullet can be caught from the tidal stretches of the river Ayr. Boat fishing in the bay can be very productive for mackerel and herring from May to October. Usually from July to November the boat fishing improves with the arrival of codling, pollack, ling, coallies, plaice, dabs, sea scorpions and spotted dogs.

Tackle: Available from Gamesport, 60 Sandgate, Ayr.

Bait: Lug and rag can be dug at the Newton shore with Doonfoot beaches producing lug and peeler crab during summer months.

Boats: Tony Medina - Tel: (0292) 285297.
Graham Johnston - Tel: (0292) 281638.
There is also a good public slipway for dinghies to launch from at the side of Ayr Multi Water Sports Centre (Yacht Club). Difficulty can be had on exceptionally low tides at low water.

Further information: Brian Burn (S.F.S.A.) - Tel: (0292) 264735.

Prestwick & Troon
Just north of Ayr, Prestwick and Troon offers some reasonable shore fishing at certain times of the year. Prestwick beaches fish for codling, flounders and coallies from usually November to January especially on evening tides. Flounders, the odd coallie and spotted dog can be caught throughout the summer months.

The Ballast Bank at Troon can produce conger, pollack, doggies, wrasse and the odd codling throughout the summer months with the better chance of a few codling and coallies during the winter. Troon Pier is a favourite mark for herring and mackerel during the summer and there is always the chance of a conger or two from this area.

Bait: Lug and rag can be dug on Prestwick shore and mussel beds also at Troon and Barassie beaches.

Boats: Jimmy Wilson, 27 Wallace Avenue, Troon. Tel: (0292) 313161.
Dinghies can be launched from Troon Marina, however there is a launching charge.

Further Information: John Fitchett - Tel: (0292) 314057.

Irvine
Irvine on the Ayrshire coast, is a rapidly developing New Town on the River Irvine. The sea is relatively shallow, with long sandy beaches. It is a fair boat fishing area. Irvine was previously a very busy port, but now the river anchorage is used by a greater number of small craft. The estuary can produce a few dabs, flounders and common eels. South of Irvine Estuary is a small island called 'The Lady Isle'. In the past few years the pollack have decreased not only in number but also in size. Just off this Isle pollack can be taken with ragworm on a long flowing trace. Pollack to 6 lbs., are not an unusual sight at some club matches. For codling close inshore is best and small coloured beads are preferred to spoon and lures. The best bait by far is a cocktail of lugworm and mussels or ragworm and mussels, all of which can be obtained locally.

Types of fish: Pollack, wrasse and coallies. Small codling after May from boat.

Bait: Rag worm, lug worm from beaches and mud flats around Irvine. Mussels from harbour walls.

Boats: Donald Findlay, Bert Harris, Robin Richmond, Davie Hollis (telephone number for any of the above can be obtained from Irvine Water Sports Club - Tel: (0294) 74981.
Easy access to boats from pier.

Season for Fishing: May to September boat angling.

Local Club: Irvine Sea Angling Club.

Further information: J. Falconer, 10 Rosemount Square, Pennyburn, Kilwinning KA13 6LZ.

Saltcoats & Ardrossan

Saltcoats with the neighbouring towns of Stevenston and Ardrossan, is situated on the Ayrshire coast 30 miles south-west of Glasgow. Shore fishing is possible in the South Bay and around the harbours.

Approximately 3 miles north is Ardneil Bay which can produce a few codling over the rough ground.

Types of fish: Pollack, wrasse, doggies, eels, cod, saithe, flatties and herring.

Further information: Please obey any private fishing signs within the area and remember dinghy anglers. No fishing within 50 meters of Ore Terminal.

Boats: Robert Reid - Tel: (0294) 601844.

Bait: Ragworm available from Saltcoats Harbour, Fairlie Pier. Lugworm from Ardrossan north shore and Fairlie sand flats.

Tackle: Light tackle is all you require for most species in the area. Fixed spool or multiplier, light rod - 8-10lb line, spinning or bait.

Season for fishing: May to October.

Local Club: Ardrossan & District Sea Angling Club.

Further Information from: Bud McClymont, 41 Corrie Crescent, Saltcoats KA21 6JL. Tel: (0294) 61830.

Largs

Largs is within easy reach of several good fishing banks, including the Piat Shoal, the Skelmorlie Patch and the east shore of Cumbrae.

Types of fish: Dogfish, flounders, gurnard, dragonets, pollack, mackerel, plaice, coalfish and dabs.

Boats: Are readily available from local hirers.

Tackle: Hastie of Largs Ltd, Department Store, 109 Main Street, Largs. Tel: Largs 673104

Bait: Lug, rag, cockles and mussels are available from Fairlie Flats.

Gourock

The coastline from Largs to Greenock was probably the most popular area in Scotland for shore angling, with many anglers from the Midlands of England and beyond making regular trips north. Now the fishing is generally poor. At Wemyss Bay, angling is not permitted from the pier, but odd good catches can still be had to the south, and the Red Rocks, about a mile to the north, are noted for

odd codling and other species. At Inverkip there is a sandy beach around the entrance to the marina where flounders, odd dabs and eels can be taken. Cloch Point, where the Firth turns east, is well known for its fishing potential, although the current can be fierce, and because of the rough bottom, relatively heavy lines are necessary. The coastline from Cloch along Gourock Promenade to the swimming pool car park provides fair fishing and is easily accessible. Further inland, at Greenock Esplanade, flounders, dabs, eels and coallies are among the species available, although the water here is shallower, and this area is more productive at night. This stretch of coastline provides the dinghy angler with easy access to many of the Clyde marks, including the Gantocks, where outsize cod and coalfish were taken many years ago, mainly on pirks. The bay beside the power station holds flatfish and the ground off Greenock Esplanade is popular for coallies, some pollock and dabs. Dinghy owners should note that no anchoring is permitted in the main navigation channels, and several other regulations must be adhered to.

Types of fish: Coalfish (known locally as saithe), odd codling, conger eel, dab, dogfish, flounder, occasional ling, plaice, pollack (lythe), pouting, whiting and wrasse. Grey mullet, herring and mackerel can also be caught during the summer months.

Tackle: Inversports, 27a Kempock Street, Gourock.
Brian Peterson & Co., 12 Kelly Street, Greenock.
Findlay & Co., 58 Lynedoch Street, Greenock.

Bait: Lug, rag, mussels, cockles and crabs can all be obtained from the shoreline.

Boats: J. Crowther, Inverclyde Boat Owners Association, 164 Burns Road, Greenock. Tel: (0475) 34341 can advise.

Isle of Arran

The island of Arran, lying in the outer Firth of Clyde, may be reached from the mainland by ferries running from Ardrossan to Brodick, the largest community on the island. Good shore fishing is found around the whole of the island, much of which remains unexplored.

Lamlash

Lamlash is the main centre for sea angling on the island, probably

because of its situation on the shores of Lamlash Bay, the large horse-shoe shaped bay which is almost landlocked by the Holy Isle. This gives excellent protection to the bay from easterly winds. Lamlash is also the starting point for boat trips to the excellent fishing grounds off Whiting Bay and those around Pladda to the south.

Types of fish: Codling, whiting, coalfish, pollack, conger, rays, flatfish, mackerel, dogfish, plaice, dabs, gurnard, wrasse and odd haddock.

Bait: Obtainable from many beaches.

Season for fishing: March-November.

Corrie

Corrie is situated on north east coast of the island.

Types of fish: Codling, haddock, conger, rays, dogfish, ling, pollack, gurnard, garfish, mackerel and wrasse.

Whiting Bay

This bay, which takes its name from the whiting, is very open to the sea. There are excellent fishing banks from Largiebeg Point to King's Cross Point.

Boats: Dinghies can be hired from the Jetty, Whiting Bay or by arrangement with Jim Ritchie, Tel: Whiting Bay (07707) 382.

Bait: Cockles, mussels, lugworm, ragworm, limpets and crabs are abundant on the banks from half-tide.

Lochranza

Lochranza is situated at the northern end of the island. The loch is surrounded by hills opening out on to Kilbrannan Sound.

Types of fish: Cod, conger, wrasse and pollack from the shore. Codling, conger, some haddock, plaice and dabs from boat.

Tackle: Available from boat hirers.

Bait: Mussels, cockles, lugworm and ragworm obtainable.

Brodick

Good fishing in Brodick Bay from Markland Point to Clauchlands Point.

Types of fish: Codling, plaice and other flatfish, conger, wrasse and pollack, can be had from the shore while cod, conger, rays, dogfish, ling, pollack, gurnard, garfish and other round fish can be fished from boats.

Bait: Mussels are obtainable from the rocks around Brodick Pier or may be purchased from boat hirers.

Isle of Cumbrae, Millport
There is good fishing at a bank between the South East Point of Millport Bay (Farland Point) and Keppel Pier. Fintry Bay and Piat Shoal provide good sport. West of Portachur Point in about 15/20 fathoms and in Dunagoil Bay, S.W. Bute are good. Fairlie Channel directly seaward of Kelburn Castle is about 12/15 fathoms. East shore northwards about 10 fathoms line.
Types of fish: Saithe, conger, coalfish, dogfish, mackerel and flatfish.
Tackle: Available locally from boat hirers.
Bait: Mussels, worms, etc. on shore. Boat hirers and local shops provide bait.

STRATHCLYDE NORTH
Sea Angling

Helensburgh

Helensburgh is a small seaside town on the Firth of Clyde at the southern end of the Gareloch, easily reached by train or car.
Types of fish: Shore and boat – flounder, coalfish, conger, dogfish, whiting, dab, pollack and mackerel.
Tackle: Spriggs Leisure Marine. Tel: (0436) 820586.
Bait: Ragworm, lugworm, may be dug locally. Mussels and crabs can be gathered from the shore. Fresh & frozen bait can be purchased from Spriggs Leisure Marine. Tel: (0436) 820586.
Season for fishing: All year.

Further information from: Mr. M.J. Partland, Drumfork S.A.C., 142 East Clyde Street, Helensburgh G84 7AX. Tel: (0436) 71937.

Garelochhead
Garelochhead is the village at the head of the Gareloch, with the whole shoreline within easy reach. Upper and lower Loch Long and Loch Goil are only a few miles away.
Types of fish: Coalfish, pollack, dab, flounder, plaice, whiting, pouting, mackerel and lesser spotted dogfish.
Tackle: Spriggs Leisure Marine. Tel: (0436) 820586.
Bait: Garelochhead – cockles and mussels. Roseneath – lugworm, ragworm and cockles. Rhu – ragworm. Kilcreggan – ragworm.

Coulport – cockles. Fresh & frozen bait can be bought from: Spriggs Leisure Marine. Tel: (0436) 820586.
Season for fishing: All year.
Further information from: Mr. M.J. Partland, Drumfork S.A.C., 142 East Clyde Street, Helensburgh G84 7AX. Tel: (0436) 71937.

Arrochar, Loch Long
The village lies at the northern end of the loch, and has waters sheltered by the high surrounding hills.
Types of fish: Shore – conger, pollack, coalfish. Boat – whiting, dabs, conger, pollack, coalfish, mackerel, dogfish and odd rays.
Tackle: Spriggs Leisure Marine. Tel: (0436) 820586.
Bait: Fresh herring and mackerel, mussels and cockles usually available from the pier. Artificial baits, lures etc. available from shops in village. Fresh and frozen bait can be bought from Spriggs Leisure Marine. Tel: (0436) 820586.
Season for fishing: All year.
Further information from: Mr. M.J. Partland, Drumfork S.A.C., 142 East Clyde Street, Helensburgh G84 7AX. Tel: (0436) 71937.

Clynder
Clynder is the fishing centre on the sheltered west side of the Gareloch and one mile north of the popular Rhu Narrows.
Types of fish: Conger, rays, plaice, flounders, dogfish, whiting, pouting and mackerel.
Tackle: Spriggs Leisure Marine. Tel: (0436) 820586.
Boats: C. Moar (0436) 831336.
Bait: Cockles, mussels, lug, ragworm, can be dug. Fresh & frozen bait can be bought from Spriggs Leisure Marine. Tel: (0436) 820586.
Season for fishing: All year.
Further information from: Mr. M.J. Partland, Drumfork S.A.C., 142 East Clyde Street, Helensburgh G84 7AX. Tel: (0436) 71837.

Isle of Bute, Rothesay
The holiday resort of Rothesay, situated on the island of Bute, only a 30 minute crossing by roll-on/roll-off ferry from Wemyss Bay, is sheltered from the prevailing south-westerly winds. Several boat hirers cater for sea anglers. There are also many excellent shore marks. The deep water marks at Garroch Head can be

productive for both shore and boat anglers.
Types of fish: Shore – cod, coalfish, pollack, plaice, mackerel, wrasse. Boat – cod, pollack, plaice, mackerel, conger, coalfish, wrasse, whiting and ling.
Tackle: Available from Bute Arts & Tackle, 94-96 Montague Street, Rothesay, Isle of Bute, Tel: (0700) 503598.
Bait: Lugworm, ragworm, cockles and mussel can be obtained from beaches around the island, and no angler should set forth without feathers or tinsel lures and a few good heavy spinner. Herring is also useful bait. **Season for fishing:** July-October.

Kilchattan Bay
Sheltered bay waters at the south end of the Isle of Bute renowned for its good all year round fishing.
Types of fish: Cod, pollack, plaice, mackerel, conger, dogfish, wrasse, whiting.
Bait: Worm, fresh cockle available locally.
Season for fishing: July to October.

Mainland Ardentinny
Ardentinny is a small unspoiled village picturesquely situated on the west shore of Loch Long, 12 miles from Dunoon by car.
Types of fish: Cod, mackerel, from the shore. Cod, conger, haddock, ray, plaice, flounder, whiting, coalfish and mackerel from boats.
Bait: Cockles, mussels, lug and ragworm easily dug in bay.
Season for fishing: All year, winter for large cod.

Dunoon
Types of fish:
Most of the shoreline around Dunoon provides catches of cod, coalfish, pollack, flounder, mackerel, plaice. Using ragworm & lugworm, cockle, mussel, razorfish & Peeler crab. Boat fishing takes mostly cod, pollack, coalfish, dogfish, dabs, plaice, flounder. Also conger over wrecks or rough ground at night.
Boats: Gourock skippers fish Dunoon waters. Approx. 3 miles from Dunoon is Holy Loch.
Bait: Can be bought at shops most of the year or obtained in East Bay shore.
Further information from: John Murray - Tel: (0475) 38241.

Tighnabruaich & Kames
Tighnabruaich, on the Kyles of Bute, is famed for its beauty and Highland scenery. Access to some

good fishing banks on the west side of the Bute and around the Kyles.
Types of fish: Mackerel and coalfish from the shore. Flatfish, whiting, dogfish, pollack, gurnard and several species of wrasse. Conger fishing can be arranged.
Bait: Supplies of fresh bait (lug, cockle, mussel, clams etc.) are locally available.
Boats: Motor dinghies available for hire. Local fishermen can take parties of anglers by arrangement. Contact: Andy Lancaster, Kames Hotel, Tel: (0700) 811489.
Season: Spring to Autumn.

Loch Fyne
This is the longest sea-loch in Scotland, penetrating into the Highlands from the waters of the lower Firth of Clyde. The depth of the water within the loch varies enormously with depth of around 100 fathoms being found not only at the seaward end but also at the head of the loch of Inveraray. Much of the shore angling potential remains unknown although access to both shores is made relatively easy by roads running down each side. Boat launching facilities are less easy to find because of the rugged shoreline. Best side is Inveraray to Furnace. Quarry is now out of bounds.
Types of fish: Mackerel, codling, pollack, flatfish, conger (at night).

Inveraray
Inveraray stands on its west shore near the head of Loch Fyne.
Types of fish: Mackerel, pollack, coalfish, ling, dogfish, conger eel and plaice.
Bait: Mussels and worms available from shore at low tide.
Season for fishing:
June-September.

Tarbert (Loch Fyne)
The sheltered harbour and the adjacent coast of the loch near the lower end of the loch on the west shore are good fishing grounds for the sea angler.
Types of fish: Mackerel, coalfish, and sea trout from the shore. Mackerel, cod, coalfish and whiting from boats.
Boats: Evening out with the boats of the herring fleet can be arranged.
Tackle: Local shops.
Bait: There is an abundance of shellfish and worms on the mud flats.
Season for fishing: June, July and August.

Oban
Good catches can be occasionally taken in Kerrera Sound near the Cutter Rock and the Ferry Rocks. Fishing is much better off the south and west coasts of Kerrera Island, particularly near the Bach Island and Shepherds Hat, Maiden Island and Oban Bay give good mackerel fishing in July and August. These places are very exposed and should only be attempted in good settled weather.
Best shore marks: Salmore Point, North Connel at road bridge, Bonawe Quarry, rail bridge at Loch Creran, Easdale Rocks.
Types of fish: Boat & Shore – Tope, conger, whiting, codling, cod, pollack, coalfish, skate, thornback ray, spurdog, dogfish, mackerel, ling, wrasse and gurnard.
Tackle Requirements: From light spinning to beachcasters. Boat rods mainly 20lb class, but for skate 50lb class. All sea and game anglers necessities stocked at "The Anglers' Corner".
Boats: Ronnie Campbell, 14 Kenmore Cottages, Bonawe, Argyll. Tel: (0631) 75213 (launching for Loch Etive best at Oban).
Bait: Mussels and lugworm, etc. can be dug from the Kerrera beaches. Frozen and preserved baits can be bought from The Anglers' Corner, 2 John Street, Oban - Tel: (0631) 66374 or from Binnie Bros., Fishmongers, 8 Stevenson Street, Oban. Tel: (0631) 62503.
Local Club: North Argyll Sea Anglers, Secretary: Andy MacArthur, Craignish, Pulpit Drive, Oban. Tel: (0631) 64657.
Season for fishing:
May-November.
Further information from: Ross Binnie, Tel: (0631) 66374.

Isle of Islay
This is the southernmost of the islands. Several of the larger communities like Port Ellen and Port Askaig have good harbours.
Types of fish: Boat – cod, haddock, whiting, mackerel, dogfish, flounder, conger, rays.
Tackle: available from J. Campbell, sub-Post Office, Bridgend.
Bait: Lugworm plentiful on most beaches. Clam skirts from fish factory waste. Bait can be purchased from fishing boats at the piers.
Season for fishing: June-October.
Further information from:

Bowmore Tourist Office, Tel: (049 681) 254.

Isle of Mull (Salen)
Salen is situated on the east coast of Mull facing the Sound of Mull in a central position, 11 miles from Craignure and 10 miles from Tobermory. The village is sited between Aros River and a headland forming Salen Bay. The Sound of Mull is on the main skate marks in the Argyll area. Many 100 lbs., plus skate have now been taken. One of the contributing factors is the sheltered nature of the Sound, which can allow practically uninterrupted angling. This area has also yielded a number of fine tope, the largest of which was a specimen of 50 lbs. It is worth noting that cod and haddock seldom frequent the sound and should not be expected. This is an area recommended for dinghy owners.
Types of fish: Coalfish, pollack, wrasse, flounder, mullet sea trout, and mackerel from the shore. Ray, skate, ling, pollack, coalfish, spurdog, tope, conger, gurnard and odd codling from boats.
Tackle: Available from the Tackle and Books, Main Street, Tobermory, 10 miles away.
Bait: Easily obtainable from shoreline. Mackerel bait from Tackle and Books, Main Street, Tobermory.
Season for fishing:
March-November.
Further information from: Mr. Duncan Swinbanks, Tackle and Books, 10 Main Street, Tobermory. Tel: Tobermory 2336.

Isle of Mull (Tobermory)
The principal town on Mull, it is situated on a very sheltered bay at the north eastern tip of the island. Apart from hitting the headlines in the national press with its treasure, Tobermory has been extensively covered in the angling press. It is Scotland's most popular centre for skate fishing. Every year an average of 50 ton-up specimens are caught, tagged and returned alive. It is this thoughtful conservation that has maintained the quality of fishing in the area. Large tope of between 35 lbs., and 45 lbs., can be numerous. Ten Scottish records, red gurnard, grey gurnard, blonde ray, spotted ray, spurdogfish, angler fish, turbot, common skate and two wrasse, have come from these Mull waters. Every year catches of migratory fish can be made. Coalfish,

whiting, haddock and cod are encountered.

Types of fish: Tope, skate, rays, pollack, coalfish, ling, conger, gurnard, spurdog, cod, haddock, flatfish (plaice, dabs, and turbot) and whiting from boats. Coalfish, pollack, cod, wrasse, flounder, grey mullet, sea trout, conger, thornback and mackerel from the shore.

Boats: Mr. Brian Swinbanks, 8 Main Street, Tobermory, has a purpose built 38 ft. sea angling boat for fishing parties with boat rods and reel available. There are 14-16 ft. dinghies for hire for fishing in and around the bay.

Tackle: A tackle shop, with a complete range of stock is on the Main Street.

Bait: Herring and mackerel available from Tackle and Books, Tobermory. Mussels and lugworms are easily obtainable from the shoreline.

Season for fishing: May-November.

Further information from: Mr. Duncan Swinbanks, Tackle and Books, 10 Main Street, Tobermory. Tel: Tobermory 2336.

Isle of Coll

Coll is one of the smaller islands seaward of Mull. Fishing vessels concentrate on the Atlantic side, but good sport can be had on the Mull side and even at the mouth of Arinagour Bay where the village and hotel lie and the mail steamer calls. Fishing from rocks at several spots round the island can give good results.

Types of fish: Mackerel, coalfish, pollack, cod, conger, haddock, skate and flounder.

Boats: Dinghies with or without outboard engines can be hired from local lobster fishermen.

Tackle: Visitors are advised to bring their own.

Bait: Mussels, worms and small crabs can readily be obtained at low tide in Arinagour Bay.

Season for fishing: May to September and later depending on weather.

FORTH AND LOMOND (EAST COAST)

Anglers going afloat from Fife and Forth Harbours are advised to contact the coastguard at Fifeness for weather information. Tel: Crail (0333) 50666 (day or night).

Tayport

Tayport, on the Firth of Tay opposite Dundee, in the northernmost part of Fife, enjoys good shore fishing in sheltered waters. There are no hotels but there is a modern caravan and camping site with showers, laundry etc.

Types of fish: Cod, flounder and plaice from shore, with occasional sea trout (permit required).

Bait: Lugworm, ragworm, mussels, cockles and crabs available locally at low water.

Season for fishing: April-January.

St. Andrews

St. Andrews is a leading holiday resort with sea angling as one of its attractions. Fishing is mainly from boats, but good sport can be had from the rocks between the bathing pool and the harbour.

Tackle: Messrs. J. Wilson & Sons (Ironmongers), 169-171 South Street, St. Andrews, KY16 9EE, Tel: 0334 72477.

Bait: Excellent supplies of Lugworm, ragworm and large mussels can be gathered on the beach.

Boarhill and Kings Barns

Good beach fishing for cod and flatfish.

Anstruther

It is a fishing village with plenty of good boat and beach fishing. A very rocky coastline but can be very rewarding with good catches of cod, saithe, flounder, wrasse, and whiting. Be prepared to lose tackle.

Types of fish: Cod, saithe, wrasse, flounder, ling, conger and mackerel.

Boats: Plenty charter boats with local skippers who know all the hot spots.

Bait: Lug, rag, white rag, cockle, crab, mussel which can be dug locally.

Season: Boat – May-October. Beach – September-January.

Pittenweem

The nerve centre of the East Neuk with a large deep water harbour which boats can enter or leave at any stage of the tide. The European Cod Festival is now held here each year and produces large catches of cod. The harbour wall is very popular with young and old alike, with some good catches.

Types of fish: Cod, saithe, flounder, wrasse, ling, conger, whiting, mackerel from boats. Cod, saithe, flounder, wrasse and whiting from beach.

Bait: Lug, rag, can be dug locally.

Season: Beach – September-January.

Leven

A holiday resort with about 2 miles of lovely sandy beaches. Beach fishing is very popular with some very good catches.

Types of fish: Flounder, cod, bass, mullet, saithe.

Boats: No charter boats.

Bait: Lug available locally.

Season: July-January.

Buckhaven

A small town on the north side of the Firth of Forth, which is renowned for its boat and beach fishing. The Scottish Open Beach Competition is fished from Buckhaven to Dysart each year with large entries from all over Scotland.

Types of fish: Cod, saithe, flounder, whiting, mackerel from beach. Cod, saithe, flounder, whiting, ling, mackerel and wrasse from boat.

Bait: Lug available at Leven.

Boats: No charter hire.

Season: Boat – June-November. Beach – October-January.

Kirkcaldy

Beach fishing at east and west end of town.

Types of fish: Cod, flatfish, saithe, mackerel.

Bait: Beach off bus station.

Pettycur and Kinghorn

Rock and beach fishing off Pettycur Harbour and Kinghorn Beach.

Types of fish: Saithe, flatfish.

Boats: Small boats can be launched from beaches.

Bait: Plenty locally. Local caravan sites.

Burntisland

Permission required to fish the beach from harbour to swimming pool.

Types of fish: Saithe, flatfish, small cod.

Boats: None locally.

Bait: Lug available locally.

South Queensferry

A picturesque burgh overshadowed by the Forth Bridges. There are 3 launching slips in the area, but currents can be dangerous and local advice should be obtained before setting out in dinghies.

Types of fish: Cod, whiting, coalfish, mackerel, flounder from boat and shore in season.

Bait: Lugworm, ragworm, mussel, cockle, clams and crabs at low water in the area.
Season for fishing: May to October.

Edinburgh
Scotland's capital city, on the south of the Forth estuary, has several miles of shoreline. Most of this is sandy, and can produce good catches of flatfish, although codling, Ray's bream, whiting, eels and mackerel can be taken in season from the shore. Best marks are at Cramond, round the mouth of the River Almond, and the Seafield to Portobello area.
Bait: Lugworm, ragworm, mussels, cockles and clams from most beaches at low water.
Season for fishing: All year round.

Musselburgh
This town stands on the estuary of the River Esk, 6 miles to the east of Edinburgh, overlooking the Firth of Forth. It has a small but busy harbour, catering mainly for pleasure craft.
Boats: Enquiries should be made at the harbour. Best shore marks range from Fisherrow harbour to the mouth of the Esk.
Bait: Lugworm, ragworm, mussels, cockles and clams at low water.

Cockenzie
Mullet can be caught around the warm water outfall to the east of Cockenzie Power station and around the harbour. Other species include flatfish, codling and mackerel.

North Berwick
There is good boat fishing out of North Berwick and the coastline between the town and Dunbar is good for shore fishing.
Types of fish: Cod, haddock, plaice, mackerel and coalfish.
Bait: Mussels, crabs and shellfish of various types available at low water.
Further information from: Information Centre, Quality Street. Tel: North Berwick (0620) 2197 January-December.

Dunbar
The coastline from Dunbar to Eyemouth is very popular for rock and beach fishing.
Types of fish: Cod, haddock, flounder, coalfish, mackerel, wrasse and coalfish.
Boats: Details can be obtained from The Tourist Information Centre, Dunbar.

Bait: Mussels, lug and ragworm available at low water, and also from tackle dealers.
Season for fishing: Best April to October.
Further information from: Information Centre, Town House, High Street. Tel: Dunbar (0368) 63353 January-December.

TAYSIDE
Sea Angling

Arbroath
Situated on the east coast of Angus, 17 miles north-east of Dundee, Arbroath is easily accessible by road and rail. It is the centre for commercial fishing, and famous for its smokies. Pleasure boats ply for short cruises to local sea cliffs and caves, from the harbour. There are about 10 boats between 15ft and 35ft used for lobster and crab fishing, taking out parties for sea angling.
Types of fish: Cod, coalfish, mackerel, flounder, conger, plaice, haddock and pollack.
Boats: Available through local fishermen and part time lobster and crab fishermen at reasonable prices.

Dundee
Dundee is situated on the estuary of the River Tay and has sea fishing in the city centre, while Broughty Ferry, a suburb of Dundee, Easthaven and Carnoustie, all within easy reach by road and rail, have sea fishing from rocks, piers or from boats. There are good marks around the Bell Rock about 12 miles offshore.
Types of fish: Cod, flatfish from shore plus cod, haddock, coalfish, ling, pouting and plaice from boats.
Tackle: available from Shotcast Ltd., 8 Whitehall Crescent, Dundee. Tel: Dundee 25621.
Bait: Available locally.
Season for fishing: All year.

NORTH EAST AND SPEY VALLEY
Sea Angling

Moray Firth
The Moray Firth has always been famous for its fishing grounds and most of the towns along the south coastline depend largely on commercial fishing for their prosperity; cod, haddock, flatfish of many kings, pollack, coalfish and mackerel being landed.

Nairn
Nairn is set on the pleasant coastal plain bordering the southern shore of the Moray Firth. There is a beautiful stretch of sands to the east. Most fishing is done from two small piers at the entrance to the tidal harbour.
Types of fish: Mackerel, small coalfish, pollack, dab and cod.
Boats: One or two, privately owned, will often take a passenger out. Enquiries should be made at the harbour.
Tackle: P. Fraser, 41 High Street, Nairn. Tel: (0667) 53038.
Bait: Lugworm available on the beach at low water. Mackerel etc. mostly taken on flies.

Lossiemouth and Garmouth
Lossiemouth, a small, prosperous town, is a unique combination of white fish centre, seaside, shops and hotels. The angler will find unlimited sport of a kind probably new to him, for off the east and west beaches sea trout and finnock abound, and spinning for these into the sea, especially into the breakers, is a magnificent sport.
Types of fish: Sea trout, conger from the pier, coalfish, flatfish, 6.5 miles of shore fishing. Haddock, cod, plaice and coalfish from boats. Shore fishing – sea trout between harbour and Boar's Head Rock and at the old cement works Garmouth.
Bait: Lugworm on the west beach and the harbour at low water. Also plenty of mussels to be collected. Spinners, Pirks.
Season for fishing: Migratory fish season, October. Best months – late July, early August.

Buckie
Buckie is a major commercial fishing port on the eastern side of Spey Bay. It has become increasingly popular over the last few years as a tourist area and is well supplied with hotels, golf courses and caravan sites. It offers a varied coastline in the form of sandy beaches and quite spectacular rugged cliff formations.
Types of fish: Cod, coalfish, conger, pollack, mackerel, haddock, whiting, flatfish.
Bait: Lugworm, ragworm, mussels, cockles and crabs freely available along the shoreline eastwards.
Season for fishing: April-October. Winter months best for cod.

Cullen
M.V. "Rosenberg" is a 30ft long, twin-engined cruiser providing

pleasure trips and catering for sea anglers (tackle for hire or for sale). The boat is licensed by the Department of Transport and, as such, meets all its survey requirements annually. The vessel, which has all modern aids to navigation, has a certificated skipper. Details may be had from Cullen Marine Services, 27 North Deskford Street, Cullen. Tel: (0542) 840323.

Portknockie
Portknockie is a quaint little fishing village to the west of Cullen Bay. The small harbour is used by two small mackerel boats.
Types of fish: Excellent rock fishing here for cod, coalfish, and some mackerel from the piers. Good boat fishing for haddock, ling and gurnard.
Boats: There are no boats for hire as such, although it is possible to get out in two small (18ft) mackerel boats.
Bait: Lugworm and mussels in the harbour at low water.
Further information from: Tourist Information Centre, 17 High Street, Elgin, IV30 1EG. Tel: (0343) 542666/543388.

Portsoy
One of the numerous small towns that line the Banffshire coast. It is a former seaport but the harbour is silting up.
Types of fish: Coalfish and mackerel from the small pier and some good rock fishing east and west for cod. From boats, mackerel, cod, haddock, plaice, coalfish and dab.
Bait: Some lugworm at low water mark.

Gardenstown and Crovie
These are traditional fishing villages. Mackerel are plentiful, June-September. Anglers would be well advised to follow local boats which are fishing commercially.
Types of fish: From shore – coalfish, pollack, flatfish, conger, From boats – mackerel, cod, haddock, flounder, plaice, conger, dab, catfish, gurnard and ling.
Bait: Available on beach, but local people prefer to use flies.

Fraserburgh
Situated on the north-east shoulder of Scotland, Fraserburgh has the Moray Firth to the west and north and the North Sea to the east. The Burgh was primarily given over to the herring and white fish industry, but has developed as a holiday resort with the decline of

commercial fishing in the North Sea. Tickets and permits for game fishing from the beaches can be had at Weelies, Grocer, College Bounds.
Types of fish: Shore – cod, coalfish and mackerel. Boat – as shore.
Bait: Mussels and lugworm can be dug from the beach.
Season for fishing: May-October.

Peterhead
Peterhead is an important fishing port situated north of Buchan Ness, the most easterly point of Scotland. Excellent breakwaters, 1900ft and 2800ft long, are the main shore marks for holiday anglers. Access to the breakwaters is dependent on weather conditions and can be restricted when vessels are being worked. A safety access procedure has been agreed with the North Breakwater Sea Angling Society to whom further queries should be directed. However passengers are at times taken out by private boats.
Types of fish: From the pier – mackerel, coalfish, dab and cod. From boats – cod, haddock, dabs, ling, coalfish and mackerel.
Boats: There are a number of privately owned boats which will sometimes take out passengers. Enquiries should be made at the harbour.
Tackle: Available from Robertsons Sports, 1 Kirk Street, Peterhead. Tel: Peterhead 72584.
Bait: Lugworm can be dug from shore at low water while mussels can be gathered from the rocks.

Stonehaven
Stonehaven is a holiday resort 15 miles south of Aberdeen on main road and rail routes. Magnificent catches of cod and haddock are taken regularly by boat. Anglers obtain great co-operation from angling boat skippers and local professional fishermen. On either side of Stonehaven there are good rock fishing marks which should be approached with care especially during strong easterly winds.
Types of fish: Cod, haddock, pollack, coalfish, flounder, catfish and mackerel from the shore. Cod, haddock, coalfish, pollack, ling, catfish, plaice and other flatfish, ballan wrasse, cuckoo wrasse, whiting and Norway haddock from boats.
Boats: Boats are available from skipper: A. McKenzie, 24 Westfield Park, Stonehaven, Tel: (0569) 63411.
Bait: Mussels available if ordered from skippers of boats.

Season for fishing: All year.
Further information from: Information Centre, 66 Allardice Street, Tel: (0569) 62806 Easter-October.

GREAT GLEN AND ISLE OF SKYE
Sea Angling

Isle of Eigg
The Isle of Eigg lies 5m SW of Skye.
Types of fish: Pollack, conger, spurdog, skate, cod, mackerel.
Season for fishing: Summer-Autumn.

Isle of Skye
The many lochs and bays around the beautiful Isle of Skye provide ideal facilities for sea angling. There is a great variety of fish, most of which can be caught from the shore because of the deep water found close inshore off rocky shores and headlands. Local residents are very knowledgeable about fishing in their own area. Loch Snizort has now been found to hold a number of large common skate and anglers could well contact these during a session there.

Isle of Skye (Portree)
Portree, the capital of Skye, is situated half way up the east coast of the island. It is a very good harbour and good fishing marks in and round it. Ample free anchorage and berthing available for visiting craft. Slipping, re-fuelling and watering facilities are easily accessible.
Types of fish: Cod, haddock, whiting, coalfish, pollack and mackerel.
Boats: Greshornish House Hotel, Edinbane, by Portree, Isle of Skye. Tel: (047082) 266, has one boat available.
Bait: Unlimited mussels and cockles available in tidal area of Portree Bay.
Season for fishing: May-September.

Isle of Skye (Camastianavaig by Portree)
To reach this sheltered bay which lies 4 miles south east of Portree, turn off the A850 to Braes. Although local tactics are the use of feathers, bottom fishing with trace or paternoster has yielded heavy bags with skate of 62.5lbs, cod 6lbs, whiting 3lbs, haddock 3lbs, spurdog 12lbs, gurnard 2lbs,

pollacks 12lbs, coalfish 14lbs, all from boats.
Types of fish: Shore – coalfish, pollack, wrasse and mackerel.
Boat – cod, haddock and spurdog.
Tackle: Obtainable at Portree.
Bait: Lugworm at Broadford Bay and Balmeanac Bay. Cockles and mussels at Portree Loch.
Season for fishing: June-October.

Isle of Skye (Uig)
Uig, a picturesque village amidst some of the finest scenery in the north west, has excellent fishing on its doorstep. Loch Snizort and small islands at its entrance, together with the Ascrib Islands opposite, are well worth fishing. Fishing can be arranged as far round the coast as Score Bay, known to some ring net fishermen as the 'Golden Mile'.
Types of fish: Shore – coalfish, mackerel, pollack, conger and dogfish. Boat – coalfish, mackerel, pollack, conger, whiting, haddock, dogfish, flatfish, skate, cod and gurnard.
Boats: Available locally at Uig, Waternish and Kilmuir.
Season for fishing: May-September.

Isle of Skye (Skeabost Bridge)
Skeabost Bridge is situated 5 miles from Portree at the south east end of Loch Snizort.
Types of fish: There is no shore fishing but many types of non fish can be caught from boats.
Bait: Available locally.
Season for fishing: July-October.

Kyle of Lochalsh
The village of Kyle, on the mainland opposite Kyleakin on the Isle of Skye, is a railhead and a car ferry link with Skye and the Hebrides.
Types of fish: Conger, coalfish, pollack and whiting from the harbour. Boat – pollack, cod, coalfish, mackerel and whiting.
Tackle: Available from John MacLennan & Co., Marine Stores, Kyle of Lochalsh IV40 8AE. Tel: (0599) 4208.
Bait: Mussels from Fishery Pier and clams and cockles at spring tides.
Season for fishing: June-September.

NORTH SCOTLAND
Sea Angling

Gairloch
Gairloch Bay is very popular with sea anglers. There is good fishing in this lovely sea loch, especially around Longa Island which lies near the entrance to the Loch.

Poolewe and Aultbea
Situated amidst magnificent scenery, the sheltered waters of Loch Ewe offer the sea angler opportunities of fine catches. Suitable accommodation is available in surrounding villages and local advice is always available.
Types of fish: Shore – pollack, coalfish, dab, codling. Boat – haddock, cod, codling, gurnard, skate, whiting, mackerel, flatfish.
Boats: Several boats available locally.
Bait: Mussels, lugworm, cockles, etc. from shore.
Season for fishing: April-October incl.

Little Loch Broom
Ten miles north east Aultbea.
Ullapool & The Summer Isles
Loch Broom and the waters encircled by the Summer Isles offer excellent sea angling. The banks can be approached from Ullapool, which is an attractive holiday village sited on a peninsula projecting into Loch Broom. The numerous banks and islands offer superb fishing and beautiful scenery in sheltered waters. Many attractions on shore via local shops; hotels and sporting facilities available throughout the season. Achiltibuie, a small village, also gives access to fishing grounds.
Types of fish: Shore – codling, coalfish, conger, pollack, mackerel, dabs, thornbacks, dogfish, flounders and plaice. Boat – as above plus haddock, whiting, wrasse, ling, megrim, gurnard, spurdog and turbot.
Season for fishing: June-October inclusive. Big skate best in autumn.

Lochinver
Lochinver is one of the major fishing ports in the north of Scotland. With a population of some 300 inhabitants it has a safe all - tides harbour with excellent shore services, including good moderately - priced accommodation and two fishing tackle shops. Excellent sea fishing within a short distance from the port, specialising in jumbo haddock, cod, skate and conger. It is one of the few areas where large halibut are caught. Boats available. A large fleet of fishing vessels operates from the harbour and bait is readily available.
Types of fish: Cod, haddock, whiting, saithe, gurnard, ling, pollack, mackerel, wrasse, conger, skate. Coalfish, pollack, cod and mackerel from the shore.
Tackle: Tackle is available from Lochinver Fishselling Co., Culag Square, Lochinver. Tel: (05714) 228/258.
Season for fishing: April-October.

Drumbeg
Seven miles north of Lochinver.

Caithness
With the prolific fishing grounds of the Pentland Firth, the north of Caithness has built up a reputation as being one of the premier sea angling areas in Scotland. It is now recognised that the chance of taking a halibut on rod and line is better in Pentland waters than anywhere else; more halibut have been taken here than in any other part of the British Isles. The presence of Porbeagle shark in these waters has been proved by the capture of two specimens, with many more hooked and lost. Among the notable fish caught were European halibut records of 194 lbs. in 1974, 215 lbs. in 1975, 224 lbs. in 1978 and 234 lbs. in 1979. This fish represented a world record catch for the species. The Scottish shore record ling of 12lbs 4oz was caught in these waters. With countless numbers of rocky coves and sandy beaches there is much for the shore angler to discover along the whole of the north coast of Scotland. Accommodation is available to suit everyone, from first class hotels, private B. & B. to caravan and camping sites with full facilities. It is also possible to have a full sea angling package holiday with full board at a hotel and all boat charges included. The number of angling boats available increases each year, but it is still advisable to book boat places in advance.

Thurso and Scrabster
Thurso is the main town on the north side of Caithness and gives access through Scrabster to the waters of the Pentland Firth, where there are first class fishing grounds. Thurso Bay and the Dunnet Head area are sheltered from prevailing winds and it is reasonably easy for anglers to get afloat to the marks. Scrabster 1.4 miles from Thurso, is the main harbour in northern Caithness. Most of the angling boats are based here. There is also some excellent rock fishing, while

conger may be caught from the harbour walls.

Types of fish: Cod, ling, haddock, conger, pollack, coalfish, dogfish, spurdog, plaice, wrasse, mackerel, dab, whiting, rays, halibut, porbeagle shark.

Tackle: Harper's Fishing Services, 57 High Street, Thurso KW14 8AZ. Tel: (0847) 63179.

Bait: Mussels, lugworm can be gathered at low water, mackerel and squid from fish shops and local fishermen. Most species take lures, feather and rubber eels, etc. and most fishing done with this type of artificial bait.

Season for fishing: April-November.

Further information from: Caithness Tourist Board, Whitechapel Road, Wick, Tel: (0955) 2596 Jan-Dec.

Dunnet
Dunnet is situated 8 miles east of Thurso at the end of the famous Dunnet Sands, which are over 2.5 miles long. Few anglers fish this beach, as there is excellent boat fishing nearby. There is plenty of lugworm and the beach is well worth trying.

Types of fish: As for Thurso.
Boats and Tackle: As for Thurso.
Bait: Mussels from the rocks at low tide and lugworm all along Dunnet Sands.
Season for fishing: Shore – July and August. Boat – April-November.

Keiss
Good shore fishing is to be had around Keiss, a small fishing village between John o'Groats and Wick. It might be difficult to get out in a boat. The shore fishing is from the rocks around Keiss, and from the beach at Sinclair's Bay to the south of the village. Here some very good plaice have been taken and also anglers have caught sea trout while spinning for mackerel.

Tackle: Tackle shops at Wick.
Bait: Mussels and lugworm can be obtained at low tide.

Sutherland and Easter Ross Brora
Brora is a village situated on the A9, 12 miles south of Helmsdale. There is a small harbour and a few boats are available to sea anglers. There are rail links to Brora from the south and ample hotel accommodation and caravan facilities.

Types of fish: Cod, coalfish, cod, ling, haddock, rays and conger from boats.
Boats: Some owners are willing to

take visitors at nominal costs.
Bait: Can be dug locally.
Season for fishing: July-September.

Grannies Heilan' Hame, Embo
This is a caravan holiday centre with extensive amenities 2 miles north of Dornoch.

Types of fish: Spinning for sea trout from the beach up to the mouth of Loch Fleet. Coalfish, mackerel and flatfish from the pier. The rocks provide good cod fishing. From boats, coalfish, mackerel, plaice, cod, haddock and whiting at times.

Bait: Lugworm can be dug at the ferry landing area and there are plenty of mussels and cockles near Loch Fleet.

Season for fishing: April-September.

Dornoch
Dornoch gives access to the fishing banks off the north coast of the Dornoch Firth. There is good shore fishing from the rocks at Embo, but to get afloat it is necessary to make arrangements in advance. Youngsters can enjoy good fishing from Embo Pier.

Types of fish: Sea trout from shore. Flat fish, haddock and cod from boats.

Boats: Boats are difficult to hire but there are one or two in Embo which is three miles from Dornoch.

Season for fishing: April-September.

Tain
Tain lies on the south side of the Dornoch Firth and gives access to excellent sea trout fishing, both shore and boat, in sheltered waters of the Firth.

Types of fish: Shore – wrasse, flatfish, pollack, mackerel. Boat – haddock, cod, skate, mackerel.

Boats: Available in Balintore, 6 miles from Tain and Portmahomack.
Bait: Available from the shore.

Balintore
The village of Balintore, near Tain, has over the past 4 years increased in status and is now one of the recognised centres for big catches. Catches of up to 1,000lbs of cod and ling have been made (8 anglers) in a single morning's fishing.

Types of fish: Cod, ling, wrasse, pollack and mackerel.
Season from mid-April to beginning of November.

Portmahomack
This fishing village is well situated in a small bay on the southern shore of the Dornoch Firth, 9 miles east of Tain and 17 miles from Invergordon to the south. There is a well-protected harbour and a good, safe sandy beach.

Types of fish: Cod from the shore. Haddock and cod from boats.
Tackle: Available at Tain.
Season for fishing: Spring to Autumn.

North Kessock, Avoch and Fortrose
These villages lie along the north-west side of the Moray Firth north of Inverness. This sheltered sea loch provides good fishing.

WESTERN ISLES

Sea Angling

The Western Isles
The Western Isles form a north-south chain of islands off the west coast of Scotland. Separated from the mainland by the Minches, much of their rod and line fishing remains to be discovered, not only due to a lack of boats in the area, but also due to a lack of communications between and within the islands. Car ferries run from Oban and Ullapool on the mainland and Uig on Skye. Regular air services to Barra, Stornoway, for Lewis and Harris and Benbecula for the Uists.

Isle of Harris (Tarbert)
The largest community on the southern part of the largest of the Hebridean islands, Tarbert stands on a very narrow neck of land where the Atlantic and the Minch are separated by only a few hundred yards of land. It is the terminal for the car ferry from Uig on Skye and Lochmaddy on North Uist.

Types of fish: Boat – mackerel, ling, coalfish, cod, rays, pollack and conger. Shore – plaice, haddock and flounder.

Boats: Check with Tourist Information Centre, Tarbert (0859) 2011.

Bait: Mussels available on the shore, lugworm, cockles.
Season for fishing: May-October.
Further information from: Tourist Centre, Tarbert.

Isle of Lewis (Stornoway)
Stornoway, the only town in the Outer Hebrides, is easily accessible by air from Glasgow

Airport (1 hour) and Inverness (25 mins.); there is also a drive-on car ferry service from Ullapool (3.5 hours crossing). Another car ferry service connects Uig (Skye) to Tarbert (Harris), which is only an hour's drive from Stornoway. Stornoway is now recognised as a mecca for sea angling in Scotland. There is an enthusiastic sea angling club with club boats and licensed premises which overlook the harbour. Each August the club runs the Western Isles (Open) Sea Angling Championships. Many skate over the 'ton' have been caught, the heaviest so far being 192 lbs. The Scottish blueshark record of 85.5 lbs. was off Stornoway in August 1972. Visiting anglers may become temporary members of the Stornoway Club (one minute from the town hall) and can make arrangements for fishing trips with club members in the club boats. Accommodation can be arranged through the Wester Isles Tourist Board, Administration and Information Centre, 4 South Beach Street, Tel: Stornoway (0851) 3088.

Types of fish: Conger, cod, skate, rays, ling, pollack, whiting, dabs, bluemouth, flounder, dogfish, wrasse, haddock.

Bait: Mussels in harbour area; mackerel from local boats.

NORTHERN ISLES

Orkney
The waters around Orkney attract many sea anglers each year as big skate, halibut and ling are there for the taking. Ling of 36 lbs. skate of 214 lbs. taken by Jan Olsson of Sweden and the former British record halibut (161.5lbs.) taken by

ex-Provost Knight of Stromness provide the bait which attracts anglers to these waters. The Old Man of Hoy, Scapa Flow and Marwick Head are well-known names to sea anglers. The Brough of Birsay, Costa Head and the Eday and Stronsay Firths are equally well known as marks for big halibut and skate. Fishing from Kirkwall or Stromness, there is easy access to Scapa Flow where wrecks of the German Fleet of the First World War provide homes for large ling and conger. In the fish rich sea surrounding Orkney the angler will find some excellent shore fishing, nearly all of which remains to be discovered. Furthermore, skate of over 100 lbs. are still common while specimens of 200 lbs. have been recorded. More halibut have been caught in the waters to the south separating Orkney from the mainland than elsewhere in the U.K. Shark have also been sighted and hooked but none so far have been landed. Around the islands, in bays and firths, there is excellent sport for the specimen fish hunter and the Orcadians are eager to help sea anglers share the sport they enjoy. There is a regular car ferry service from Scrabster (Thurso) to Orkney and daily air services from Edinburgh, Glasgow and other points of the U.K.

Types of fish: Sea trout, plaice, pollack and coalfish, mackerel, wrasse from the shore. Skate, halibut, ling, cod, pollack, haddock, coalfish, plaice and dogfish from the boats.

Tackle: available from Stromness and Kirkwall.

Bait: Available from most beaches and piers.

Season for fishing: June-October.

Shetland
Shetland offers the best skate fishing to be had in Europe; during the years 1970-74 more than 250 skate over 100 lbs. were caught. These included a European record of 226.5lbs., and 12 other skate over 190 lbs. During the same period, Shetland held nine British records, ten Scottish records and six European records, giving some indication that the general fishing is of no mean standard. Halibut and porbeagle of over 300 lbs. have been taken commercially in the Sumburgh area with porbeagle shark now being landed by anglers from this area. The Scottish record porbeagle shark of 450 lbs. has been landed here and bigger fish have been taken by commercial boat. Shore-fishing remains for the most part to be discovered.

Types of fish: Shore – coalfish, pollack, dogfish, mackerel, dabs, conger and cod. Boat – skate, halibut, ling, cod, tusk, haddock, whiting, coalfish, pollack, dogfish, porbeagle shark, Norway haddock, gurnard, mackerel, cuckoo and ballan wrasse.

Boats: Many boats available for hire throughout the islands. Boats can also be arranged through the Shetland Islands Tourism, Market Cross, Lerwick, Shetland.

Tackle: Available from J.A. Manson, 88 Commercial Street, Lerwick and Cee & Jays, 5 Commercial Road, Lerwick.

Bait: Fresh, frozen or salted fish bait available from fishmongers. Worm bait, crabs, etc. from beaches.

Season for fishing: Limited to May to October by weather conditions.

SCOTLAND FOR FISHING
A Pastime Publication

I/We have seen your advertisement and wish to know if you have the following vacancy:

Name ....

Address ....

....

Dates from pm ....

Please give date and day of week in each case ....

To am ....

Number in Party ....

Details of Children ....

(*Please remember to include a stamped addressed envelope with your enquiry.*)

SCOTLAND FOR FISHING
A Pastime Publication

I/We have seen your advertisement and wish to know if you have the following vacancy:

Name ....

Address ....

....

Dates from pm ....

Please give date and day of week in each case ....

To am ....

Number in Party ....

Details of Children ....

(*Please remember to include a stamped addressed envelope with your enquiry.*)

MAPS

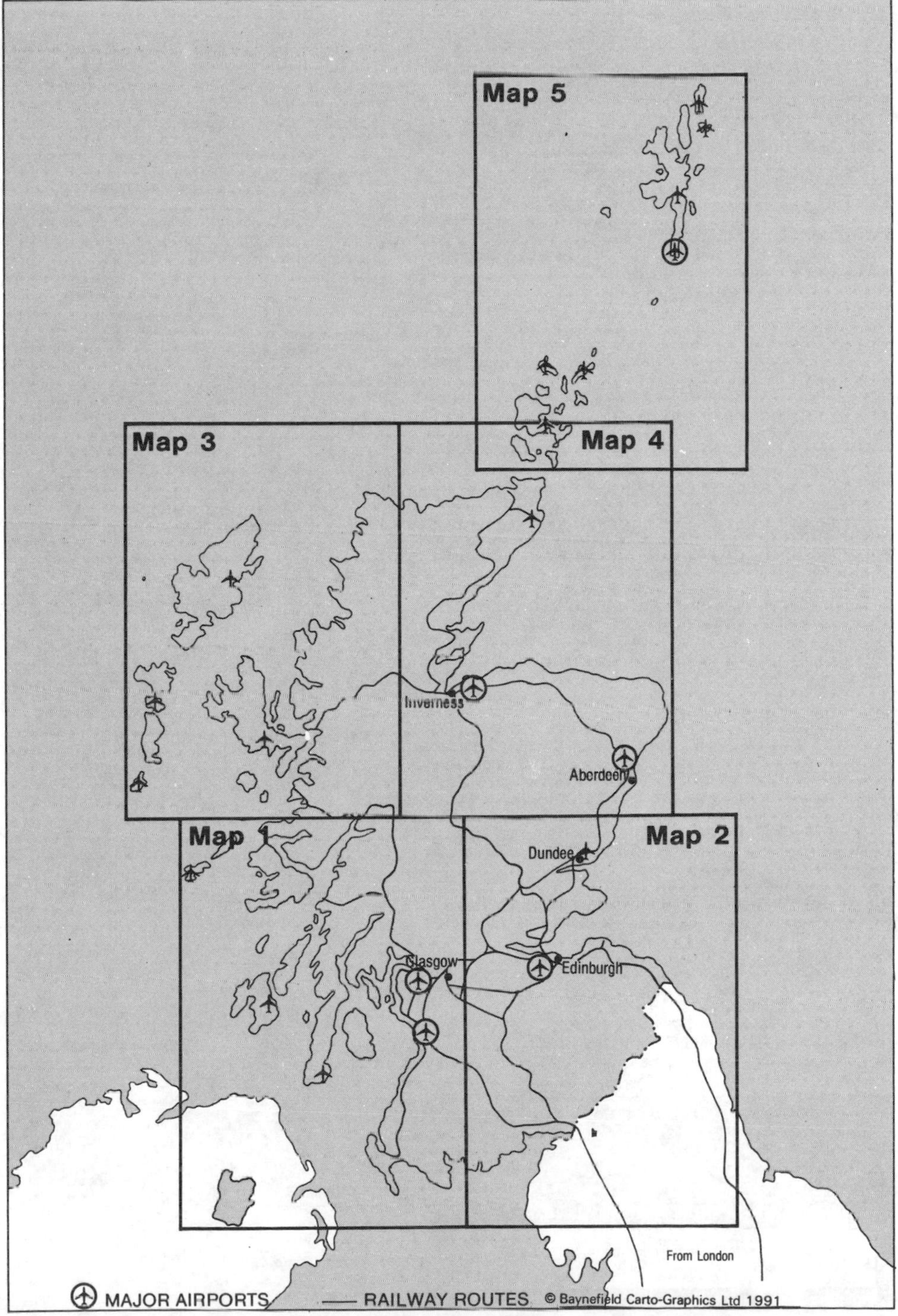

Map 5

Map 3

Map 4

Inverness

Aberdeen

Map 1

Dundee

Glasgow

Edinburgh

Map 2

From London

✈ MAJOR AIRPORTS   —— RAILWAY ROUTES   © Baynefield Carto-Graphics Ltd 1991

MAP 1

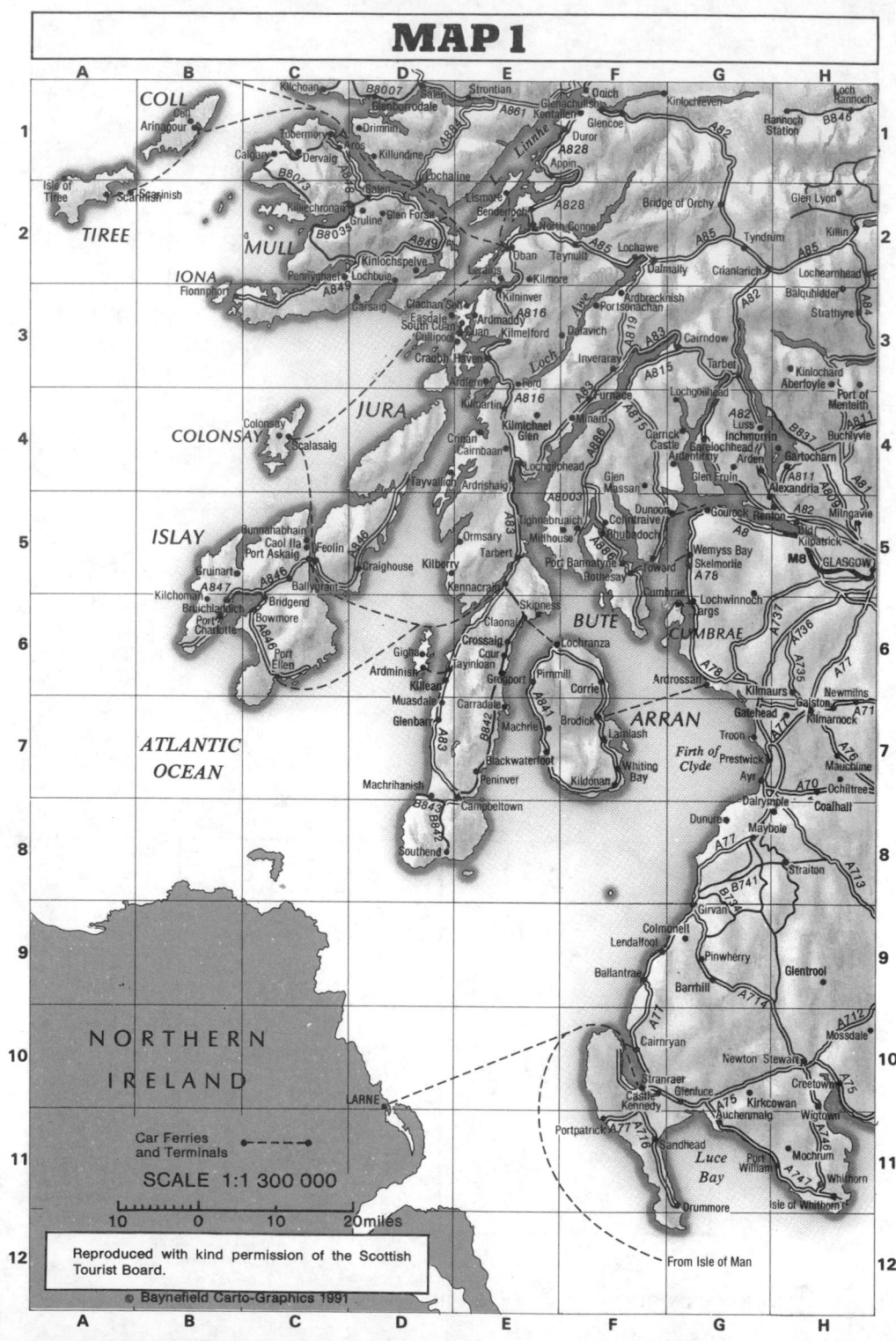

Reproduced with kind permission of the Scottish Tourist Board.

© Baynefield Carto-Graphics 1991

Car Ferries and Terminals

SCALE 1:1 300 000

10   0   10   20 miles

MAP 2

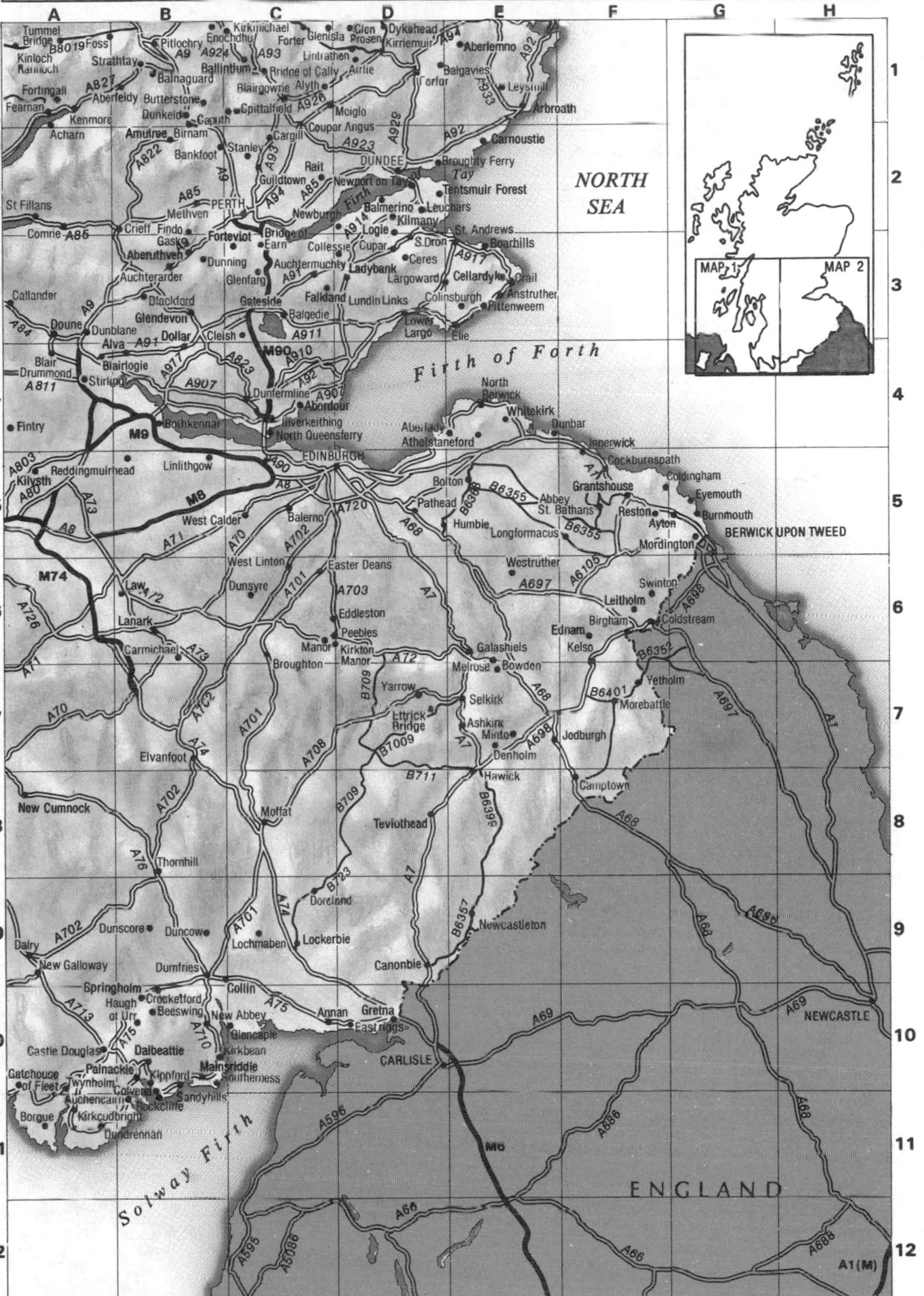

Tummel Bridge
B8019
Foss
Pitlochry
Enochdhu
Kirkmichael
Forter
Glenisla
Glen Prosen
Dykehead
Kirriemuir
A94
Aberlemno
A92
Kinloch Rannoch
Strathtay
A9
A924
Ballintium
A93
Lintrathen
Bridge of Cally
Airlie
Balgavies
Balnaguard
Fortingall
A827
Aberfeldy
Butterstone
Blairgowrie
Alyth
Forfar
Leysmill
Fearnan
Kenmore
Dunkeld
Caputh
Spittalfield
A926
Moiglo
A929
A933
Arbroath
Acharn
Amulree
Birnam
Cargill
Coupar Angus
A92
Carnoustie
Bankfoot
Stanley
A923
A822
A93
Rait
DUNDEE
Broughty Ferry
Tay
Guildtown
Newport on Tay
Tentsmuir Forest
A85
A94
A85
Firth
St Fillans
PERTH
Methven
Newburgh
Balmerino
Leuchars
Kilmany
Comrie
A85
Crieff
Findo
Gask
Forteviot
Bridge of Earn
A914
Logie
St. Andrews
Boarhills
Aberuthven
Dunning
Collessie
Cupar
S.Dron
A917
Ceres
Auchtermuchty
Ladybank
Auchterarder
Glenfarg
A91
Largoward
Cellardyke
Crail
Callander
Falkland
Colinsburgh
Anstruther
Blackford
Gateside
Balgedie
Lundin Links
Pittenweem
A9
A84
Glendevon
Doune
Dunblane
Dollar
Cleish
A911
Lower Largo
Elie
Alva
A91
M90
A910
Blair Drummond
Blairlogie
A977
A823
A92
A811
Stirling
A907
Dunfermline
A907
Aberdour
Firth of Forth
North Berwick
Whitekirk
Fintry
M9
Bothkennar
Inverkeithing
North Queensferry
Aberlady
Athelstaneford
Dunbar
Innerwick
A803
Reddingmuirhead
Linlithgow
A90
EDINBURGH
Cockburnspath
Kilsyth
A80
A8
M8
A73
Bolton
Grantshouse
Coldingham
Eyemouth
Pathead
B6368
B6355
Abbey St. Bathans
Reston
Burnmouth
West Calder
Balerno
A720
A68
Humbie
Ayton
A8
A71
A70
A702
Longformacus
B6355
Mordington
BERWICK UPON TWEED
West Linton
Easter Deans
Westruther
A6105
M74
Law
A72
Dunsyre
A701
A703
A7
A697
Swinton
Leitholm
A698
A726
Eddleston
Lanark
Peebles
Birgham
Coldstream
Ednam
Kelso
Manor
Kirkton Manor
A72
Galashiels
A71
Carmichael
A73
Broughton
Melrose
Bowden
B6352
B709
Yarrow
Selkirk
Yetholm
A7C2
A68
B6401
A697
Morebattle
A70
A701
Ettrick Bridge
Ashkirk
A1
Minto
A698
Jodburgh
A708
B7009
A7
Denholm
Elvanfoot
A74
B711
Hawick
New Cumnock
A702
B709
Camptown
Moffat
B6399
Teviothead
A68
A76
Thornhill
A7
B723
A74
Doreland
B6357
A702
Dunscore
A701
Duncow
Newcastleton
A68
A695
Dalry
Lochmaben
Lockerbie
New Galloway
Dumfries
Canonbie
Springholm
Collin
Crocketford
Haugh of Urr
Beeswing
A75
Annan
Gretna
A69
A69
NEWCASTLE
A713
A75
New Abbey
A710
Glencaple
Eastriggs
Castle Douglas
Dalbeattie
Kirkbean
CARLISLE
Catchouse of Fleet
Palnackie
Mainsriddle
Southerness
Twynholm
Kippford
Colvend
Sandyhills
Auchencairn
Rockcliffe
A596
A686
A68
Borgue
Kirkcudbright
Dundrennan
M6
Solway Firth
ENGLAND
A66
A595
A5086
A66
A688
A1(M)
NORTH SEA
MAP 1
MAP 2

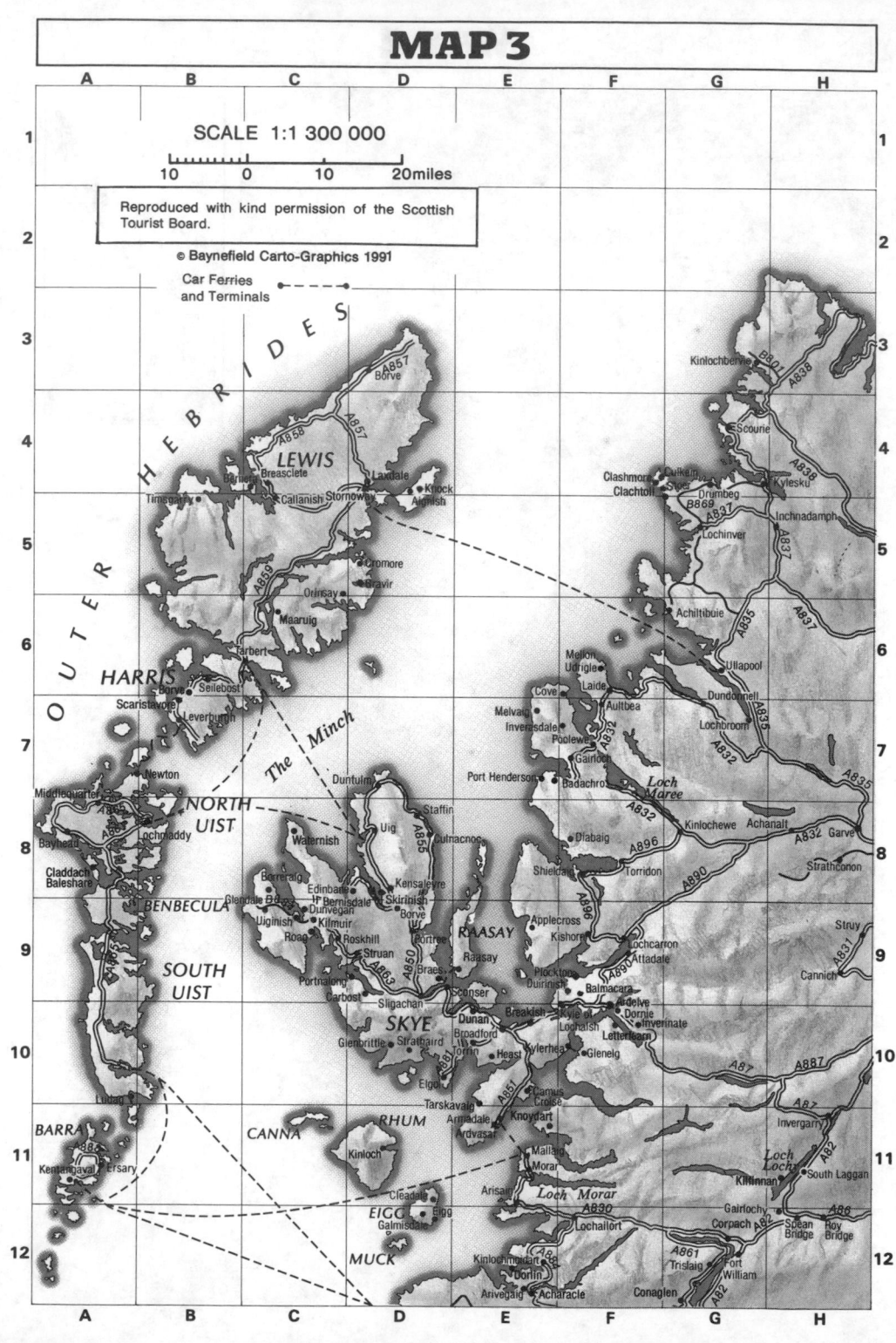

MAP 3

SCALE 1:1 300 000

10   0   10   20miles

Reproduced with kind permission of the Scottish
Tourist Board.

© Baynefield Carto-Graphics 1991

Car Ferries
and Terminals

OUTER HEBRIDES

LEWIS

Borve
A857
A858
Bragar
Breasclete
Timsgarry
Callanish   Stornoway
Laxdale
Knock
Aignish

Cromore
Orinsay
Bravir
A859
Maaruig

Tarbert

HARRIS
Borve   Seilebost
Scaristavore
Leverburgh

Newton
Middlequarter
Bayhead
NORTH UIST
Lochmaddy
Claddach
Baleshare
BENBECULA

SOUTH UIST

BARRA
Kentangaval   Eriskay
Ludag

CANNA

Kinloch

RHUM
Cleadale
EIGG
Galmisdale   Eigg

MUCK

The Minch

Duntulm

Waternish
Uig
Staffa
Staffin
A855
Culnacnoc
Borreraig
Edinbane
Glendale   Dunvegan
Uiginish   Kilmuir
Roag   Roskhill
Portnalong   Struan
Carbost
Sligachan
Glenbrittle   Strathaird
Elgol

Bernisdale   Skirinish
Borve
Portree
Braes
Duirinish
Dunan
SKYE
Broadford
Torrin   Heast
Kylerhea
Tarskavaig
Armadale   Knoydart
Ardvasar
Mallaig
Morar
Arisaig
Kinlochmoidart
Dorlin
Arivegaig   Acharacle

RAASAY
Raasay

Applecross
Kishorn
Plockton
Balmacara
Kyle of
Lochalsh   Ardelve
Dornie   Invernate
Letterfearn
Glenelg

Diabaig
Shieldaig
Torridon
A896
Lochcarron
Attadale

Loch Morar
A830
Lochailort

Conaglen

Port Henderson

Mellon
Udrigle
Cove   Laide
Melvaig   Aultbea
Inverasdale
Poolewe
Gairloch
Badachro

Loch
Maree
A832
Kinlochewe   Achanalt

A896
A890

A87   A887
A87

Invergarry

Loch
Lochy
Kilfinnan   South Laggan
Gairlochy
Corpach   A82
Spean
Bridge   Roy
Bridge
Trislaig   Fort
William
A861

Kinlochbervie
B801
A838
Scourie
Clashmore   Culkein
Clachtoll   Drumbeg
Kylesku
B869   A837   Inchnadamph
Lochinver   A837
Achiltibuie
A835   A837
Ullapool
Dundonnell
Lochbroom   A835
A832
A835   Garve
Strathconon
Struy
A831
Cannich

Balmacara
A890

OUTER HEBRIDES

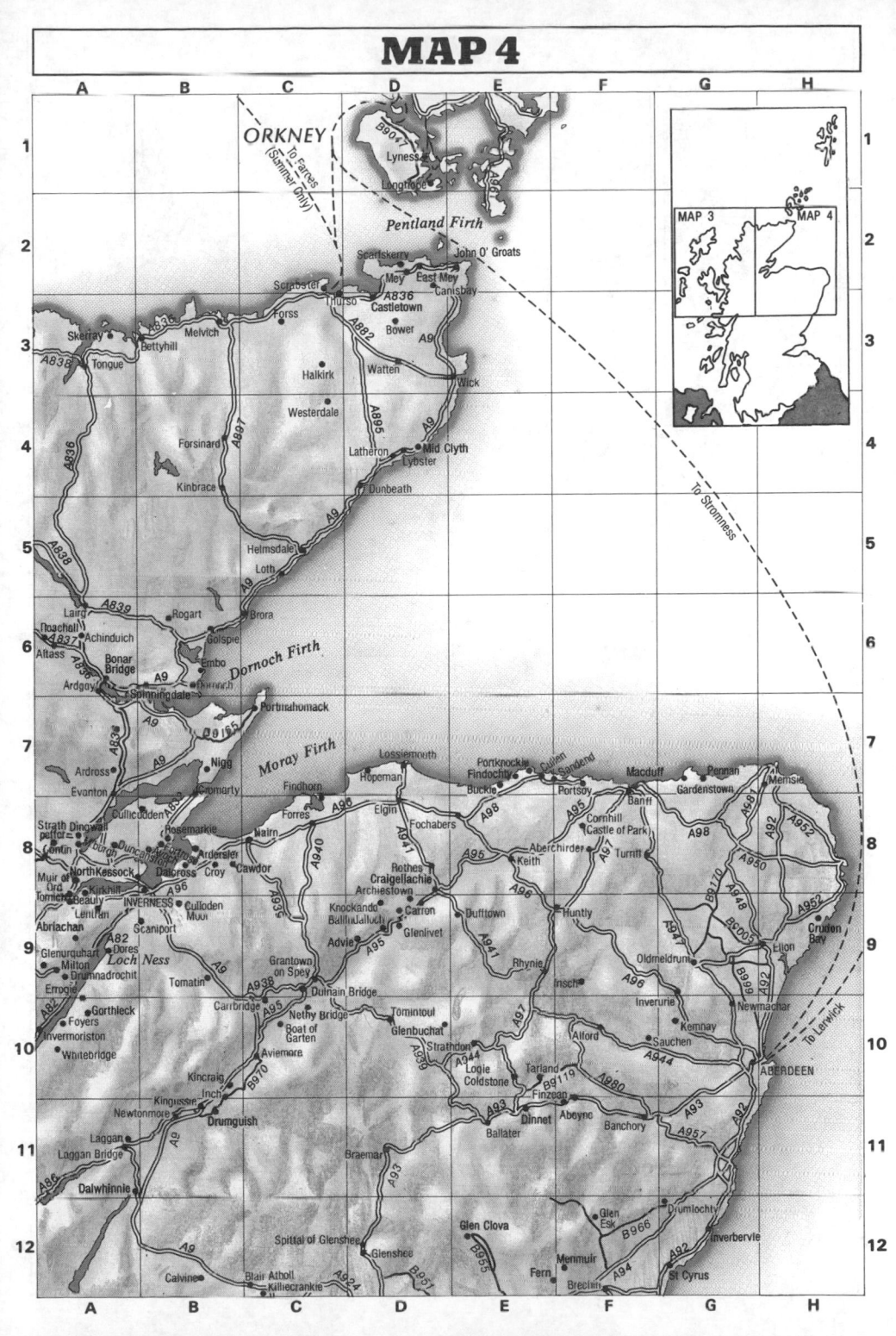

MAP 4

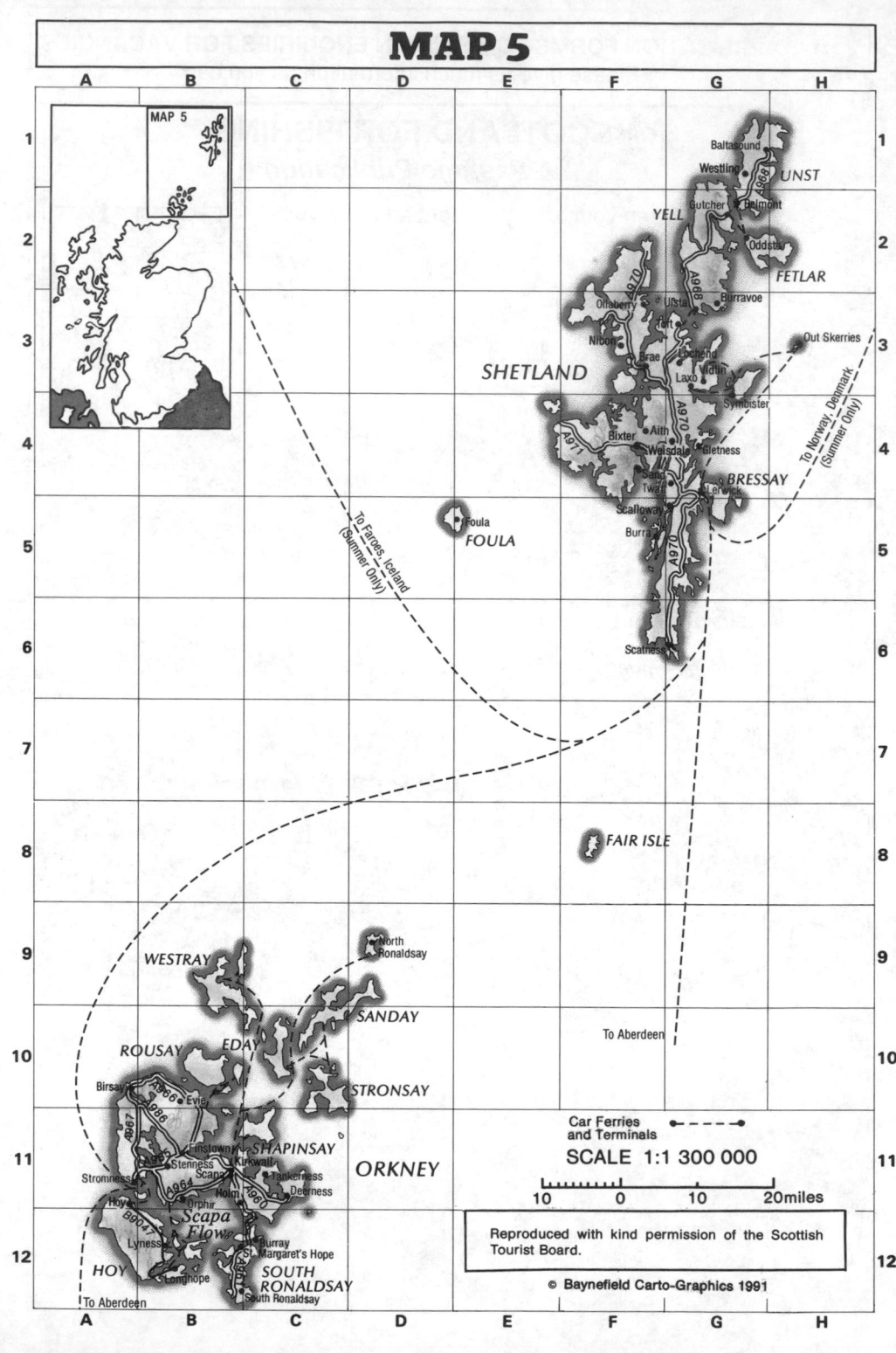

SCOTLAND FOR FISHING
A Pastime Publication

I/We have seen your advertisement and wish to know if you have the following vacancy:

Name ....

Address ....

....

Dates from pm ....

Please give date and day of week in each case ....

To am ....

Number in Party ....

Details of Children ....

(*Please remember to include a stamped addressed envelope with your enquiry.*)

SCOTLAND FOR FISHING
A Pastime Publication

I/We have seen your advertisement and wish to know if you have the following vacancy:

Name ....

Address ....

....

Dates from pm ....

Please give date and day of week in each case ....

To am ....

Number in Party ....

Details of Children ....

(*Please remember to include a stamped addressed envelope with your enquiry.*)

PASTIME GUIDES FOR 1994

Pastime Publications Ltd is one of the leading Holiday Guide Publishers for U.K. Bed & Breakfast, Self Catering and Farm & Country Holidays as well as Activity and Motoring Holidays in Scotland.

The following publications are useful guides and make wonderful gifts throughout the year.

Whilst our guides are available in leading bookshops and Tourist Board Centres for your convenience we will be happy to post a copy to you or send books as a gift for you. We will post overseas but have to charge separately for post or freight.

The inclusive cost of posting and packing your selection of guides to you and your friends in the U.K. is as follows:

☐ **Farm & Country Holidays**
This guide gives details of over 300 farms, many of them working with livestock, as well as activity holidays. **£4.20**

☐ **Scotland for Fishing**
Permits, fishing rights, boat hire, season/dates, rods, fly fishing and spinning....it's all here. **£4.20**

☐ **Bed & Breakfast Holidays**
A comprehensive guide to over 300 hotels, guesthouses, farms and inns throughout Britain. **£4.20**

☐ **Scotland Home of Golf**
Over 400 golf clubs featured. Also places to stay. Editorial by well-known celebrities. **£4.20**

☐ **Self Catering Holidays**
Includes details of hundreds of houses, chalets, boats, caravans, cottages, farms and flats throughout Britain. **£4.20**

☐ **Scotland for the Motorist**
Over 1,000 places of interest plus road maps and where to stay. **£4.20**

☐ **Scotland Activity Holidays**
The finest walks and trails as well as hill walking, cycling, skiing, yachting, canoeing and trekking.
£4.20

Tick your choice and send your order and payment to:
Pastime Publications Ltd., 32/34 Heriot Hill Terrace, Edinburgh EH7 4DY.
Telephone: 031-557 8092.
Deduct 10% for 2 or 3 titles and 20% for 4 or more titles.

Send to: NAME ....

ADDRESS ....

....POST CODE ....

I enclose Cheque/Postal Order for £ ....

SIGNATURE .... DATE ....